G000299734

Victorian Farming

Henry Stephens

A Sourcebook

Victorian Farming

Edited by C. A. JEWELL

Barry Shurlock

BARRY SHURLOCK & Co. (Publishers) Ltd
174 *Stockbridge Road*
WINCHESTER
Hants, SO22 6RW

First published 1975

ISBN 0 903330 12 1

Printed in Great Britain by
REDWOOD BURN LIMITED
Trowbridge & Esher

Preface

This book provides a conspectus of the tools, implements, methods and machines which belonged to a style of hand and horse-powered husbandry practised during the middle years of the nineteenth century. The illustrations and associated text are from *The Book of the Farm* by Henry Stephens. To put them and Stephens' work into a fresh perspective, Dr. Collins has written an Introduction which outlines the technical, economic and social anatomy of Victorian farming.

There are, of course, a number of other nineteenth century sources from which a miscellany of illustrations of farm equipment could have been chosen. Both J. C. Loudon's *An Encyclopaedia of Agriculture* (1825) and J. C. Morton's *A Cyclopaedia of Agriculture* (1855), for example, have as many or more woodcuts than *The Book of the Farm.* Neither, however, have anything to compare with the drawings which Stephens used to illustrate farm operations. These were executed by the Edinburgh artist Gourlay Steell and are generally to be distinguished by the use of silhouette to draw attention to the more important elements in the illustrations. Furthermore, Stephens wrote clearly and concisely from a basis of sound practical knowledge so that his text has been used with advantage to extend the figure captions by reproducing all or part of relevant paragraphs.

All the illustrations and captions have been taken from the 3rd edition of *The Book of the Farm* which Stephens revised about 1870. To make further reference to the original work easier, the paragraph numbers have been retained. With a few exceptions the sequence of illustrations is also as Stephens arranged it and follows the main farming activities of each season of the year.

I am very grateful to Alexander Fenton for drawing my attention to the existence of Stephens' manuscript revisions in the National Museum of Antiquities of Scotland and to that Museum for permission to reproduce the photographs included in the Introduction.

Institute of Agricultural History
University of Reading

ANDREW JEWELL

Publisher's Note

The text and illustrations for *Victorian Farming*, taken from *The Book of the Farm* (3rd ed. 1876), have been assembled in the following pages and enlarged photographically by one third. Editorial notes have been set in italics and placed within square brackets. No attempt has been made to indicate editorial deletions or rearrangements of the text, and the inclusion of Stephens' original paragraph numbers should not be taken to imply that the whole of the relevant paragraph has been included.

A microfiche edition of the complete text of *The Book of the Farm* is available from the publishers.

Contents

Introduction

by E. J. T. Collins

The career of Henry Stephens, from 1820, when he began farming at Balmadies in Forfarshire, to his death in 1874, spans almost precisely a phase in the history of British farming, called by Professor F. M. L. Thompson 'The Second Agricultural Revolution'. The year 1820, or thereabouts, was a watershed in a number of important respects. Hitherto, agricultural progress has been associated with reclamation and enclosure and technically with root and fodder cropping, that is, with improvements which had been generated by and within farming itself. Thereafter, with enclosure already reclaimed, higher output could be secured only at the 'intensive margin', that is by raising average yields per acre. Yet at the same time, because of the risk of diminishing returns, there were definite limits as to the extent to which this could be done profitably within the existing technology. Moreover, many farmers were soon to discover, as some already had, that as the demand for manpower increased so its supply tended to diminish, as labour migrated from the countryside to the industrial towns, and as the great historic sources of casual labour—village women, country craftsmen, and itinerant Irish and Scottish Highlanders, upon whose timely help farmers had so much relied at haytime and harvest—began to dry up. The industrial counties of northern England and southern Scotland were earliest and worst affected but by the mid-1830s, and more generally after 1850, eastern and southern Britain felt the similar pinch of a deteriorating labour market.

The situation demanded, therefore, new and better techniques by which to increase output, reduce production costs and save labour. Thus were forged during the second quarter of the nineteenth century new links between agriculture and the wider economy as more and more the farmer came to rely on imported and manufactured sources of feed, fertility, motive power, plant and machinery. Agriculture ceased to be self-contained; biological efficiency was dependent on the support energy supplied by other industries, and through the network of international trade, of other lands.

The period 1820–1880 witnessed the first stage in this process, with industrial inputs competing with, sometimes displacing, sometimes supplementing the older, more traditional methods, and scientific principles beginning to break down the traditional regime of ritual and rule of thumb.

I

The chemical analysis of plants and manures had been pioneered by Sir Humphrey Davy (1778–1829), but it was the German scientist, Justus von Liebig (1803–1873) who advanced the first comprehensive theory of plant nutrition embodying the proposition that growth could be stimulated 'artificially' by the application of 'minerals'. But having determined the amounts of nitrogen, phosphorus and potassium in the different plants, he made the mistake of assuming that they should be applied in the same proportions; that, for example, because turnips contained by analysis only small quantities of phosphorus, phosphatic manures were relatively unimportant to the plant's growth and development. Although Liebig's 'mineral theory' was later refuted by Gilbert and Lawes at the Rothamsted Experimental Station alert agricultural minds had nevertheless been roused to the possibilities of artificial manuring.

Until the nineteenth century farmyard dung was the chief fertilizing agent. apart from a few areas where alternative manures, such as woollen rags, soot, wood-ash, town refuse and, in the seaboard counties, fish and seaweed, were conveniently to hand. Of the new 'portable' manures, bone-meal was first used about 1800, having then been introduced into Lincolnshire and Yorkshire by a Hull merchant. It became so popular between 1815 and 1840 that Liebig accused English merchants, in their insatiable hunger for bones, of digging up the battlefields of Europe and ransacking the catacombs of Sicily. The 1830s saw the introduction of phosphatic guano (accumulated bird droppings) from South America, imports of which, under the source names of Mejillones, Booby Island, Peruvian and Patagonian, had risen by the 1870s to over 200,000 tons per annum. Mineral nitrates in the form of 'cubic nitre' imported from Chile made their debut in the next decade, mineral potash from Germany.

The first properly 'manufactured' manure was superphosphate of lime produced by treating animal bones or mineral phosphate with sulphuric acid, a process developed by John Bennett Lawes in 1842. Within a few years it had become the favourite artificial fertilizer and by the 1870s total usage exceeded half a million tons per annum. In many areas roots were grown with superphosphate alone, applied at a rate of 3–4 cwts per acre while in Yorkshire some farmers manufactured their own fertilizer from acid and bones. Sulphate of ammonia, hitherto a waste product of the gasworks, came into agricultural use after 1860.

By the late 1870s sales of artificial fertilizer are estimated to have approached £3 for every acre of arable land, and to have been sufficient to treat upwards of 16 million acres at the usual rates of application. In 1871 there were over 1200 manure manufacturers in England and Wales, while the total market for portable manures, home produced and imported, amounted to over 650,000 tons. As the use of artificials grew so some traditional methods of manuring, such as marling and liming, fell out of favour.

The revolution in animal feeding centred around oil-seed cake, the residue of the oil-seed crushing process, which, until the late eighteenth century, was little used in agriculture, and then rather as a manure than a feeding stuff. Consumption of linseed and cotton-seed cake rose from an estimated 35,000 tons per annum in the early 1820s to 160,000 tons in the late 1840s, and, by the late 1870s to over

600,000 tons. One major problem which was eventually overcome by legislation, was adulteration. Indeed, oil cake was often sold at prices well above its actual feeding value. Lawes at Rothamsted showed by analysis that cake at £40 per ton was of no more nutritive worth than straight cereals at £8–£9, although the difference was partly, and in the minds of many farmers, more than offset by the value of its dung. Between them sales of oil-seed cake and American maize totalled almost £16 million per annum by the late 1870s, enough, if exclusively fed to cattle, for about three million animals, half the British herd.

Another important area of technological advance was field drainage. Up to the 1820s the standard method was either the mole drain, or on heavy arable land, the ridge or stetch, drawn ten to thirty feet apart along the slope of the field, and sometimes so deep that men sitting in adjacent furrows might be hidden from each other. In parts of Essex and Suffolk a method of hollow-draining, known as brushwood-draining, after the nature of the filling, had been 'anciently' employed, while in Warwickshire, after the example of Joseph Elkington, drains were sometimes filled with small stones. A new era opened in 1831 when John Smith of Deanston, Perthshire, published his *Remarks on Thorough Draining and Deep Ploughing*, which advocated a system combining Elkington's stone drains with subsoil ploughing to help percolation in the upper soil. The more significant breakthrough, however, was the development in the early 1840s of a cylindrical drain-pipe made by machinery which met the demand for a cheaper and more efficient means of conduit. Stones were expensive in a stoneless district, as also were handmade tiles, which had been used, though not extensively, since 1810. By the early 1850s machines were capable of producing 20,000 tiles a day at a cost of 6 shillings per 1000 where a decade earlier they had cost 21 shillings. After 1846, government loans, administered by the Inclosure Commissioners, were available to landowners wishing to drain their estates. Within 25 years about two million acres had been drained by public funds, and a much larger area by private landowners. Where skilfully and thoroughly done—which in the early days of the one-inch pipe and imperfect understanding of the art, especially in respect to depth of drain, was a rare event—the improvements could be striking. Whether, as was originally hoped, underdrainage turned the same productive wheel on the waterclogged clays as had turnips and clover on the freer working soils, is another matter. Caird, for one, thought that not one fifth of the land which ought to have been drained had received that benefit by 1873. Nor was underdrainage ever a panacea where, as sometimes happened, landowners found themselves committed to large interest repayments without a corresponding increase in rents, or when tenants failed to make the necessary complementary improvements by way of better cultivations or larger purchases of cake and fertilizer.

It was in farm equipment—tools, implements and machinery—where the record was most impressive, and where *The Book of the Farm* is most instructive. 'The present age' wrote James Slight in the 1844 edition, 'is perhaps the most remarkable that time has produced, from the perfection of almost every kind of machine or tool required in the various departments of art and manufacturers'. Better and cheaper raw materials, more accurate machine tools, and a more perfect understanding of the principles of machine design and construction, brought about, during the second quarter of the nineteenth century, a revolution in the agricultural engineering industry. Helped by the railway building boom of 1835–46, many new firms were founded, and a few older firms, such as Ransomes, Garretts and Howards, had grown by the time of the Great Exhibition of 1851 into large international companies employing many hundreds of workers.

The period 1830–1880 can be regarded as the first major phase in the mechanization of British Agriculture. It saw iron displace wood in the manufacture of many field implements, a trend towards more standardized products, some with interchangeable parts, the general adoption of labour-saving machinery, and the selective employment of a new source of motive power, namely steam. Threshing machines, though commonplace in parts of Scotland and northern England before 1820, conquered the main cereal areas of southern and eastern Britain only after 1835. They were powered first by water or horses, but, from the late 1840s, increasingly by steam. An efficient portable steam engine adapted for agricultural purposes was developed about 1840. Overall, north Britain preferred stationary engines installed in the farmstead, while south Britain relied on portables, usually operated by firms of specialist contractors that travelled the farms for that purpose. By the 1870s the flail had almost disappeared from lowland Britain, and survived chiefly on smallholdings, and otherwise only for beans and sometimes malting barley.

By 1850 it had been demonstrated that steam was an economic proposition for barn tasks, especially threshing. The logical development from the portable was the self-propelled engine, which in turn opened up the possibilities of applying steam power directly to field cultivation. The prospect of the steam plough fired the agricultural imagination, which saw it as the complete answer to the mechanical problems of clayland farming. Attempts to develop a self-moving plough, spectacular but never very successful, gave way to the more practical alternative of direct hauling across or around the field by means of a steel-wire rope, a system perfected in the 1850s by John Fowler of Leeds and James Howard of Bedford. On account of its low weight-to-power ratio, crude immobility and high cost, the steam plough never lived up to its early promise. At the peak of its popularity it could be numbered only in hundreds where steam threshers ran into many thousands.

Worthwhile savings of labour were secured primarily in barn work and harvesting. In the one, a wide range of hand, horse and steam powered equipment—for threshing, winnowing, dressing, chaff-cutting, root-slicing, oil-cake breaking and cereal crushing and milling—was in general use by the 1870s. In the other, the sequence of technological change was more complex because although reaping and mowing machines, of American design, were available from the early 1850s, more modest but still considerable savings had already been, and continued to be made within hand-tool technology, through the substitution of the faster-working scythe and heavy hook for the traditional sickle and reap hook. J. Algernon Clarke's claim that 'fully three fourths of white corn in England' was reaped by machine in 1878, was probably near the truth, and is striking testimony to the speed with which mechanical harvesting gained ground during the closing years of the great third quarter. The grass mower and hay tedder were slower to take command but had largely done so by the 1890s. Elsewhere, the 'High Farming Era' saw the general uptake of the seed-drill and, latterly, the introduction of the stack-elevator. Conversely, because of the nature of the tasks and the small average size of farms, mechanical innovation in dairying was less dramatic than in arable farming. However, the barrel and box churns gradually replaced the traditional plunger type, while metal replaced wood in the manufacture of dairying utensils and the construction of cheese presses. On large farms, horse-works, water-wheels and sometimes steam engines were occasionally employed to drive churn and curd-cutters but otherwise butter and cheese making was a tedious business and remained so until foreign competition eventually brought about the collapse of the farmhouse industry. Technological progress, such as it was, occurred mainly off the farm, in the new dairy factories, which, after the American style, sprang up in a number of districts after 1869.

The new techniques did not always displace the old, but often only supplemented them. Mixed farming—the interlock of crops and stock with yarded bullocks, folded sheep and tight rotations alternating white straw and fodder crops—remained, as before, the basis of agricultural prosperity, but with its potential now greatly enhanced. The new husbandry demanded from the landowners a more positive involvement in the farming activities of their tenants by way of more and better farm buildings, underdrainage, compensation for unexhausted improvements, longer leases and greater security of tenure. Farming became increasingly a joint enterprise of landlord and tenant, with the one assuming responsibility for fixed improvements and the other for working capital. How many landowners were able or willing to invest on the lavish scale regarded by the farming textbooks as necessary for the efficient practice of high-farming husbandry is a moot point. The low returns realized by some of the richer landowners—whose capital often originated outside agriculture—suggests that their numbers were few, and that the average scale of investment was relatively modest and, at the lower end, totally inadequate.

It is more likely that the leadership in this joint enterprise was increasingly in the hands of the tenants. There is no doubt that the new husbandry engendered a different type of entrepreneur—more knowledgeable, more innovative, and more managerial than his predecessors. Stephens himself had carried out extensive improvements on his farm at Balmadies which he took over in a dilapidated condition, with no dwelling house and a ruinous steading, and which he transformed within the short space of ten years into a capital holding. He introduced several techniques hitherto unknown in the district, such as stall-feeding of cattle, the enclosing of sheep on turnips by means of nets instead of hurdles, swede culture, and anticipating by several years the publication of the Deanston plan, the use of furrow drains filled with small stones.

II

Why Stephens ceased active farming in 1830, to settle near Edinburgh and devote the rest of his life to agricultural journalism, is not clear. Perhaps, like Arthur Young and William Ellis before him, he was a better publicist than a practitioner. By accident or design he began his new career at an important stage in the evolution of the farming press. 1828 saw the first *Quarterly Journal of Agriculture,* published in Edinburgh for northern farmers; the 1830s the *Mark Lane Express* and the *Farmers Magazine,* and the 1840s the *Agricultural Gazette,* a monthly publication edited by John Chalmers Morton. The period saw also a spawning of farmers' clubs and agricultural societies, culminating in the formation of the Royal Agricultural Society in 1839, although the Highland and Agricultural

THE BOOK OF THE FARM.

INITIATION.

ON THE BEST OF THE EXISTING METHODS FOR ACQUIRING A THOROUGH KNOWLEDGE OF PRACTICAL HUSBANDRY.

1. No doubt exists, I believe, that the best way, among existing ones, for a young man to acquire a thorough knowledge of farming, is to become a pupil in the house of a good practical farmer. On a fine farm, and with a competent tutor, the pupil will not only live comfortably, but may thoroughly learn any system of husbandry he chooses. The choice of locality is so far limited, that he must take up his residence in a district in which the particular system he has chosen is practised in a superior manner.

2. Many farmers are to be found who accept pupils, amongst whom a proper selection should be made, as it would be injudicious to engage with one who is notoriously deficient in the requisite qualifications — and those qualifications are numerous. A tutor-farmer should possess a general reputation of being a good farmer — that is, a skilful cultivator of land, a successful breeder, and an excellent judge of stock. He should possess agreeable manners, and have the power of communicating his ideas with ease. He should occupy a good farm, consisting, if possible, of a variety of soils, and situate in a tolerably good climate, — neither on the top of a high hill nor on the confines of a large moor or bog, nor in a warm sheltered nook, but in the midst of a well cultivated country. Such circumstances of soil and locality should be requisites in a farm intended for the residence of *pupils*. The top of a hill, exposed to every wind that blows, or the vicinage of a bog overspread with damp vapour, would place the farm in a climate in which no kind of crop or stock could arrive at a state of perfection; while a very sheltered spot and a warm situation, would give the pupil no idea of the disappointments experienced in a precarious climate.

3. The inexperience of the pupil renders him unfit to select these requisites for himself in either a qualified farmer or a suitable farm: but monitors are never awanting to render assistance to their young friends in every emergency; and as their opinion should be formed on a knowledge of farming, and especially on an acquaintance with the farm, and the personal qualifications of the farmer they recommend, some confidence may be placed in their recommendations. For the pupil's personal comfort, I would advise him to choose a residence where are *no young children*.

4. A residence of one year must pass ere the pupil can witness the course of the annual operations of the farm. His first engagement should, therefore, be made for a period of *not less than one year*; and at the expiry of that period he will not be qualified to manage a farm. The time he

Figs. i. and ii. Pages from Henry Stephens' revision of his second edition of *The Book of the Farm* for the third edition.

left. The coulter is slightly oblique to the land-side plane, the point standing towards the left; the rake of the coulter varies from

upper line is straight and the breast ~~vertical sectional lines approximate to straight lines,~~ giving the character of ap-

15. I prefer the Tweeddale plough to all others because of its wide ... which enables the horses to plough the acre of land with fewer ...ings; because of its deep furrow and loose furrows which renders the ...oration of the soil easier, and because of its easier draught in proportion to the quantity of soil turned over.

Small's plough makes neat rectangular furrows, but it packs them too ...ly and it cannot go deep, not ordinarily than 8 inches, which is 5 inches ... than the Tweeddale plough. See Fig. 12. looking at fig. 12, which is a

a c g d f e h

Plan of Small's plough.

... of Small's plough, from d the middle of the [illegible] its ear, its ... section is too great to allow the plough to go deep, and the bosom of the mould ... from d to f is too concave and increases the draught.

Wilkie's plough cuts a trapezoidal furrow with a high crest, clasps the furrow too closely and cannot go deep for the same reason as Small's plough.

Most of the English ploughs are provided with wheels, which, while allowing the plough to be easily held by the ploughman, prevent them going beyond a given depth ... and they also compress the furrows too much.

The ~~resistance to the~~ draught of this furrow is ~~generally below the average of~~ ploughs, with their furrows ~~and this plough is employed for every kind of soil.~~

509. A necessary accompaniment of every plough is the *plough-staff*, or plough-spade, ~~as it is called in some places~~, fig. 13. Its ~~use consists in~~ shovelling ~~off~~ the mould that may ~~happen to~~ adhere to the front of the mould-board, between d and *f*, fig. 9, which ~~in~~ pushes away ~~any~~ stubble or weeds ~~that~~ may accumulate in the angle ~~formed by~~ the coulter *e* and beam *a*, ~~fig.~~ and ~~in~~ strikes out the stones that may ~~become~~ have

PLOUGH-STAFF.

swing-trees consist of 3, as represented in fig. 14, where *a* points out the bridle of the plough, *b b* the main swing-tree attached immediately to the bridle, *c c* the furrow or off-side small swing-tree, and *d d* the land or nigh-side small tree, arranged in the position in which they are employed in working: *h* is a section of a swing-tree at the centre of attachment, with clasp and eye mounting; the scale of which is double the size of the principal figure in the cut. Swing-trees are for the most part made of wood, oak or ash, ~~being most generally used; but the former, if~~ sound English oak, is by much the most durable—though good Scotch ash is the strongest, so long as it remains sound, but it is liable, by long exposure, to a species of decay resembling dry rot. The small trees are furnished

Society, of which Stephens was a member, had been founded as far back as 1784, Stephens, together with John Chalmers Morton, John Wilson and Samuel Copland. ('The Old Norfolk Farmer'), rose to prominence as a new generation of authors and editors of agricultural encyclopaedias, which were masterly works of synthesis, whose compass and intrinsic quality have probably never since been exceeded in the field of agriculture. In 1832 Stephens was appointed editor of the *Quarterly Journal of Agriculture*,, and he continued until 1852 to edit the *Transactions of the Highland Society*. In addition to *The Book of the Farm*, which, in his own lifetime, went through three editions in Britain and two in America, and soon achieved a recognized position as the standard work on practical agriculture, Stephens wrote also on underdrainage, farm implements and machines, farm buildings, and animal and plant physiology.

Stephens presided over, as chief literary doyen, the so-called 'High Farming Era', which began about the time of the accession of Queen Victoria, and ended in the late 1870s, with the onset of the Great Depression. It was the technologically most impressive phase of the Agricultural Revolution and, by reputation, the high-water mark of nineteenth century farming prosperity, the Golden Age which preceded the Deluge. Its achievement, as Caird pointed out, was less in the advance of absolute standards as in the general upheaval of the middling and the worst towards the higher standards formerly practised by the few. Contrary to expectations, the Repeal of the Corn Laws in 1846 did not result in a flood of cheap foreign grain because until the 1870s foreign competitors were in no position to undercut the home producer. Meanwhile, as corn prices held steady, livestock prices forged ahead. 'Thirty years ago', wrote Caird of the 1840s, 'probably not more than one third of the people of this country consumed animal food more than once a week ... now nearly all of them eat it, in meat or cheese or butter, once a day.'

Market conditions were right for a swing away from cereal-growing towards livestock production and by the 1870s the latter comprised over half the value of national agricultural output where fifty years earlier it had barely exceeded one-third. As far as we know the dairyman and stockbreeder reaped the benefits of rising prices for their products. The mixed farmer on the other hand, despite his technical superiority, may have wasted opportunities because of his preoccupation with corn growing, to which end livestock were often but a means. Thus, bullocks were machines for converting straw into dung, just as on light soils the sheep fold was a device for maintaining soil fertility. Artificial fertilizers and oil-cake were employed to the same end, the former being fed mainly to the root crop, and the latter, often with scant regard to its value as a flesh maker, to winter stock. The need for improvement in grassland management and dairying was recognized only in the 1860s, too late either to make good two centuries of neglect, or to prepare arable farmers for the Great Depression. Small wonder, therefore, that mixed farming, as it became more intensive, became also more subject to diminishing returns. Technical excellence and the sheer biological productiveness of the system tended to conceal the fact, apparent in the 1850s, but not generally admitted till the 1880s, that mixed farming was not only an expensive, but also an unprofitable method of food production. According to Lord Ernle the tide of prosperity ceased to flow after 1862; some clayland arable farmers may have put it even earlier, from the end of the Crimean War. Fortunate indeed were those Berkshire sheep and corn farmers, of whom it was said money was not so much made as brought home by the bucketful and thrown down at their doors!

The appeal of mixed farming lay partly in its elegance—that of the self-contained system; partly in its flexibility—of being able to switch between one product and another; and partly in the belief that it alone, through its succession of white straw, fodder and cleaning crops, could keep the land in good heart. Stephens was entirely convinced that no other system was so demanding of skill and intelligence or so deserving of capital and enterprise. 'No doubt', he said, 'the farmers of some of the other modes . . . became very skilful in adapting their practice to the situations in which they are actually placed, but his [the mixed farmer's] more varied experience increases versatility of talent and quickness of discernment; and accordingly, it will be found that farmers of the mixed husbandry prove themselves to be the cleverest and most intelligent agriculturists of the country.'

But while he correctly analysed its strengths, he failed, like many others, to detect its weaknesses. Mixed farming was flexible only at the margin, never at the core, and was so tightly integrated as to discourage specialization. In the final event high-cost, high-output farming proved no answer to falling prices. Indeed, already by the late 1850s, the system had become susceptible to rising costs—higher rents and wages—it being often complained that satisfactory profits could be bought only at the expense of increased capital investment and diminishing returns. It was only in retrospect, from the vantage point of the Great Depression, that farmers knew the wisdom of Caird's warning, issued in 1852, that in a world of free trade, the future of British agriculture lay not in the barn but the stall. Their preoccupation with mixed farming led agricultural writers to neglect other forms of enterprise, such as dairying, market gardening and stock rearing, with the result that our knowledge of them is slight and the overall impression is one of backwardness and slow and imperceptible progress.

At the apex of the agricultural pyramid, outstanding in their pursuit of technical excellence and commitment to scientific husbandry, where the 'Leviathans', men such as John J. Mechi of Tiptree, Essex, the Rev. Huxtable of Sutton Waldren, Dorset, James Prout of Sawbridgeworth, Hertfordshire, and Mr. Middleditch of Badon near Swindon, Wiltshire, who all believed that the application of industrial techniques would allow fortunes to be made out of land in the same way as out of a mine or factory. Prout, for example, was by the early 1860s practising continuous corn-growing using artificial manures and steam power alone. Middleditch, the real-life 'Man of Progress' depicted by Richard Jefferies in *Hodge and his Masters*, sank an enormous fortune into industrialized farming, throwing all his arable into one huge field and draining the whole to a depth of six feet. He constructed an engine shed with a centrifugal pump to draw water from a nearby stream and laid a light railway across the widest part of the estate to transport men and materials. Everything was done by machine—cultivation, harvesting, barn work—the crowning glory a set of steam-ploughing tackle which, to quote Jefferies, having once commenced its work, 'the beat of the engines never seemed to cease'.

The most remarkable of them all, the Leviathan-in-chief, was John Joseph Mechi, 'No permanent grass', he proclaimed, 'can keep so much stock per acre as turnip culture and green crops, folded and fed in stalls.' Deep drainage, thorough cultivation, intensive manuring and liberal feeding were the cornerstones, and steam power, ceramics, oil and cotton cake, guano, lime, superphosphate and the Norfolk Four Course Rotation, the instruments whereby a poor 170-acre clayland farm was transformed into an agricultural showpiece. His greatest contribution was as a publicist. The most controversial farming figure of his day, he preached, with missionary zeal, the gospels of high farming.

Less colourful, but more influential, was John Bennett Lawes, the first manufacturer in this country of superphosphate of lime, and founder, in 1842, of the Rothamsted Experimental Station. Together with Joseph Henry Gilbert, he laid the foundations of agricultural scientific research in Britain. Experimental work was carried out on plant and animal nutrition. He demonstrated experimentally what Prout was later to put into practice, that soil fertility could be maintained, for some years at least, by means of chemical fertilizers unaccompanied by dung or other organic manures. Trials were conducted to determine the relative economy, as meat producers, of different breeds of sheep. The results of these experiments were diffused through the agricultural journals and by public lecture, and while it is probably true that many, perhaps the majority, of farmers tended to associate scientific husbandry with a dwindling bank balance, the figures of oil-cake and chemical fertilizer consumption suggest that by the 1870s some at least of their scepticism had been overcome.

Predictably, only a select few had the means or the inclination to emulate the 'Leviathans'. As Jefferies remarked, no class was more jealous of a rapid rise than 'old fashioned farming people' so that the ultimate failure of Mechi, Middleditch and many other lesser 'men of progress' in the decade after 1875 satisfied the rural appetite for bathos and tightened the purse-strings of would-be imitators.

What then of the average Victorian farmer? It is doubtful whether he could have lived, as we are sometimes led to believe, 'in the manner of the best country squires, in a capital and superior residence seated on a lawn'. Contemporaries compared Old and New Style farming in the jingle:

Man to the plough,
Wife to the cow,
Girl to the yarn,
Boy to the barn,
And your rent will be netted,
Man Tally ho',
Miss piano,
Wife silk and satin,
Boy Greek and Latin,
And you'll all be gazetted.

Such comparisons confused categories of farmers. Statistics show that in the 1870s less than 20 per cent of farmers in England and Wales were owner-occupiers, while most were tenants of large estates. Moreover, 82 per cent farmed less than 100 acres and, of the rest, only 5000 farmed more than 500 acres, the income threshold for upper-middle class living. For every farmer who could run to a groom, a carriage, and a high-stepping mare, who could afford 'unlimited hospitality' and educate his sons at boarding schools and university, there were ten or twenty whose standard of living was little, if at all higher than that of village shopkeepers and tradesmen. Kendall observed that it was normally only the very rich who were able to follow their sports; and that as for the others, 'their business and working hours were far too arduous, far too long, to permit them to carry on after school days . . . the only exception an odd half-day with the gun, a little coursing or a day with the hounds'. Moreover, such wealth was often not amassed in agriculture. Jefferies' 'man of progress' brought a colonial fortune to his farming; 'Fine Lady Farmer' was the wife of a city gent, while the 'Borrower' and the 'Gambler' were agricultural speculators, living and farming on permanent credit. Ordinary farmers, like the exceptionally shrewd and practical 'Agricultural Genius', could, if they practised rigid economy, garner a fortune, but such men were rare. Indeed, those who could save fifty pounds a year thought themselves prosperous. Many small farmers had to engage in by-employments to make ends meet, and most occupiers of less than 100 acres would have worked in the fields alongside their sons and hired hands. Few had the means of extravagance, although during the high farming period many would have graduated from rushes to carpets and from wagons to pony and traps. As Jefferies remarked of their womenfolk, 'You cannot blame these girls, for thinking of something higher than the cheese tub . . . the world has gone on since then, it is a world of education, books and wider sympathies.'

Inertia was of a rather different kind. Many farmers were muddlers, unable to perceive long-term trends and forced to live from season to season, buffeted by events. Others, further-sighted, may often have lacked the means to improve, and, if a yearly tenant under a bad landlord, the encouragement to do so. The most able ascended the farming ladder adding acre to acre; the least so, knowing neither how to spend nor to save, descended it, eventually to sell up and leave the district, but often to remain in the village and merge and be lost in the multitude of the rural poor.

III

Henry Stephens was not the intellectual match of James Caird, J. C. Morton or C. S. Read. He was more a master of the art of description than of commentary, and was less perceptive of general trends than of minutiae. *The Book of the Farm* is thus primarily of value to historians of farming techniques. Being concerned with the material world, it is able to provide, what other contemporary writings do not, an insight into the daily routine of Victorian farming. Its purpose, clearly stated in the introduction to the first edition, was to serve as a textbook for the farm pupil; that is 'the young man, who, having finished his scholastic and academical education, directs his attention for the first time to the acquirement of practical farming; or who, though born on a farm, having spent the greater part of his life at school, determines at length, on following his father's profession.' It was not intended for ordinary farmers but for model farmers. Yet at the same time it was concerned less with scientific principles, which could be learnt elsewhere, than with the labour of the farm—its distribution, variety, and connection between the task and its ultimate ends. *The Book of the Farm* was organized not by product or type of enterprise but by season. Special emphasis was given to mechanics, 'of all the sciences . . . the most useful to agriculture.' As was explained, 'If implements may be characterised as the right hand of agriculture, mechanical science in improving their form and construction may be said to have given cunning to the right.' Here Stephens was assisted by the Edinburgh engineer, James Slight, who supplied the descriptions of implements, and by his son, George Henry Slight, who executed all the drawings of machinery. The striking silhouette drawings of field operations were supplied by Gourlay Steell of Edinburgh, an Associate of the Royal Scottish Academy.

The Book of the Farm has its shortcomings. Its bias towards mixed farming has already been noted. As a historical source for British agriculture its value is diminished by its primary concern with practice in Scotland, to the exclusion, misunderstanding, and sometimes denigration of practice elsewhere. Agriculture north and south of the Border differed in a number of important respects, such as, land tenure, design of farmstead, labour and conditions of employment, as well as in technical details. Alas, the inbalance is not easily redressed, because, for some inexplicable reason, most encyclopaedists were native or ex-patriate Scots! These strictures apart, *The Book of the Farm* stands out as the leading practical text of its day, affording the agricultural historian a wealth of unique and detailed information about Victorian farming, its means and mechanisms.

Winter

The subjects which court attention in winter are of the most interesting description to the farmer. Finding little inducement to spend much time in the fields at this torpid season of the year, he directs his attention to the more animated work conducted in the steading, where all the cattle and horses are collected, and preparation of the grain for market affords pleasant employment within doors. The progress of live stock towards maturity is always a prominent object of the farmer's solicitude, and especially so in winter, when they are comfortably housed in the farm-stead, plentifully supplied with wholesome food, and so arranged in various classes, according to age and sex, as to be easily inspected at any time. 411.

The labours of the field in winter are confined to a few great operations. These are ploughing the soil in preparation of future crops, and supplying food to live stock. The commencement of the ploughing for the year consists in turning over the ground which had borne a part of the grain crops, and which now bears their *stubble*—which is just the straw left uncut of the previous crops. 412.

PLOUGH, SWING-TREES, AND PLOUGH-HARNESS.

The *plough* serves the same purpose to the farmer as the spade to the gardener, both being used to *turn over* the soil; and the object of both in doing so is to pulverise the soil, and to enclose manure within it. 495.

The operation of the plough upon the soil is to imitate the effect of the *spade* upon it; but the plough being too large and heavy to be wielded by hand, it is not under man's control, as is the spade. The ploughman is obliged to call in the aid of horses to wield it, and through their means, in combination with harness, he can command its motions effectively. It is not so much by man himself, as by his horses, that the soil is turned over by the plough; but he is thereby a great gainer in the end, inasmuch as a larger extent of soil can be turned over by the plough in a given time than he could turn with the spade. 496.

The common plough used in this kingdom is made either wholly of iron, or partly of wood and partly of iron. Until a few years ago it was universally made of wood and iron, but now as universally entirely of iron. It is now made so, because iron withstands the changes of weather better than wood — a desirable property in any implement that must necessarily be much exposed to weather—and also because, when old, iron is worth something—whereas ash timber is now scarce, dear, and worthless when decayed. A wooden plough with iron mountings weighs 13 stones imperial, and an iron one for the same work 15 stones. The cost of a wooden plough is £3, 16s., of an iron £4, 4s., both capable of service, with repairs, for a lease of 19 years. 497.

Two varieties of ploughs, Small's and Wilkie's, are used in Scotland, and I do not know how many in England. A recent kind in Scotland, the Tweeddale, is the best in my estimation, and is the one I shall recommend and fully explain Its constructor is the Marquess of Tweeddale; hence its name. 498.

Fig. 1 is the *furrow-side* elevation of the Tweeddale plough in iron. The ploughman holds and guides the implement by the *stilts*. The *bridle*, with the hook, is that by which the horses are attached to the beam. The *coulter* is the cutting instrument that severs the slice of earth or furrow from the firm land. The *sock* severs the slice below from the subsoil. The *mould-board* receives the slice from the sock, turns it gradually over, and deposits it continuously at an angle. The coulter has a sharp cutting edge in front, and is slightly inclined, that it may cut the cleaner. 499.

Fig. 1

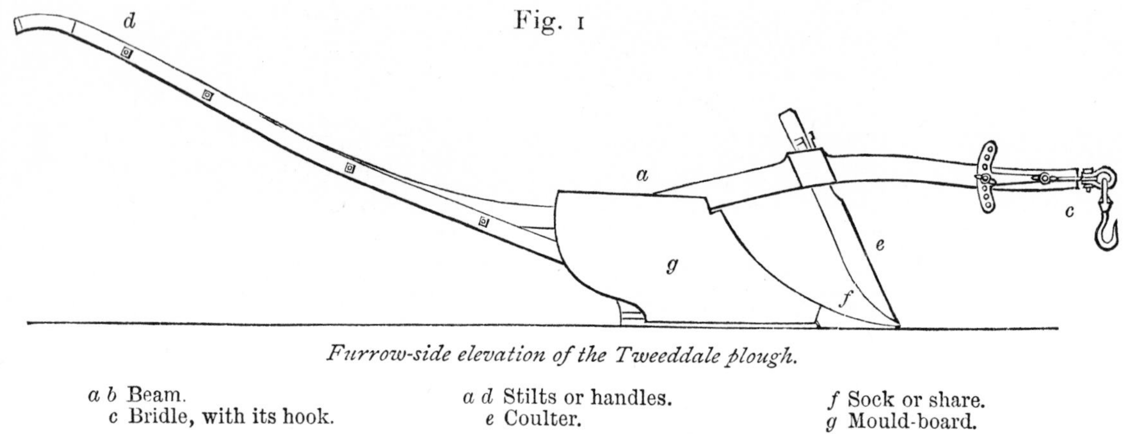

Furrow-side elevation of the Tweeddale plough.

a b Beam.
c Bridle, with its hook.
a d Stilts or handles.
e Coulter.
f Sock or share.
g Mould-board.

Fig. 2 is the *land-side* elevation of the same plough. The *land-side plate* presents a straight broad surface to the firm land, and prevents the earth falling within the body of the plough. The sole-shoe supports the plough, and slides upon the firm subsoil below. The attachment of the sock is with the lower end of the head of the plough, which is concealed in the figure, and which is fixed to the beam by its upper end. The ear of the mould-board prevents the earth falling into the bosom of the plough on that side. 500.

Fig. 2

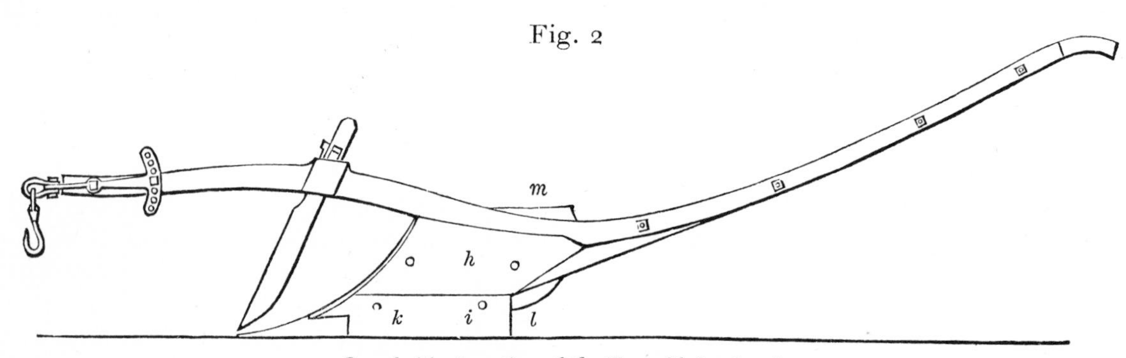

Land-side elevation of the Tweeddale plough.

h Land-side plate.
i Sole shoe.
k Onset of the sock.
l Heel.
m Ear of mould-board.

Fig. 3

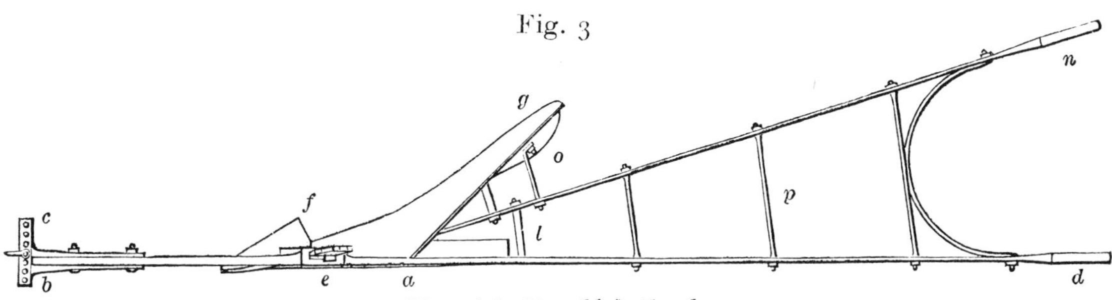

Plan of the Tweeddale plough.

b d Straight line of body.
a b Beam.
c Bridle.
a d Great stilt.
a n Little stilt.
e Head of coulter.
f Feather of sock.
g Ear of mould-board.
l Heel.
o Bolts fastening the mould-board to the little stilt.
p Stays to support the stilts.

Fig. 3 is a plan of the same plough. The lines of the body of the plough on the land-side are in one plane from the bridle to the end of the great stilt. The head of the coulter is fastened in a socket in the beam by means of iron wedges. The rake of the coulter varies from 55° to 65°. In the mould-board the upper line is straight, and the breast bulged forward in a convex form, the fore part of which is truncated. The sock is pointed, with a feather having a breadth of at least two-thirds the breadth of the furrow, and its cutting edge lying nearly as low as the plane of the sole. The neck of the sock is prolonged backward, joining and coinciding with the curve of the mould-board at its truncated end. This plough cuts a furrow-slice of 12 inches in breadth by 13 inches in depth, leaving the sole open level and clean. Its draught is more than in the common ploughs, but with this deep furrow the horses draw it without distress. 501.

I prefer the Tweeddale plough to all others, because of its *wide* furrow, which enables the horses to plough the acre of land with fewer turnings; because of its deep and loosened furrow-slices, which promote the pulverisation of the soil quicker; and because of its easier draught in proportion to the weight of soil turned over. 502.

Small's plough makes neat rectangular furrows, but it packs them too close, and cannot go deeper, by reason of its outspread mould-board, than 8 inches, which is 5 inches less than the Tweeddale plough. 503.

Wilkie's plough cuts a trapezoidal furrow with a high crest, claps the furrows too close, and cannot go deeper than Small's plough, for the same reason. 504.

Most of the English ploughs are provided with wheels, which, while allowing the ploughs to be easily held by the ploughman, prevent them going beyond a given depth, which in Scotland is deemed shallow for substantial ploughing, and they also compress the furrows too much. 505.

Fig. 4

Plough-staff.

A necessary accompaniment of every plough is the *plough-staff,* or plough-spade, fig. 4. It shovels the mould that adheres to the breast of the mould-board, pushes away stubble or weeds which accumulate in the angle of the coulter and beam, and strikes out the stone when one fixes itself between the points of the coulter and sock. It lies upon the stilts, the spade being inserted into a staple in the bosom of the plough. The plough-staff has often a slanting cross-head for the hand of the ploughman. 506.

Horses are yoked to the plough by means of a set of levers named *swing-trees,* arranged so as to cause the united strength of the horses to be exerted at one point, by linking the ring of the swing-trees to the hook of the bridle of the plough. Swing-trees are used for attaching any number of horses to other implements besides the plough, such as harrows, small ploughs, &c. 507.

[*In England commonly Whipple Tree*]

Fig. 5

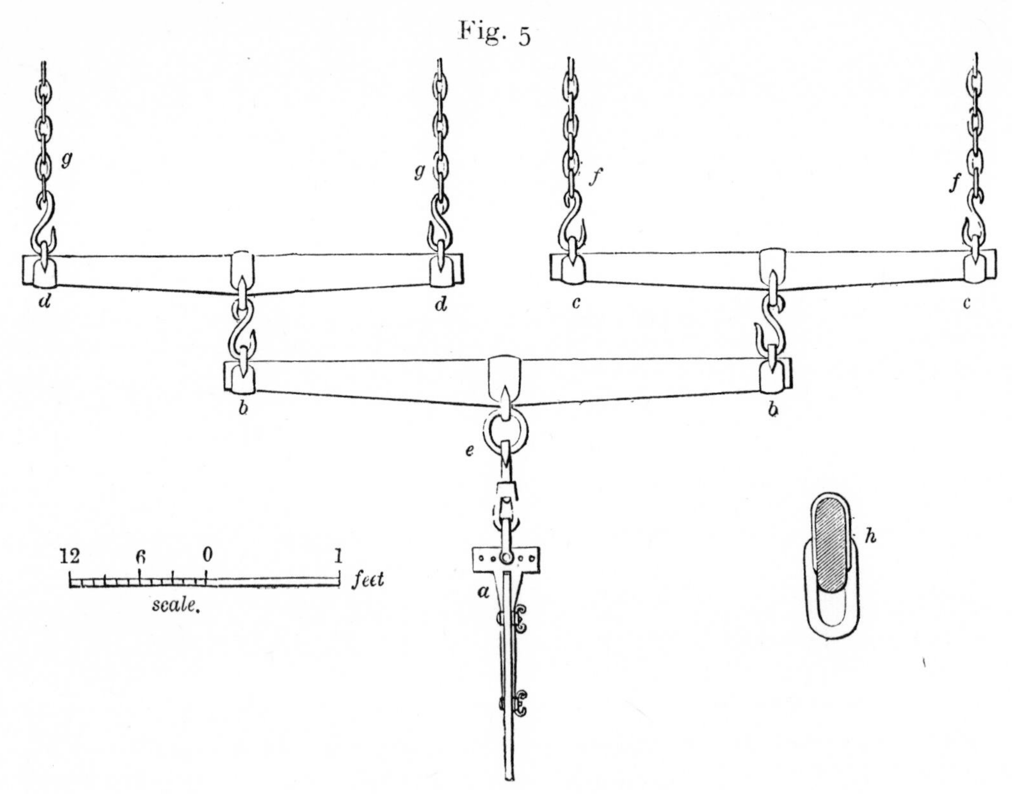

Swing-trees for two horses.

a Bridle of the plough.
b b Main swing-tree.
e Ring of main swing-tree.

c c Furrow or off side swing-tree.
d d Land or near side swing-tree.

f g Trace-chains from the harness.
h Section of main swing-tree.

Fig. 6

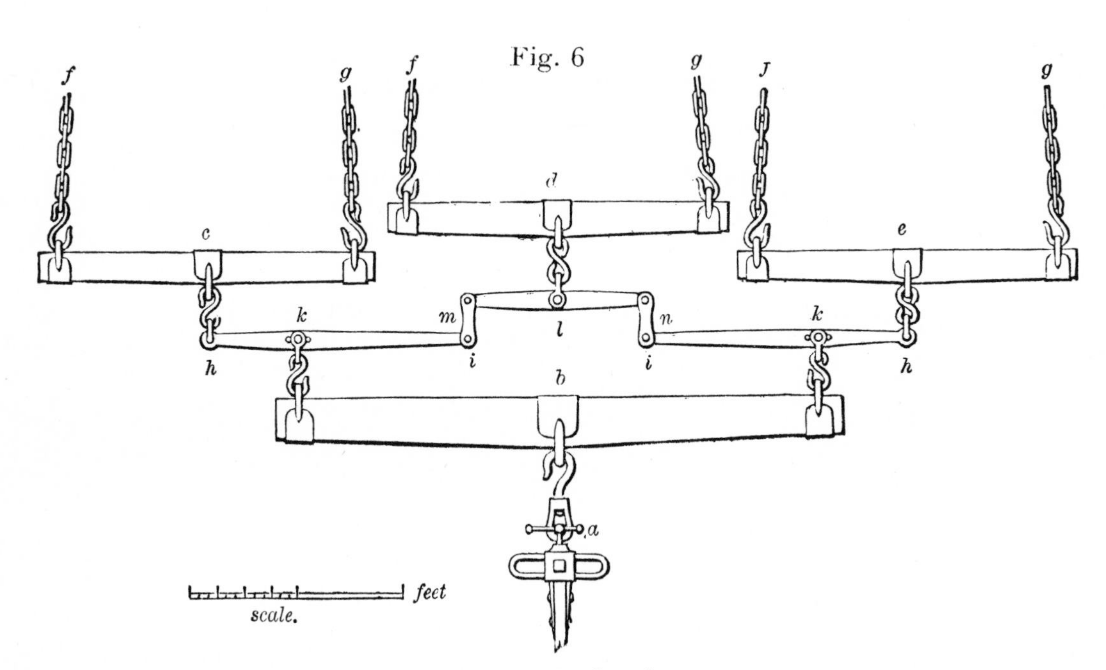

Swing-trees for three horses.

a Bridle of the plough.
b Main swing-tree.

c d e Common swing-trees for a horse each.
f g Trace-chains from harness.

h i k l m n Compensating apparatus of three levers of iron.

Fig. 7

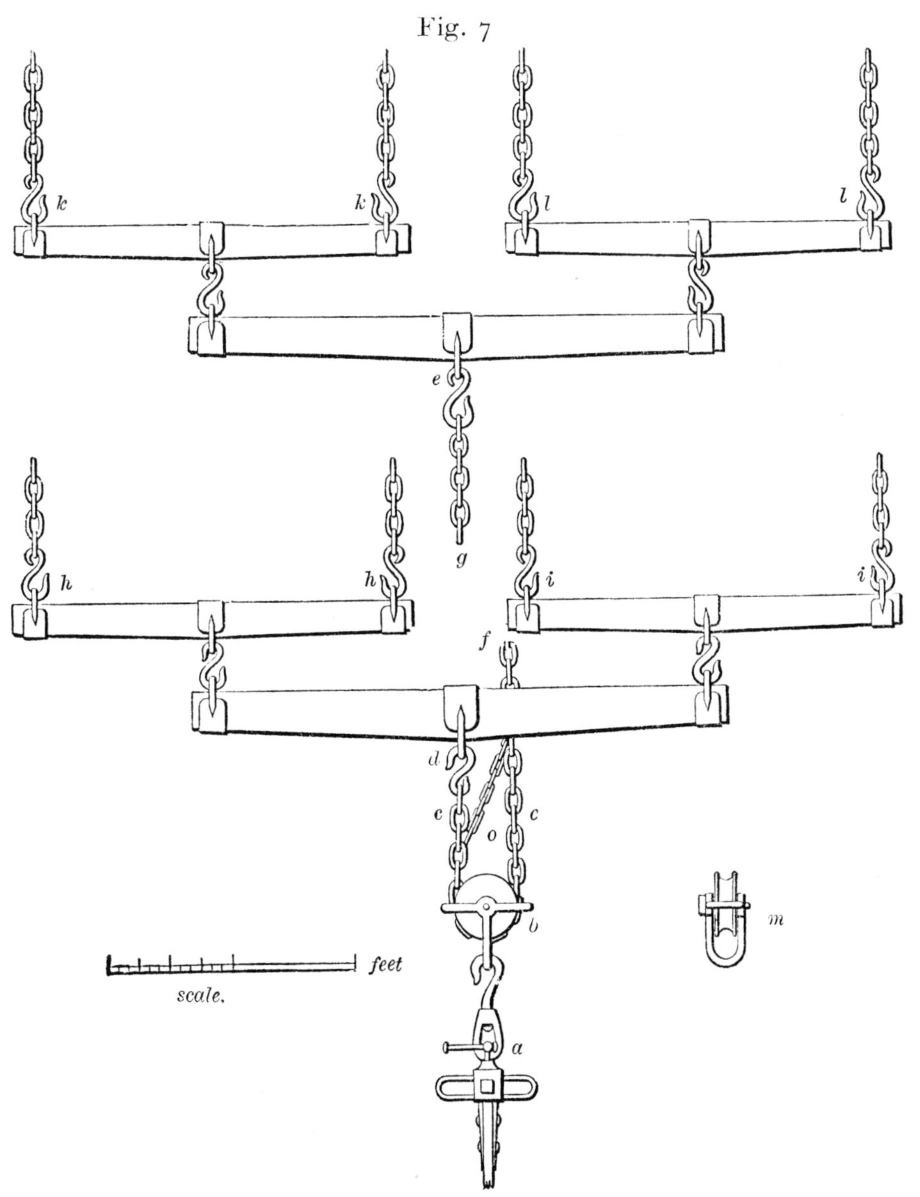

Swing-trees for four horses.

a Bridle of the plough.
b Pulley of cast-iron.
m Edge-section of pulley.
c Link-chain wove round the pulley.
d A set of common swing-trees.
e Another set of common swing-trees.
g f Chain connecting the two sets of swing-trees through the pulley.
h i k l Trace-chains from the harness.
o Check-chain.

On examining the particulars of ploughing with two horses, fig. 8, the *collars* are round the horses' necks; the top of the *haims* is seen at the upper part of the collar. The horses are yoked to the swing-trees by light *trace-chains*, linked on one end to the hooks of the haims, and hooked at the other into the eyes of the swing-trees. *Back-bands* of leather cross the back, near the groins of the horses, supporting the trace-chains by means of simple hooks. The *bridles* have blinders, and the *bearing-reins* are supported on the top of the haims. The *swing-trees* are hooked to the draught-swivel of the bridle of the plough; and being yoked abreast, the horses are enabled to exert their united strength much more effectually than if yoked one before the other. The two horses are kept together either

Fig. 8

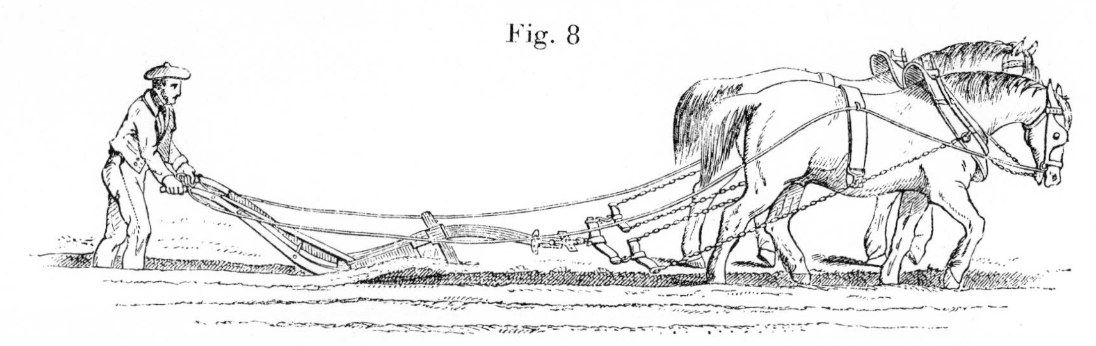

Scotch plough at work with two horses.

by a *leather strap*, buckled at each end to the bridle-ring, or by *short rein-ropes* passed from the bridle-ring to the shoulder of each horse, where they are fastened to the trace-chains. The strap only prevents the horses separating beyond its length, and allows their heads to move about loosely; but the short reins not only prevent them separating, but keep their heads steady; and on this latter account, horses fastened with them can be turned round more quickly and simultaneously than with the strap. The *reins* proceed from the ploughman's hands to the horses' heads. The off-side horse—that is, the one nearest to the spectator in the figure —is walking in the *last* made open furrow — the nigh horse walking on the *firm land*. The plough is in the act of turning over a furrow-*slice* of land, and the ploughman is walking in the *new*-made open furrow, leaning forward slightly upon the stilts, to steady himself and the plough at the same time.

525.

Fig. 9

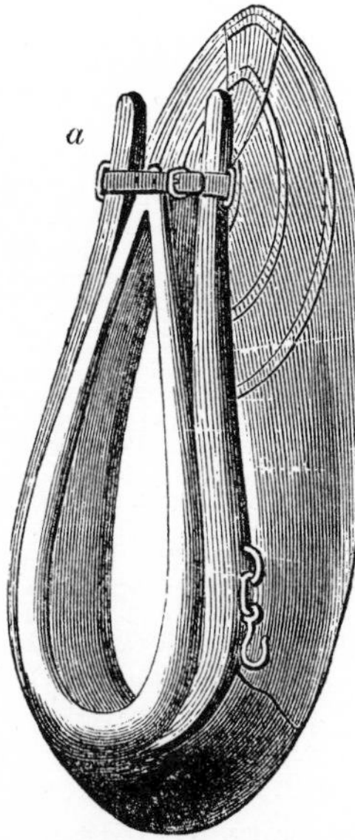

Scotch draught-horse collar and haims.

Besides swing-trees, horses require *harness* to enable them to apply their strength to the plough. The harness, as used in Scotland, is simple and efficient. It consists of a collar, fig. 9, which surrounds the neck of the horse, and serves as a padding to protect the skin of the neck and the points of the shoulder, while the horse exerts his strength in the draught. This form of collar is used in the Lothians, and its covering consists of one piece of leather stiffened in its upper part with stripes of whalebone to form the cape. The body of the collar is stuffed with wheat-straw, or what is better, rye-straw, and covered with strong tweelled woollen cloth.

516.

Fig. 10 is a form of cape common in England, which answers no purpose of protection from rain, but rather to catch the wind, and thereby obstruct the pro-

Fig. 10

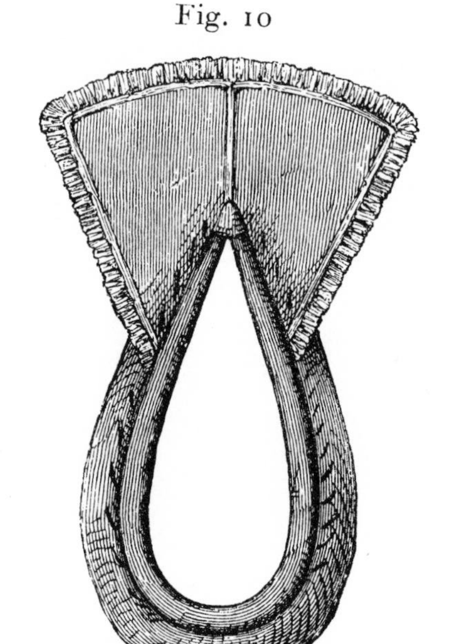

English draught-horse collar.

gress of the horse. Such a cape is frequently ornamented with flaring red worsted fringes round the edge, or with large tassels from the corner and middle, and even with bells.

518.

Fig. 11 shows the Tweeddale plough at work with three horses. The yoking of the three horses through the instrumentality of the apparatus described in fig. 6 will at once be understood. The off horse—that is, next the spectator in the figure—is walking in the last-made furrow, the other two horses are on the firm land, while the ploughman is stepping in the new-made furrow. The depth of the furrow in this case is 13 inches, instead of 7 or 8 inches—the usual depth of ploughing. The three horses plough to this depth with great ease. 526.

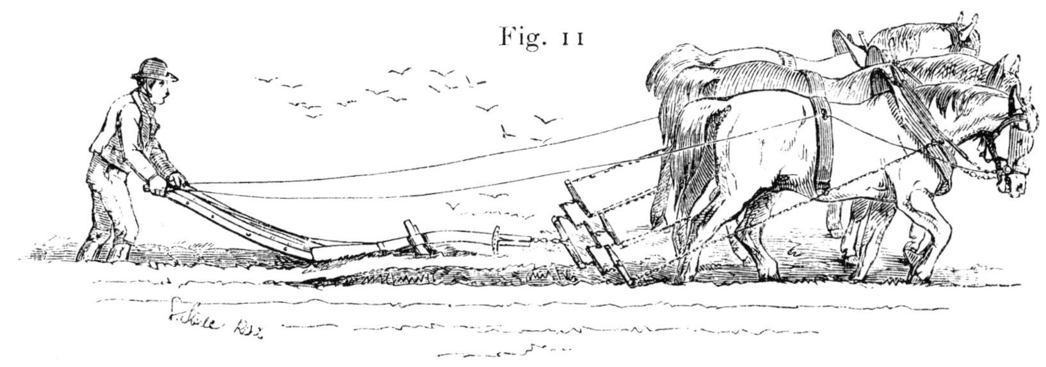

Tweeddale plough at work with three horses.

ACTIONS OF VARIOUS PLOUGHS IN USE.

It would be well to make a comparison between the actions of the various ploughs in use before entering on the different methods of ploughing land; and first, of Small's plough, fig. 12 :—

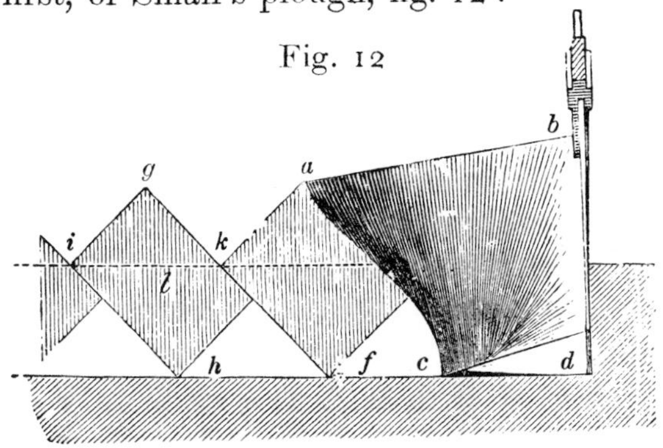

Effects of a rectangular furrow-slice.

a b c d Transverse section of mould-board.
a f, g h Sections of furrow-slice.
g k a Right angle.
i g k Triangle equal to breadth of furrow-slice.
i g, g k Equal sides of triangle.
g l Half the breadth of furrow-slice.
h f c d Level sole of furrow.

In this example, the rectangular furrow-slice is 10 inches broad by 7 inches deep. 530.

Next of Wilkie's plough, fig. 13 :—
In comparing the furrow-soles in figs. 12 and 13, besides the loss of time and labour in ploughing a breadth of furrow 8½ inches, compared with a 10-inch furrow, the crested furrow-sole leaves part of the ground unploughed. Thus, in ploughing

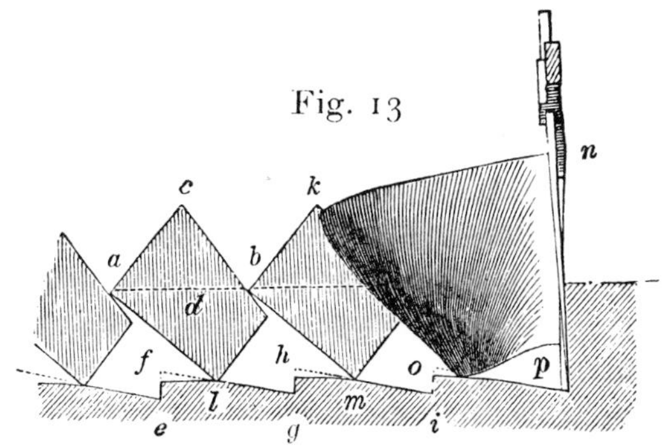

Effects of a crested furrow-slice.

k n p o Transverse section of mould-board.
k m, c l Sections of furrow-slice.
c Angle 84° or 75°.
a c b Isosceles triangle.
a c 6½ inches, upper end of furrow-slice.
l h 4½ inches, lower end of furrow-slice.
f h o p Crested furrow-sole.
e f g, g h i Triangular spaces 1½ inch left unploughed.

an imperial acre with a 10-inch furrow—leaving out of view the taking up of closings, turnings, &c.—the distance walked over by the man and horses will amount to 9.9 miles; with a 9-inch furrow the distance will be 11 miles; with 8½-inch furrow, it will be 11½ miles; and with a 7½-inch furrow, 13¼ miles. 531.

The Tweeddale plough cuts a right-angled furrow-slice and level sole as well as Small's, but its furrow-slice is deeper and broader, and the angle of inclination about the same. Fig. 14 gives the same view and mode of action of the mould-board of the Tweeddale plough as figs. 12 and 13 of Small's and Wilkie's. Its right-angled furrow-slice is 13 inches deep and 12 inches broad, laid over at a higher angle than 45°, or it might be 15 inches deep and 14 inches broad. The furrow-slice is not left whole, but much broken by the projecting breast of the mould-board, the soil being thus quite open for the free action of the air, rain, and frost; the valuable consequence of which is, that by spring the soil is completely pulverised for any purpose it may be put to. The mould-board was not formed on any theory or preconceived notion of what form a mould-board should have. It was attained by trial and error, and corrected and altered according to the suggestions of the ploughman who held the plough. At length the plough cut its furrow-slice of the above dimensions, and cleared its way in the furrow with perfect ease. 532.

A balance-plough was introduced by Fowler adapted to steam-power. It is simply two sets of four ordinary ploughs placed in opposite directions, and bal-

Fig. 14

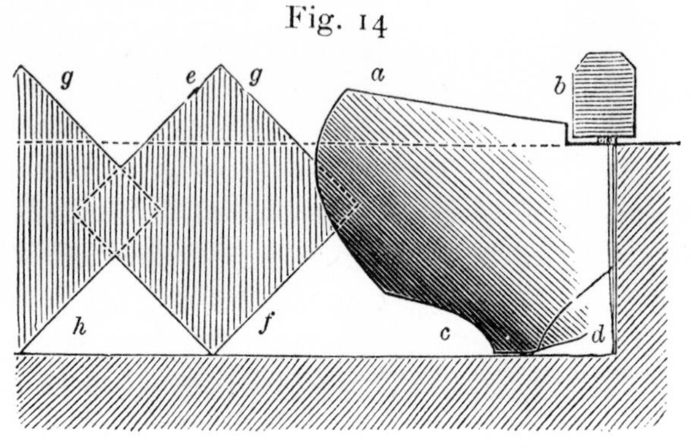

Effects of the Tweeddale furrow-slice.

a b d c Transverse section of mould-board.
e f, *g h* Sections of furrow-slices.
g Right angles.
h f c d Level sole of furrow.

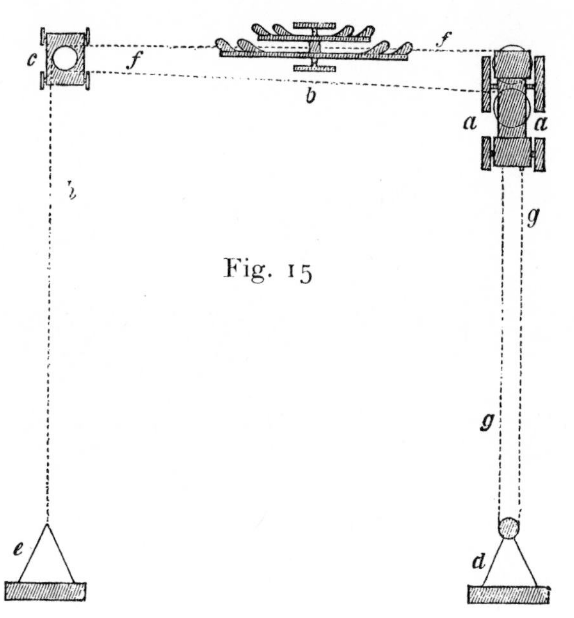

Fig. 15

Traction of Fowler's steam-plough.

a a Steam-engine, with drum and windlass.
b Balance ploughs.
c Movable anchor.
d Fixed anchor and snatch-block.
e Fixed anchor.
f f Wire rope.
g g Wire rope.
h Wire rope.

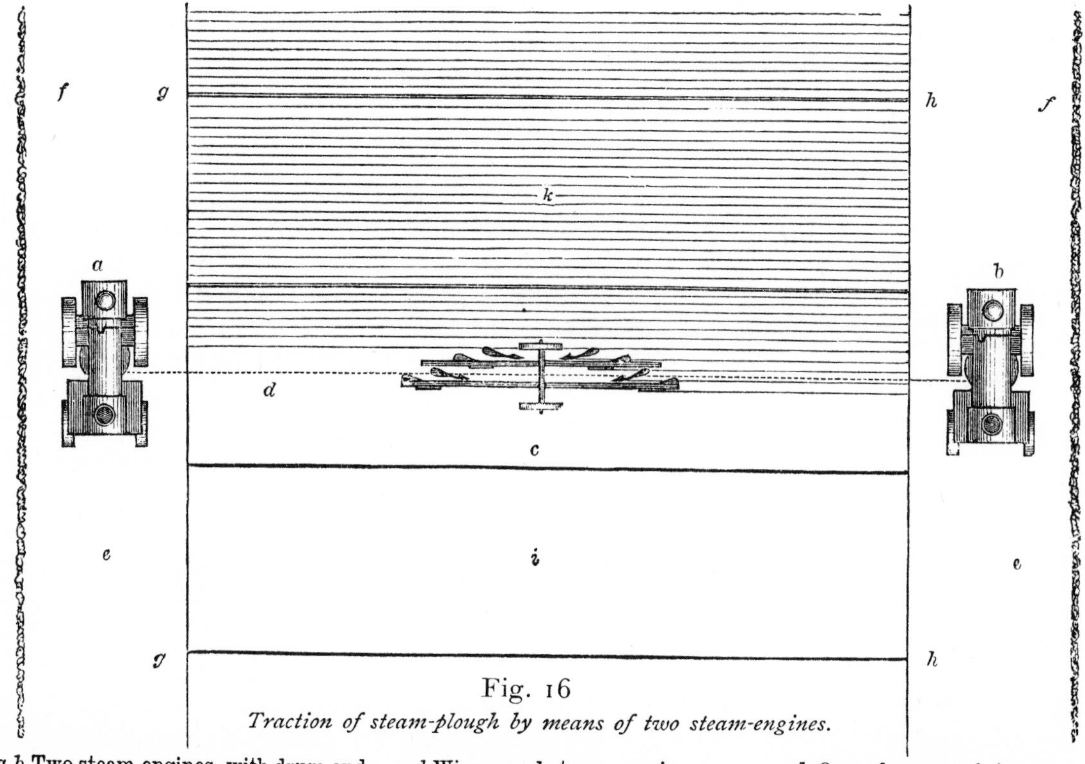

Fig. 16

Traction of steam-plough by means of two steam-engines.

a b Two steam-engines, with drum and windlass.
c Balance plough.
d Wire rope between engines.
e e Headridges.
f f Fences of the field.
g h Open furrows of ridges.
i Unploughed land.
k Ploughed land.

anced on an axle supported on two wheels. Its furrow-slice is right-angled, furrow-sole level, and inclination of furrow-slice 45°. It works much in the same fashion as Small's plough. In fig. 15 the steam-engine and windlass are combined. Two drums, worked by the engine alternately, wind up the wire rope which works the plough. There is a movable anchor, and two fixed anchors. The movable anchor and the engine progress forward as the plough turns over the soil. The wire rope moves round a pulley in the movable anchor, and finds points of resistance in the two fixed anchors, round the snatch block of one of which the wire rope winds. The wire rope in connection with the plough is kept off the ground by grooved pulleys in wooden frames, which are shifted as the plough progresses. The arrangement forms a parallelogram, the breadth of which is that of the field; the engine and movable anchor being placed on opposite headlands. Eight furrow-slices of 8 inches in depth are turned over in two journeys of the plough, at the rate of 3/4 acre per hour.* 534.

A simpler, easier, and more certain method of traction is given in fig. 16 Two steam-engines are placed on the opposite headridges of the field. A wire rope winding round in combination with the drum and windlass moves the ploughs; and as they progress in the ploughing, the engines follow along the headridges. The wire rope is supported from the ground upon grooved wheels mounted on wooden frames which are shifted forward as the ploughing progresses. 535.

A third kind of traction is by one steam-engine placed at a corner of the field, and the wire rope traverses along its four sides round fixed anchors. 536.

Fig. 17

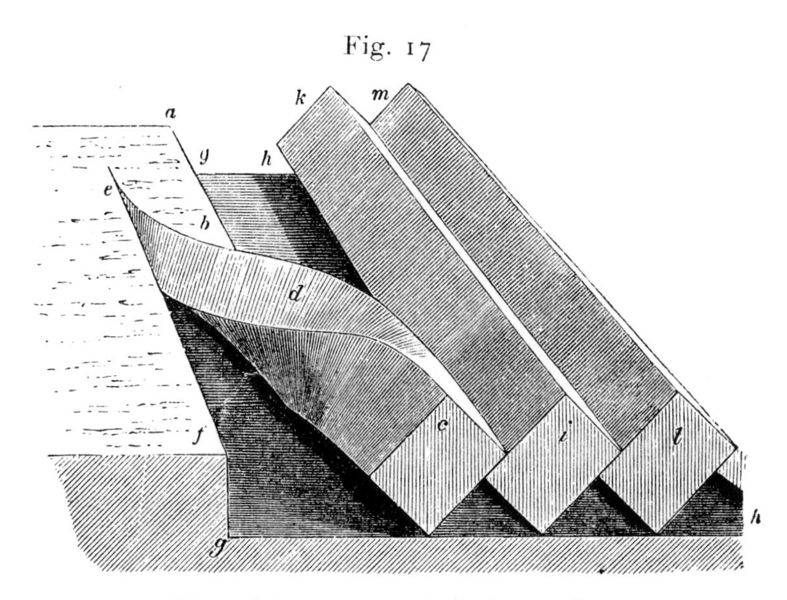

View of the movement of the furrow-slice.

a b Edge of land cut by preceding furrow.
c d Slice being turned over by the plough.
e f Edge of land being left by the ploughing furrow.
i k, *l m* Furrow-slices previously laid over.
g h Level sole of furrow.

The steam-plough, laying all its furrows in the same direction, by means of its balanced mould-boards, dispenses with ridges and open furrows. The even surface proves advantageous in certain operations—as drilling for potatoes and turnips—and it looks well; but in sowing grain by hand or machine, or drill, the guidance for the breadths in sowing the ridges will be missed, and some expedient must be substituted to have as sure a one as defined ridges. 629.

* For a complete description, with figures of the Tweeddale, Usher's, and Fowler's steam-ploughs, see *Book of Farm Imp.*, 223-238, by H. Stephens and R. S. Burn, 1858.

Fig. 18

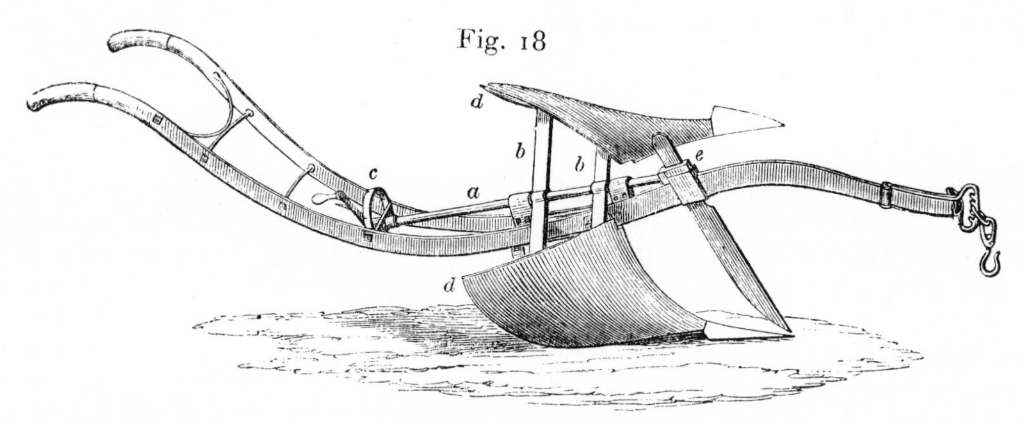

Wilkie's turn-wrist plough.

a Turn-wrist spindle.
b b Bars supporting the mould-boards.
c Crank handle for moving the spindle.
d d Mould-boards with opposite faces.
e Coulter-box to fit the coulter to each sock.

The turn-wrist plough turns over the furrows in one direction; and the one invented by Wilkie, fig. 18, is the best in Scotland. This plough acts in the same manner as the common plough, when the mould-board is set as seen in the figure, the furrow-slice being turned over to the right hand; and on coming to the land's end, the other mould-board is brought down on the left-hand side of the plough, and by it the furrow-slice is turned over to the left hand—where it is placed in the same position as did the ploughing in turning over the furrow-slice to the right hand, while moving in the opposite direction. The even surface without open furrows, executed by this mode of ploughing, is highly favourable to the action of reaping-machines in harvest. 630.

Correct ploughing possesses these characteristics:—The furrow-slices should be quite straight; for a ploughman that cannot hold a straight furrow is unworthy of the name: They should be quite parallel as well as straight, which shows they are of an uniform thickness; for thick and thin slices lying upon one another present irregularly parallel and horizontal lines: They should be of the same height, which shows that they have been cut of the same breadth; for slices of different breadths, laid together at whatever angle, present unequal vertical lines: They should present to the eye a similar form of crest and equal surface; because, where one furrow-slice exhibits a narrower surface than it should have, it has been covered with a broader slice than it should be; and where it displays a broader surface than it should have, it is so exposed by a narrower slice than should be: They should have their back and face parallel; and to discover this property after the land has been ploughed requires minute examination; but it is easily ascertained in the Tweeddale ploughing: They should lie easily upon each other, not pressed hard together: The ground, on being ploughed, should feel equally firm under the foot at all places, for slices in a more upright position than they should be, not only feel hard and unsteady, but will allow the seed-corn to fall between them and become buried: When too flat, they yield considerably to the pressure of the foot; and they cover each other too much, affording insufficient mould for the seed: They should lie over at the same angle, presenting crests in the best possible position for the action of the harrows: Crowns of ridges formed by the meeting of opposite furrow-slices, should neither be elevated nor depressed in regard to the rest of the furrows in the ridge; although ploughmen often commit the error of raising the crowns too high into a crest, the fault being easily committed by not giving the first furrow-slices sufficient room to meet, and thereby pressing them against each other: The last furrow-slice should be uniform with those of the rest of the ridge; but ploughmen are very apt to miscalculate the width of the slices near the edges of the ridges; for if the specific number of furrow-slices into which the whole ridge should be ploughed are too narrow, the last slices of the open furrow will be too broad, and will therefore lie over too flat; and should this too broad space be divided into two furrows, each slice will be too narrow, and stand too upright: When the last furrows are ill made, the open furrow cannot be proportionately ploughed out; because, if the space between the last furrows is too wide, the open furrow must be made too deep to fill up all the space; and if too narrow, there is not sufficient mould to make the open furrow of the proper size: If the last furrow-slices are laid too flat, the open furrow will throw too much mould upon the edges next the open furrow, and make them too high: When the last furrows of adjoining ridges are not ploughed alike, one side of the open furrow will have less mould than the other. From consideration of these particulars, it is obvious that ploughing land correctly, which is best exhibited in lea-ploughing, is an art which requires a skilled hand and correct eye, both of which are much interfered with in the management of the horses. Hence a ploughman who has not his horses under strict command cannot be a good hand. 557.

Ploughs should always be provided with the useful appendage of an *iron hammer*, fig. 19. The hammer and handle are forged in one piece of malleable iron, the handle being formed into a nut-key. With this simple but useful tool the ploughman has always at hand the means by which he can, without loss of time, alter and adjust the position of his plough-irons—the coulter and share—and perform other little operations which circumstances or accident may require, for the performance of which most ploughmen are under the necessity of taking advantage of the first *stone* they can find, merely from the want of this simple instrument. 573.

Fig. 19

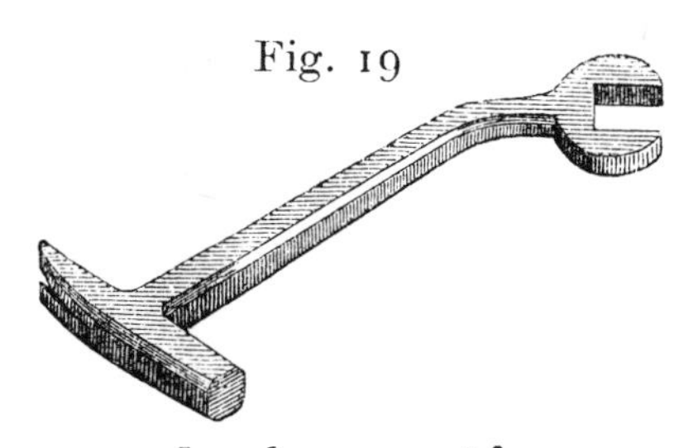

Iron hammer nut-key.

In removing ploughs from one field to another, or along a hard road to a field, instead of sliding them upon their sole-shoe, which is difficult to do when they have no hold of the ground, or upon the edge of the feather of the sock and the side of the mould-board—which is a more easy mode for the ploughman than the former, and is consequently more commonly taken—every ploughman should be provided with a plough-slide, a simple and not costly implement, as in fig. 20.

Fig. 20

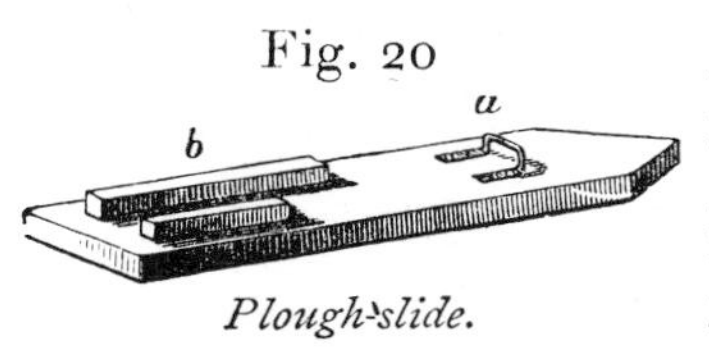

Plough-slide.

It consists of a piece of hardwood board 3 feet 4 inches long, 8 inches broad, and 2 inches thick, in which a long staple *a* is driven to take in the point of the sock;

and at *b* are fastened two small bars of wood, longways, and at such distance from one another as to take between them the sole-shoe of the plough. On the under side of the board are nailed two pieces of flat bar-iron, to act as skeds to the slide. Upon this implement the plough may be conveyed with comparative ease along any road or headridge. 574.

PLOUGHING DIFFERENT FORMS OF RIDGES.

The first process in the ridging of land upon the flat surface is *feering*, which is done by placing upright, in the direction of the ridges, not fewer than three, and as many more poles, fig. 21, $8\frac{1}{2}$ feet in length, graduated into feet and half-feet, and each painted at the

Fig. 21

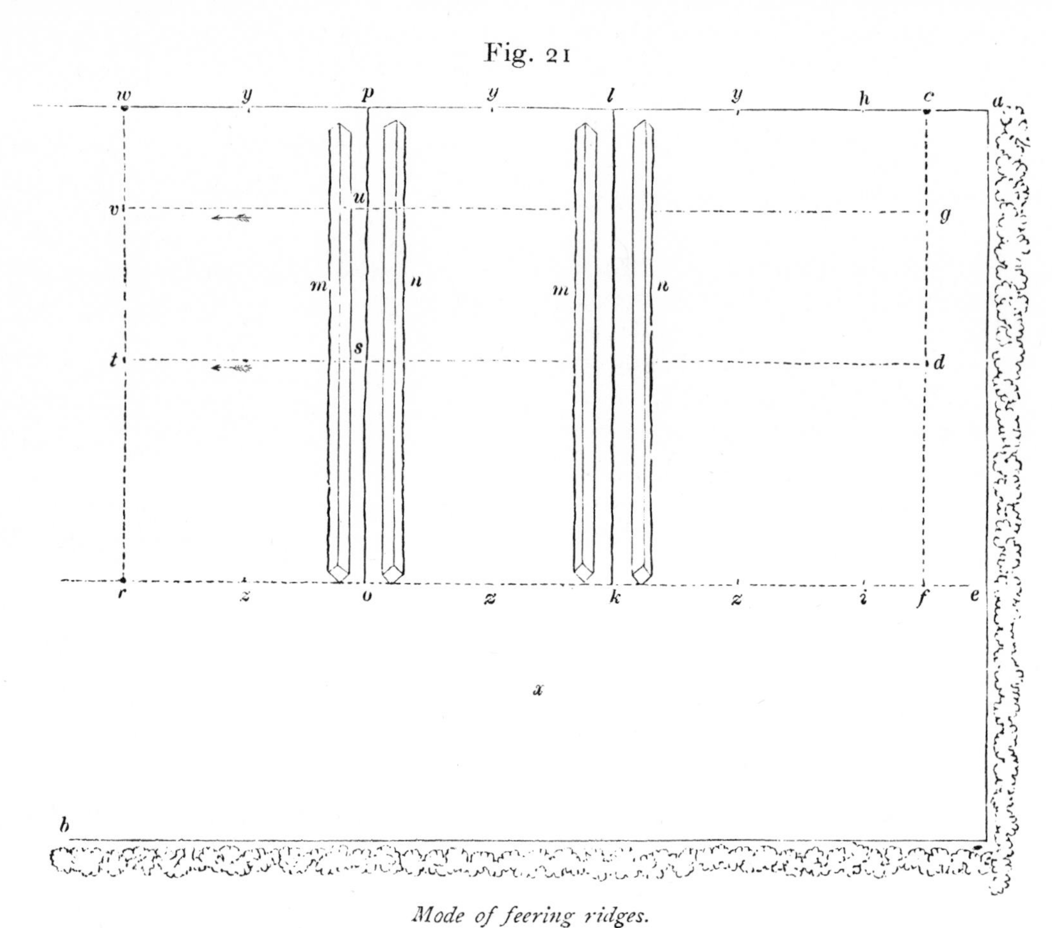

Mode of feering ridges.

a to *b* Fences of field.
x Headridge of field.
k l, *o p*, Second and third feering of ridges ; *f c* first feering of ridges
m and *n*, Furrow-slices of feerings.

Fig. 22

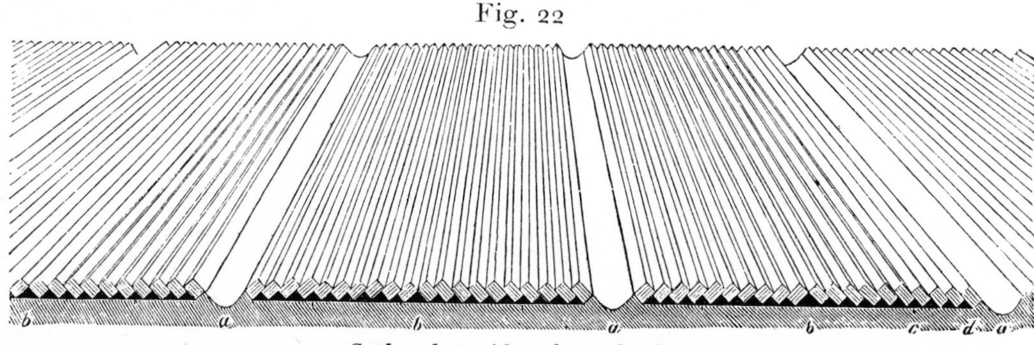

Gathered-up ridges from the flat.

a a a Three open furrows of two ridges.
a b Furrow-slices lying from left to right.
b a Furrow-slices lying from right to left.
b b Crown of two ridges.
c d Furrow-brow.
d Mould-furrow.

top of a different colour, with bright blue, red, and white, to form decided contrasts with one another when set in line, and also with green trees and hedges, and brown ground. 583.

[*The mould or water furrow was a method of draining a ploughed field before underdraining with tiles became general. On heavy soils it was used in addition to underdraining.*]

Fig. 23

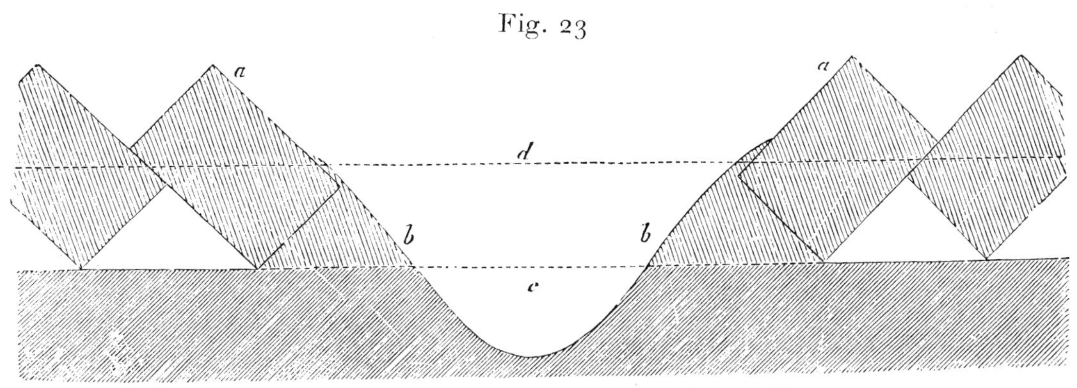

Open furrows with mould or hint-end furrow-slices.

a a Two last-ploughed furrow-slices, and open furrow between them. *b b* Two mould furrow-slices closing up the open furrow between *a* & *a*. *c* Finished open furrow.

Fig. 24

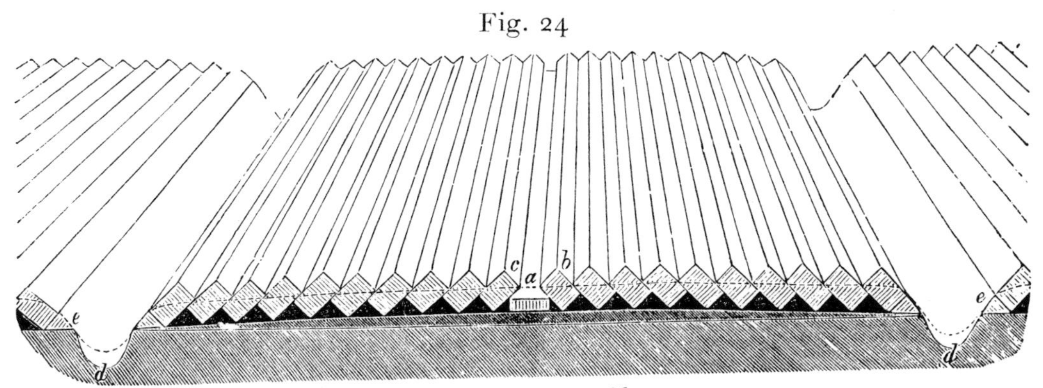

Twice-gathered-up ridges.

d to *d* Section of the ground by the first gathering-up. *e* to *e* Dotted line indicating the rise in the ground after the second gathering-up.

Fig. 25

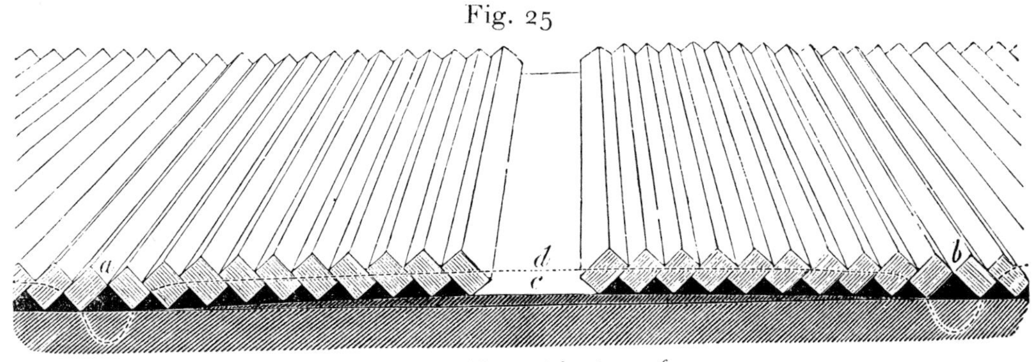

Cleaved-down ridges without gore-furrows.

d Dotted line showing the former surface of the ground. *a* and *b* Dotted line showing the former open furrows.

Fig. 26

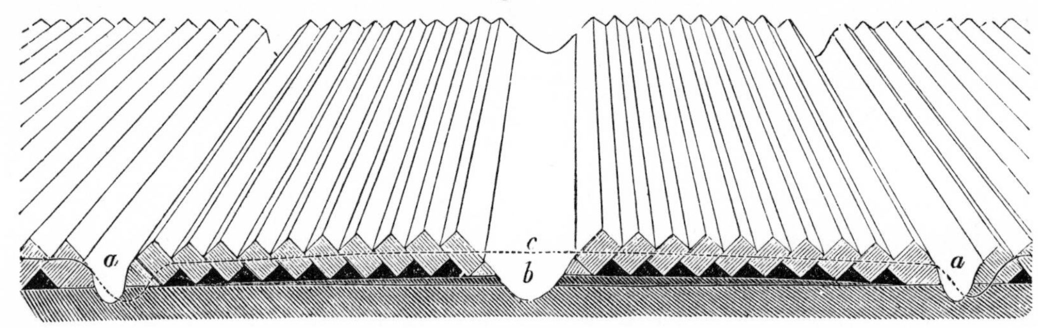

Cleaved-down ridges with gore-furrows.

c Dotted line showing the former surface of the ground. *a* and *a* Dotted line showing the former open furrows.

PULLING AND STORING TURNIPS.

Fig. 27

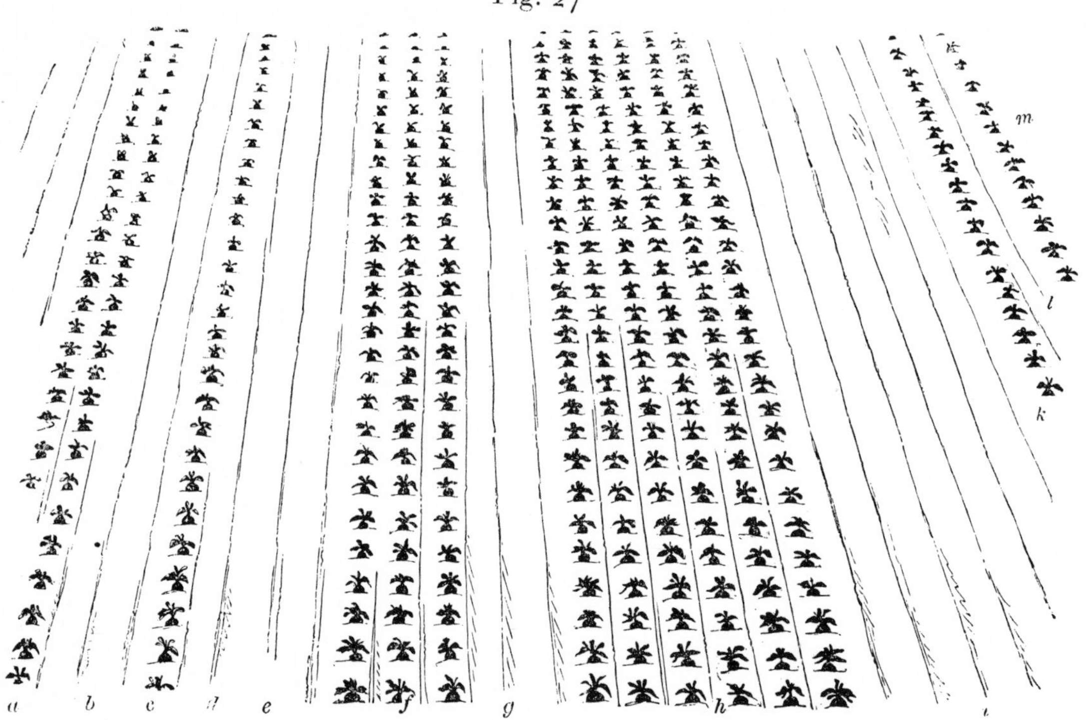

Methods of stripping the ground of turnips in given proportions.

a 2 drills left, and *b* 2 drills pulled, when half is left on.
b 2 drills pulled, and *c* 1 drill left, when one-third is left on.
d e 3 drills pulled, and *c* 1 drill left, when one-fourth is left on.

[*Removing part of the crop from the field for stall feeding cattle without damaging the remainder, which will be folded by sheep* (see below).]

Fig. 27 shows how turnips are stripped off the ground in the various proportions enumerated above. The *half* can be pulled in various ways, but not all may be left, by pulling 3 drills at *e*, and leaving 1 at *c*. taking away 2 drills *b*; or by taking away 3 drills *e* and leaving 3 drills *f*; or by taking away 6 drills *i* and leaving 6 drills *h*; or by taking away 1 drill *l* and leaving 1 drill *k*. 681.

Fig. 28

Method of pulling turnips in preparation for storing them.

a and *b* 2 pulled drills. *e* and *f* 2 drills left with turnips. *c* and *d* 2 heaps of prepared turnips.

The tops and tails of turnips are easily removed by means of very simple implements. Figs. 29 and 30 represent these in their simplest form, fig. 29 being an old scythe reaping-hook, with the point broken off. 690.

Fig. 29 Fig. 30

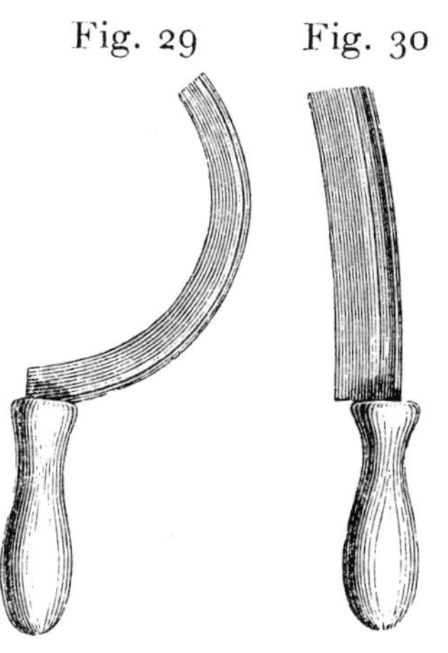

Implements for topping and tailing turnips.

The mode of using these implements in removing tops and tails from turnips is this: When 2 drills are pulled and 2 left, the field-worker moves along between the 2 drills of turnips to be pulled, at *a*, fig 28, and pulling a turnip with the left hand by the top from either drill, holds the bulb in a horizontal direc-

Fig. 31

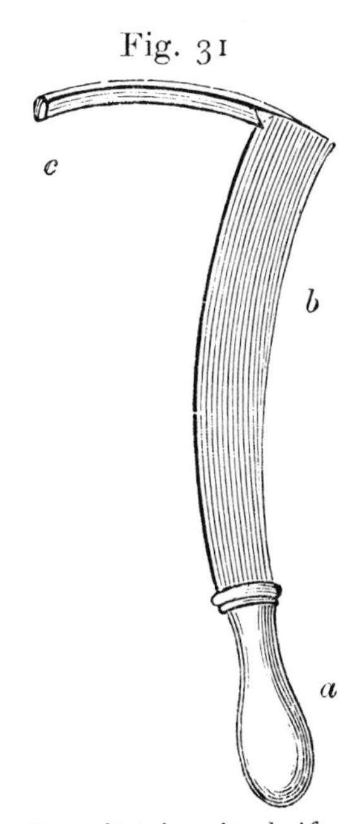

Turnip trimming-knife.

a Handle.
b Cutting edge.
c Claw welded to the extremity of the back.

tion, as in fig. 32, over and between the drills *e* and *f*, fig. 28, and with the knife first takes off the root with a smart stroke, and then cuts off the top between the turnip and the hand with a sharper one, on which the turnip falls into the heaps *c* or *d*, the tops being thrown down on the cleared ground. Thus, pulling one

Fig. 32

Mode of topping and tailing turnips.

b, root, first cut off. *a*, top, where cut off.

or two turnips from one drill, and then as many from the other, the two drills are cleared from end to end. Another field-worker is a companion by going up *b*, pulling the turnips from the drills on either side of her, and dropping them, topped and tailed, into the same heap as her companion. 692.

The storing of turnips is well done in this manner. Choose a piece of lea ground, convenient to access of carts, near the steading, on a 15-feet ridge, running N. and S., for the site of the store. Fig. 33 gives the form of a turnip-store. The cart with topped and tailed turnips is backed to the spot of the ridge chosen to begin the store, and there emptied of its contents. The ridge being 15 feet wide, the store should not exceed 10 feet in width at the bottom, to allow a space of at least 2½ feet on each side towards the open furrow of the ridge, to carry off surplus water. The turnips are piled by hand up to the height of 4 feet; but will not pile to 5 feet on that width of base. The store may thus be formed of any length; but it is more desirable to make two or three stores on adjoining ridges, than a very long one on the same ridge, as its farthest end may be too far off to use a wheel-barrow to remove the stored turnips. Straw drawn out lengthwise is put 6 inches thick above the turnips for thatch, and kept down by means of straw ropes arranged lozenge-shaped, and fastened to pegs driven in a slanting direction into the ground, along the base of the straw. Or a spading of earth, taken from the furrow, may be placed upon the ends of the ropes to keep them down. The straw is not intended to keep out either rain or air—for both preserve turnips fresh—but to protect them from frost, which causes rottenness, and from drought, which shrivels them. To avoid frost, the end, and not the side of the store should be presented to the N., which is generally the quarter for frost. If the ground is flat, and the open furrows nearly on a level with the ridges, so that a fall of rain might overrun the bottom of the store, a furrow-slice should be taken out of the open furrows by the plough, and laid over to keep down the ropes, and the furrow cleared out as a gaw-cut with the spade. 705.

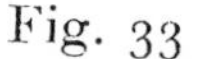

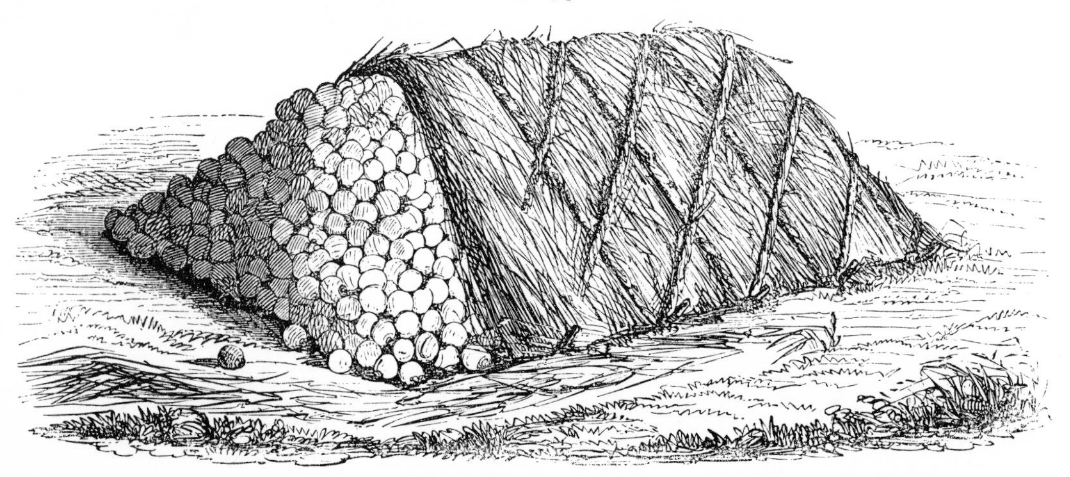

Triangular turnip-store.

FEEDING SHEEP ON TURNIPS IN WINTER.

Room having been prepared on turnips for sheep to be fed upon them, by removing half the crop in the manner described in fig 27, the first thing to be done is to carry the articles on carts to the field to construct a temporary enclosure of a given space. It is the duty of the shepherd to erect the enclosure, and he requires in any case but little assistance from other labourers. 813.

Fig. 34

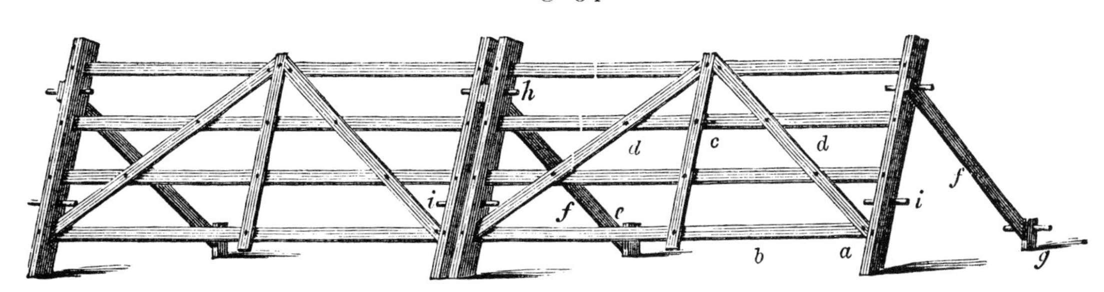

Wooden hurdles or flakes set for confining sheep on turnips.

A very common hurdle used in England is shown in fig. 35. It is formed of any sort of willow or hardwood, as oak-copse, ash-saplings, or hazel. It con-

Fig. 35

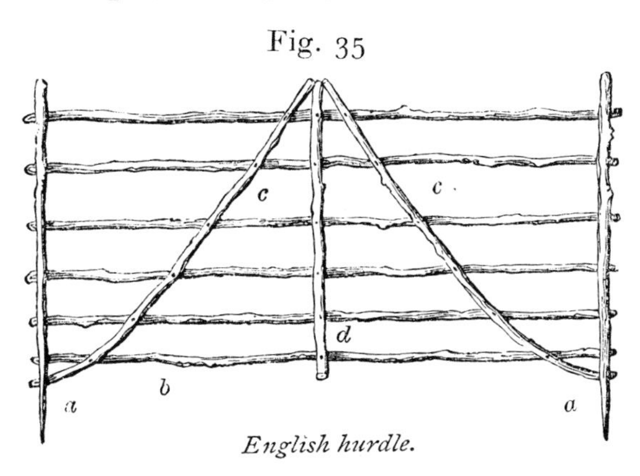

English hurdle.

sists of 2 heads *a a*, 6 slots *b*, 2 stay-lots *c c*, and an upright slot *d*. The slots are mortised into the heads and nailed with flattened fine-drawn nails, at 6d. per lb., which admit of being very firmly riveted, upon which the strength of the hurdle mainly depends: 100 poles at 18s. make 36 hurdles, which, including nails and workmanship, cost £1, 11s. 6d., or 10s. 6d. per dozen. Although the horizontal slots are cut 9 feet long, the hurdle, when finished, is only somewhat more than 8 feet, the slot ends going through the heads 1 or 2 inches: 2 hurdles to 1 rod of 16 feet, or 8 to 1 chain of 22 yards, are the usual allowance. 816.

[*The fold pitcher and the driver are used to make holes 9 inches deep to accommodate hurdles and stakes.*]

Fig. 36 Fig. 37

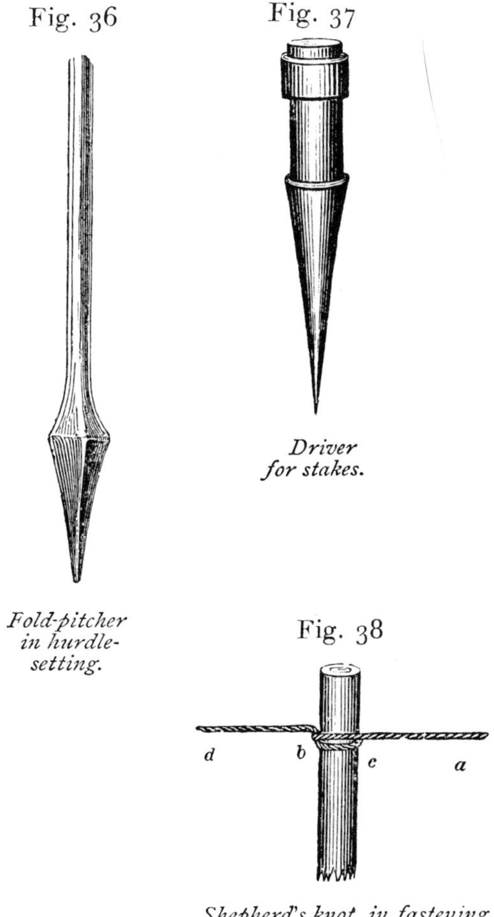

Fold-pitcher in hurdle-setting.

Driver for stakes.

Fig. 38

Shepherd's knot, in fastening a net to a stake.

Nets, made of twine of the requisite strength, form a superior enclosure for sheep; and, to constitute them into a fence, they are supported by stakes driven into the ground. 820.

Fig. 39

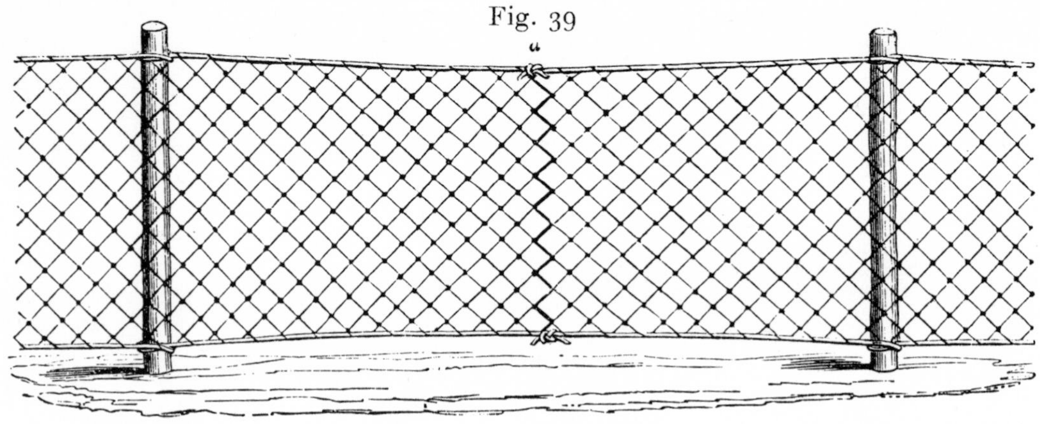

Net set for confining sheep.

When sheep are on turnips they are supplied with dry fodder, hay or straw; clover-hay is the best and most nutritious, but fresh oat-straw answers the purpose very well. The fodder is supplied them in racks, which are of various forms; some are so elevated that sheep can with difficulty reach the fodder; and others are mounted on too high wheels. I have found an elegant, strong, and useful fodder-rack for sheep, fit for grass or tares in summer, or turnips in winter, in fig. 40.

Fig. 40

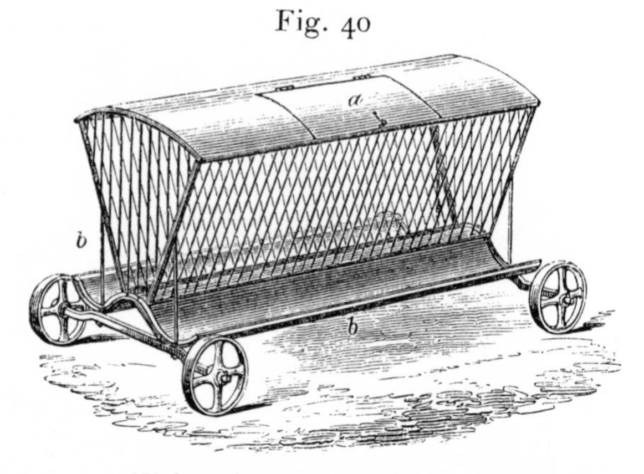

Kirkwood's wire sheep-fodder rack.

Rack of wirework 6 feet long, 2 feet 9 inches wide at top, 8 inches wide at bottom, and 2 feet 3½ inches deep.
a Curved cover of sheet-iron with a hatch.
b b Sheet-iron troughs to contain corn, &c.

It was invented by Mr Kirkwood of Tranent. The troughs are provided with a hole at each end to allow the rain to drain off, and might be used in dry weather for holding salt or oilcake for the day. The rack is mounted on axles and 4 wheels, to be moved anywhere. The iron supports and axles are malleable, and the implement costs £4, 4s., and its strength and durability are great. 848.

Until of late years, sheep helped themselves to turnips, and when the bulbs were scooped out to the ground their *shells* were raised with a *picker*, the mode of using which is seen in fig. 41. By this

Fig. 41

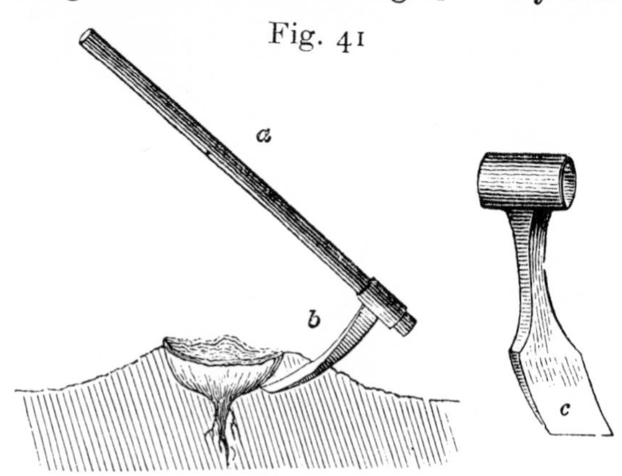

Best form of turnip-picker.

a Handle 4 feet long.
b Blade 10 inches long, including eye for handle.
c Breadth of blade 2 inches.

mode of action, the tap-root of the turnip is cut through and the shell separated from the ground at one stroke. The tap-root contains an acrid juice detrimental to the stomach of sheep, and should be left in the ground. Notwithstanding the general use of turnip-slicers, a turnip-picker is useful on small farms. 851.

The mode now adopted of serving turnips to sheep, is to cut them into small pieces with a turnip-slicer into troughs conveniently placed, while the sheep have liberty to eat turnips from the ground. A most efficient slicer is Samuelson's improved Gardner's *cylinder turnip-slicer for sheep*, fig. 42. In working this turnip-slicer, the field-worker picks up the turnips along 2 drills with the picker, fig. 41,

Fig. 42

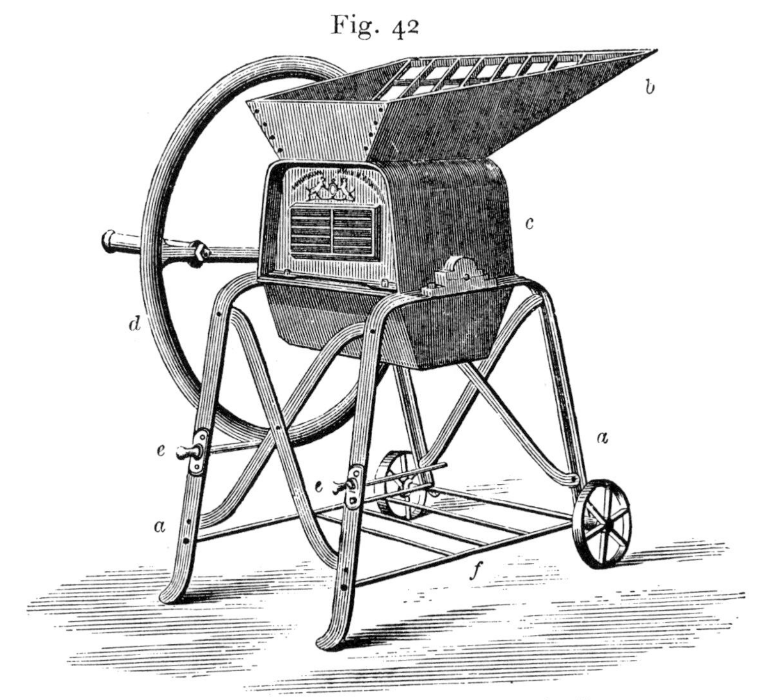

Samuelson's Gardner's cylindrical turnip-slicer.

a a Malleable-iron framing.
b Hopper.
c Box of cylinder, with the cutter.
d Fly-wheel with handle.
e e Where handles are fixed for moving the machine.
f Frame for skep to receive the sliced turnips.

then cuts off their tops. She throws the prepared turnips into the hopper—as many as it will hold—drives the fly-wheel with the handle, and fills the skep on the frame below the machine, which she empties into the turnip troughs. On wheeling the machine along the drills of turnips she uses the handles, from trough to trough.* 853.

Fig. 43

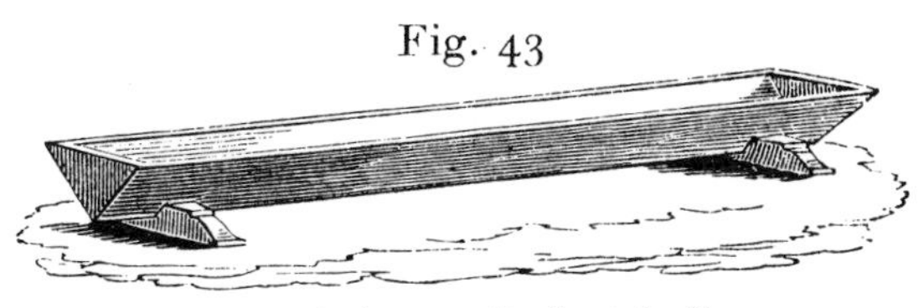

Trough for turnip sheep-feeding.

Having prepared the ground with every requisite for the reception of the sheep, fig. 44 gives a bird's-eye view of a break of turnips in a turnip-field occupied by sheep. Of the turnips, *a*, *a*, *a*, half have been pulled. The ground is bare beyond the turnip-slicer *b* in its advance along one side of the break to the other. The turnip-slicer *b* is proceeding up beside the two drills *c*, and depositing the sliced turnips into one of the small troughs *d*, while out of another some of the sheep are eating, as also in the drills *c*. The sheep are scattered over the ground as they usually are, some following one another in a string *f* towards the place where their food is preparing for them, whilst others *g* are lying resting, regardless of food. Some *h* are standing, as if meditating what next to do, and others *i* examining matters about the nets. Some nibble at the dry fodder in the racks *r*, whilst a group *k* lie under their shelter. Such are the usual occupations of sheep when they have abundance of food at their command. The field-worker *l* is slicing the turnips with the machine. The nets *m m* enclose two sides of the break, the other two sides being supposed to be the fences of the field. The remainder of the net along the upper part of the break is coiled round the top of a stake at *p*, and there also the mallet and driver await their use. The turnips *n* to the right of the nets are undrawn, while those *o* above the nets are stripped, indicating that the progress of the break is upwards towards the top of the field, in

* Gardner's original and wheel-barrow disc turnip-cutters for sheep are fully described and figured in the *Book of Farm Imp.*, 436-41, by H. Stephens and R. S. Burn.

Fig. 44

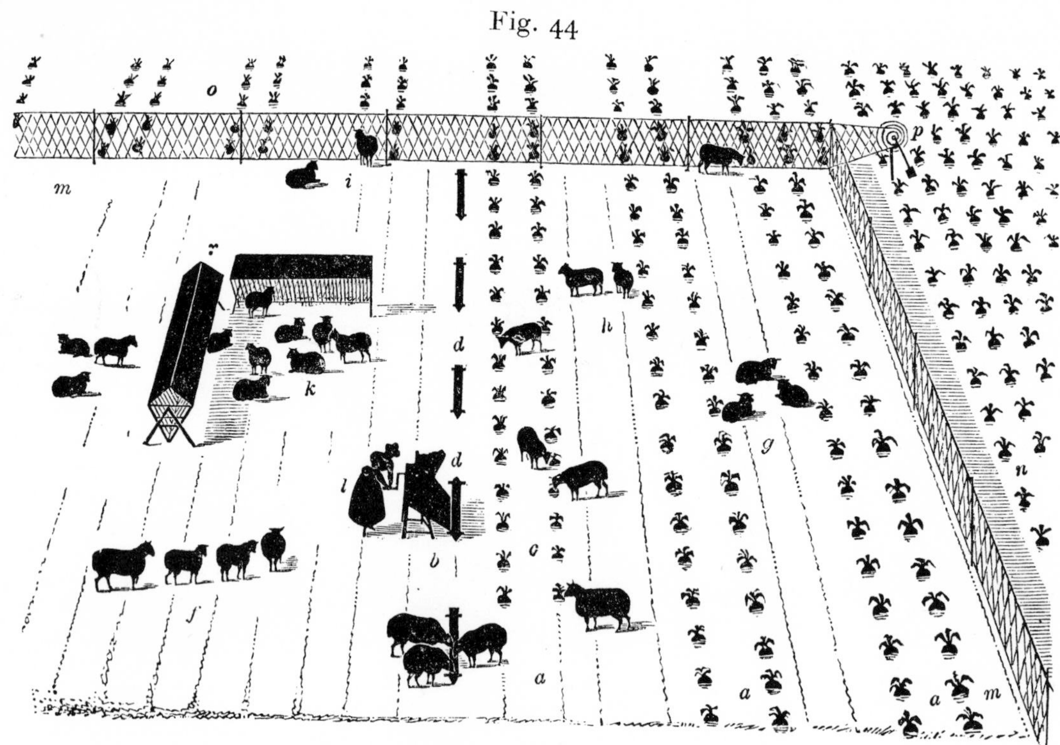

Mode of occupying turnips with feeding sheep.

Fig. 45

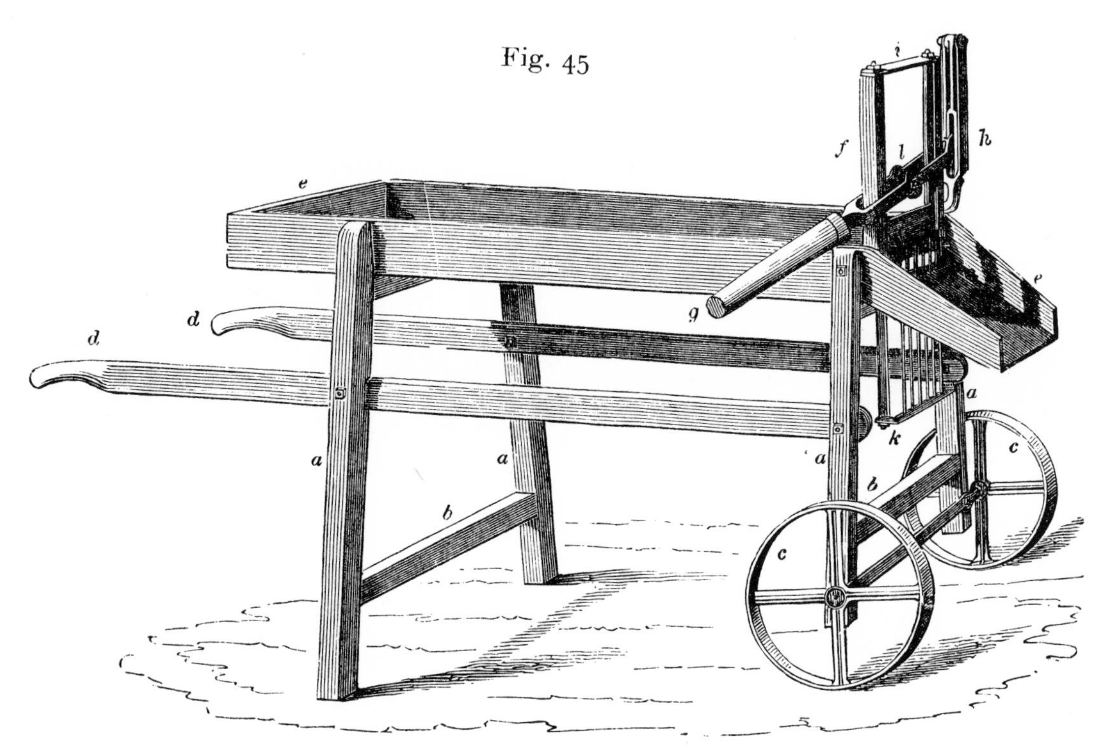

Lever turnip-slicer for sheep.

a a Frame.
b b Cross rails.
d d Bars forming handles.
c c Cast-iron wheels.
e e Trough for turnips with spout.
f Grooved frame of iron.
g Lever handle.
h Forked support to handle.
i Swing-link jointed.
k l Gridiron cutter jointed to the handle.

a line with the drills and the ridges; and this part of the arrangement is not a matter of chance, because the breadth of each break should succeed one another across the field, that the land, when cleared of turnips, may be ploughed into ridges. 855.

I have known one field-worker supply 220 sheep with sliced turnips by this lever turnip-slicer, fig. 45. It is worked by moving the handle with the right hand, while the left pushes forward each turnip, rooted and shawed, successively to be sliced by the gridiron cutter, while the finger-form slices fall down the spout into the trough below. 858.

Sheep while on turnips are fed on oilcake or corn. Either of these is best served in a covered trough, fig. 46, to protect it from the weather. Its construction requires no explanation. 859.

Oilcake or corn, or both, may be served in these troughs to sheep on grass in winter as their entire food. Oilcake renders the dung of sheep moist. It is given them in a bruised form, partly in powder and partly in pieces, as it falls from the oilcake-breaker. There is no use measuring the quantity of oilcake to sheep when on turnips, as they will eat it when inclined, and some sheep eat it more heartily than others, but 1 lb. to each sheep a-day is the usual allowance, as is also of corn. 860.

Fig. 46

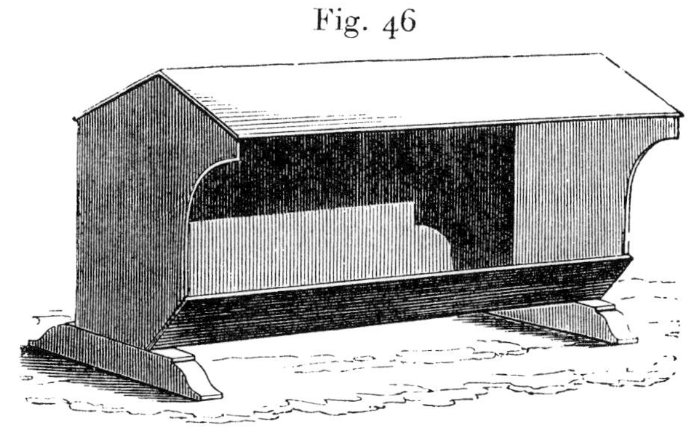

Oilcake or corn box for feeding sheep.

In fig. 47 is a perspective view of Ransome and Sim's oilcake-breaker. The oilcake is put into the hopper, the mouth of which is open upwards. The two rollers bruise it to any degree of smallness by means of pinching-screws. The bruised cake falls down the spout into any vessel below. The price of this oilcake-breaker is £4, 10s., and is very compact in its form. 861.

Fig. 47

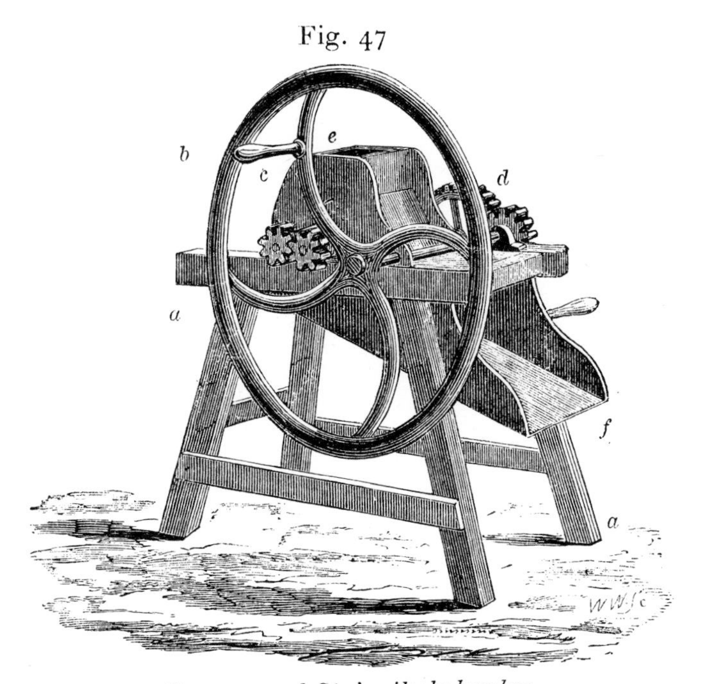

Ransome and Sim's oilcake-breaker.

a a Frame. *b* Fly-wheel with handle. *c* Box containing 2 bruising rollers. *d* Spur-wheel connected with a roller. *e* Hopper for oilcake. *f* Delivery-spout.

STELLS FOR SHEEP ON HILL FARMS.

[*A stell is a walled enclosure in which sheep can find shelter in hard weather.*]

Fig. 49 is a stell of 18 yards diameter inside, surrounded by a wall 6 feet high, the first 3 feet of stone, the other 3 feet of turf; costs 2s. 4d. per rood of 6 yards if erected by the tenant, and if wholly of stone, with a cope, by the landlord, 7s. per rood; will embrace 9⅓ roods, at a cost of £3, 5s. 4d., including quarrying and carriage of stones—a trifling outlay compared to the permanent advantage derived from it on a hill-farm. The opening into the stell should be from the side towards the rising ground, and its width 3 feet. Such a structure as this will easily contain 10 score of sheep for weeks, and even 15 or 16 score may be put into it for a night without being too much crowded. 929.

Fig. 48

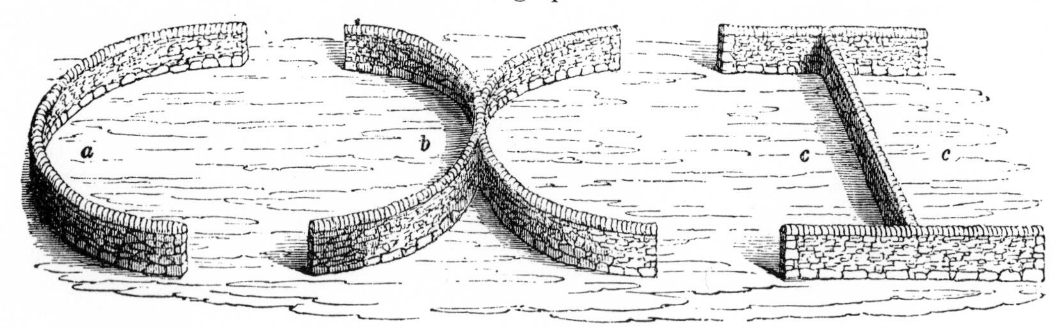

Ancient stells.

Fig. 49

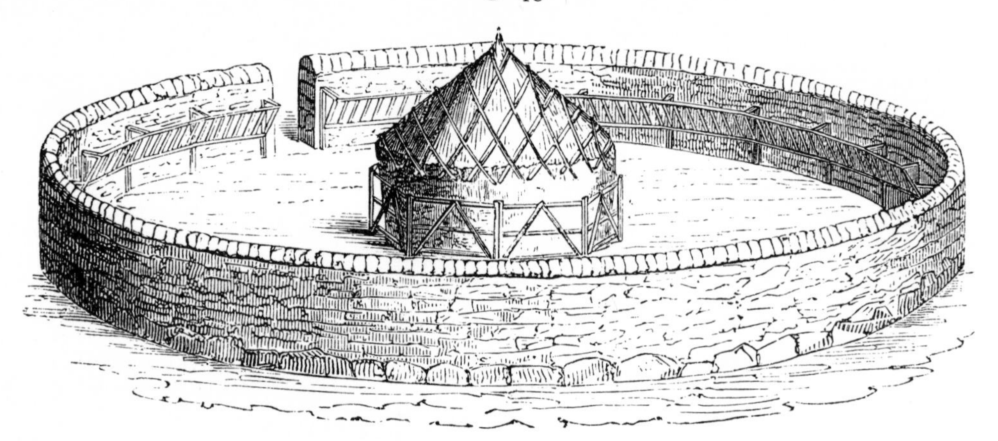

Circular stell, with hay-racks and hay-stack.

Fig. 50

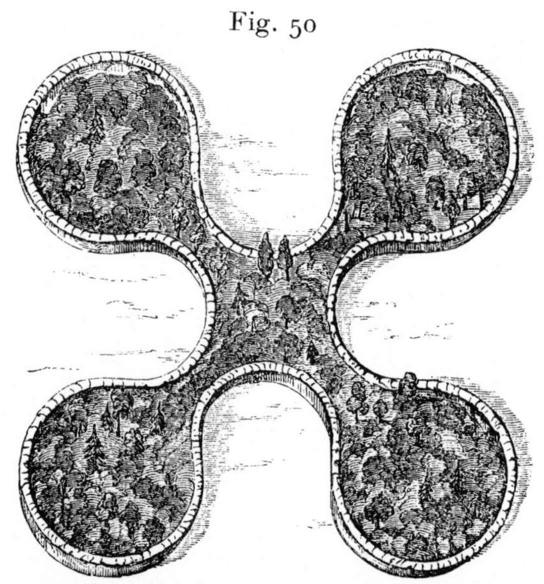

Outside stell sheltered by plantation on every quarter.

[*The description given for fig.* 49 *is typical of the other stells.*]

Fig. 51

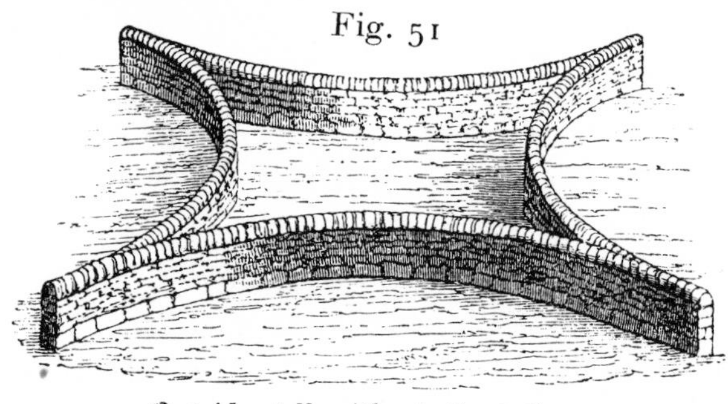

Outside stell without plantation.

Fig. 52

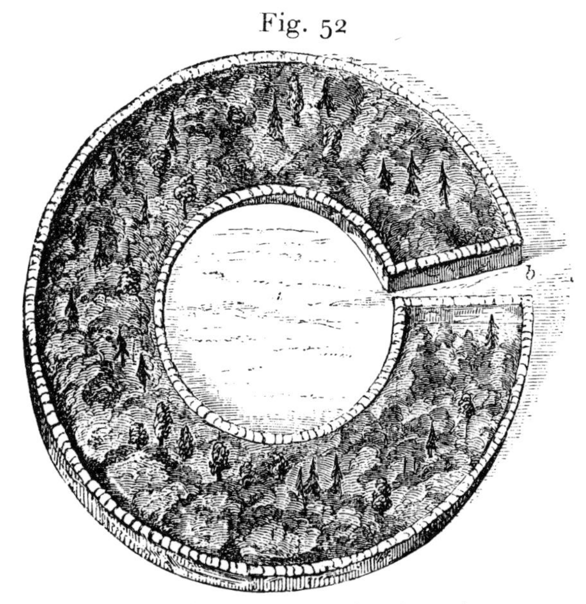

Inside stell sheltered by plantation.

BRATTING SHEEP.

There are other modes of protecting hill-sheep from the severities of weather besides stells, and which may be regarded as more personally comfortable to them. One of these is *bratting*, which is covering the sheep with a cloth. Cloth, well suited for the purpose, may be made from the refuse wool of carpet manufactories, as thick and warm as a blanket, and at only a 6d. per yard. If sacking is employed, it may be had for 4d. per yard. The brats are dipped in coal-tar to resist wet and rotting, and if taken care of will last 5 seasons. They should be made early in summer to be in good state for use in November. This cloth rendered waterproof with Indiarubber would be more comfortable, clean, and durable. 949.

Fig. 53

Bratted sheep.

a A tie below the belly behind the shoulder.
b One before hind legs.
c Under the middle of the belly.
d e Across the breast.
f Behind the hind legs.

ACCOMMODATION FOR CATTLE IN WINTER IN THE STEADING.

All cattle-courts and hammels should be provided with *troughs for turnips*, and they are placed conveniently against the walls, as in fig. 54. Some board the bottom with wood; and, where that is plentiful, it is cheap, and answers the purpose, and is pleasanter for cattle in wet and frosty weather; but where pavement can be easily procured, it is more durable. 1001.

Fig. 54

Turnip-trough for courts.

a The wall.
b Building to support bottom of trough.
c Pavement bottom of trough.
d f Planking of front and end of trough.
e Iron bar to strengthen the planking.

Cows stand in stalls, and stalls, to be easy for them to lie down and rise up and be milked in, should never be less than 5 feet in width. Four feet is a more common width, but is too narrow for a large cow, and even 7 feet is considered in dairy districts a good double stall for two cows. My opinion is, that every cow should have a stall for her own use in lying, standing, eating her food, and being milked, and of such length and breadth as she may lie at ease betwixt the manger and the gutter. The width

Fig. 55

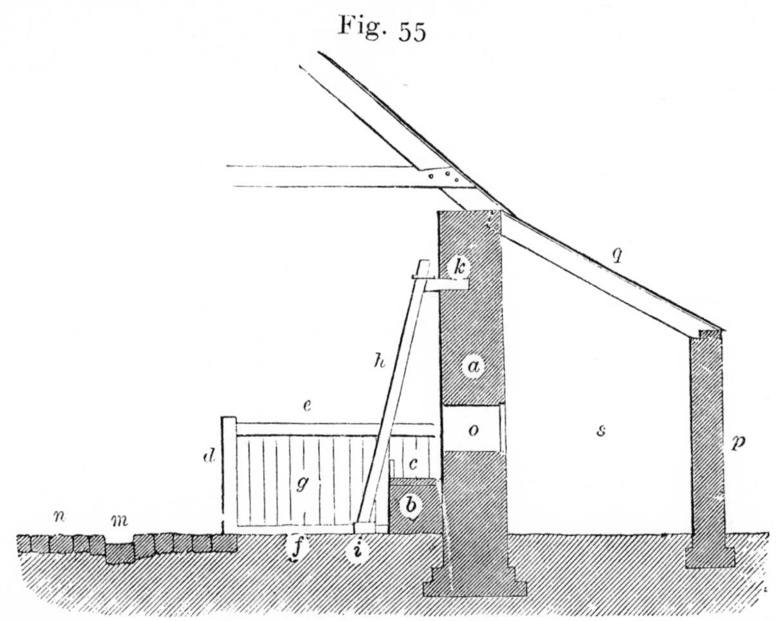

Byre travis, manger, and stake.

a Wall of byre.
b Building supporting manger.
c Manger with a front of wood.
d Hardwood hind post.
e Hardwood top rail.
f Curb-stone.
g Travis of wood, 6 feet long.
h Hardwood stake for the binder.
i Stone base for stake.
k Block of wood for top of stake.
m Dung-gutter of pavement.
n Paved floor.
o Opening through wall for turnips.
p Wall of shed.
q Roof of shed.
s Shed for food.

of byre should be 18 feet; made up of the manger 2 feet in width, length of a large cow 8 feet, the gutter 1 foot broad, leaving 7 feet behind the gutter for a passage for containing the different implements used in milking cows and removing the dung. If a passage of 3 feet for food is given at the head of cows, the passage for milk-work will be curtailed from 7 to 4 feet, which may be inconvenient for dairy purposes, but may do for feeding cattle. A stall of 4 feet in width will suffice for a feeding ox, or even, for the sake of economy, a double stall of 8 feet for two oxen. In every other respect feeding cattle should have the same accommodation as cows. 1017.

Fig. 55 is a section of *travis and manger of a byre.* The opening through the wall is not necessary, and the shed behind it may be dispensed with; but where it is, it forms a convenient turnip-store, to which access might be obtained from the byre by a back door. 1018.

Cows and oxen are bound to a stake in stalls by means of a ligature which goes round the neck behind the back of the head. One method of binding is with the *baikie*, made of a piece of hardwood, *e*, fig. 56, standing upright, and flat to the neck of the cow. A rope *g* fastens the lower end of it to the stake, upon which it slides up and down in a perpendicular direction, by means of a loop which the rope forms round the stake. This rope passes *under* the neck of the animal, and is never loosened. Another rope *k* is fastened at the upper end of the piece of wood *e*, and, passing *over* the neck of the animal and round the stake, is made fast to itself by a knot and eye, which serves the purpose of fastening and loosening the animal. The neck, being embraced between the two ropes, moves up and down, carrying the baikie along with it. This method of binding, though quite easy to the animals themselves, is objectionable in preventing them turning their heads round to lick their bodies;

Fig. 56

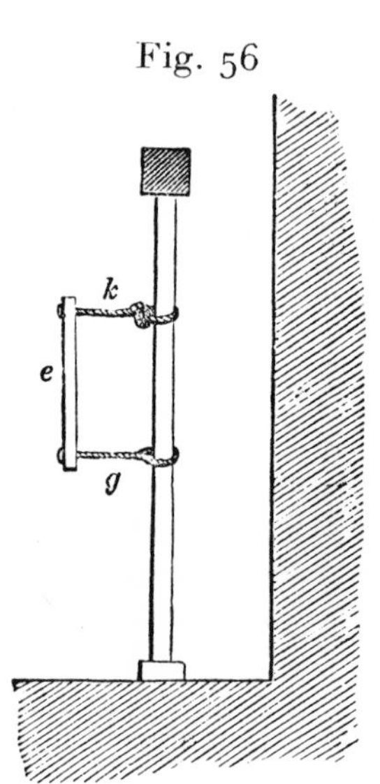

Baikie.

and the stake being perpendicular, the animals can only move their heads up and down, and are obliged to hold them always over the mangers. 1022.

A much better binding of cattle is with the *seal*, which consists of an iron chain, fig. 57, where *a* is the large ring of the binder, which slides up and down the inclined stake *h*. The iron chain, being put round the neck of the cow or ox, is fastened to itself by a broad-tongued hook at *c*, which is put into any link of the chain that gauges the neck, and it cannot come out until turned on purpose edgeways to the link of which it has a hold. This sort of binder is in general use in the midland and northern counties of Scotland. It is most durable, and gives the animal liberty, not only to lick itself, but to turn its head in any direction it pleases; and the inclination of the stake *h* gives the animal farther liberty of lying down or standing back free of the manger. 1023.

Fig. 57

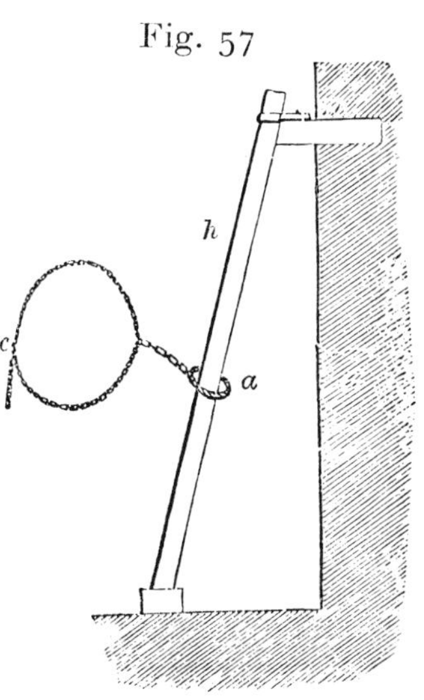

Cattle seal or binder.

FEEDING CATTLE IN WINTER.

A more useful and efficient implement of its kind cannot be found than the lever turnip-slicer, fig. 59. It was contrived by Mr Wallace, Kirkconnell, as an improvement on a pre-existing machine of the same kind. In using this portable machine, the workman takes hold of the lever end with his right hand, and, having raised it sufficiently high, throws a turnip into the cradle with the left hand. The lever is now brought down by the right hand, which with a moderate impetus, and by means of the block, sends the turnip down upon the cutters, through the openings of which it passes while the cutters are dividing it, and falls in uniform slices into a basket beneath. In most cases it is found more convenient to have a boy to throw in the turnips, to expedite the work. The cost of this machine is 30s. When this lever turnip-cutter is furnished with an additional set of cutting-knives, six in number, fixed at right angles to those referred to above, the machine is rendered useful for cutting turnips for sheep; and it will cut them in long narrow parallelopipeds, well suited in shape for being taken into the mouths of sheep. It will still be a cheap implement, not exceeding 40s. in price. 1074.

Turnips are reduced into smaller pieces than is effected by turnip-slicers for cattle or sheep by implements named root-graters; and they are also brought to a still finer state of subdivision by the root-pulpers, which reduce turnips to the state of pulp. The pulped turnip is mixed with cut straw or hay when given to cattle. Fig. 60 is a perspective view of Bentall's root-pulper, which is reckoned the best in use. The turnips, topped and tailed, are put into the hopper, and they fall down in a pulped state into a basket, by the action of the working barrel, which is provided with a series of hooked teeth on the barrel, and are set in a helical form round its periphery. As the barrel revolves, these teeth pass between the threads of the screw; the tearing of the teeth and the squeezing of the worm-screw very speedily reduce the roots to a pulp. This machine is made by Mr Bentall, of Heybridge, Maldon, Essex, and costs for hand £5, 5s., and for power, with a 10-inch pulley, £6, 6s. 1142.

A handy form of *lantern* that will distribute a sufficient intensity of light around, and yet be safe to carry to any part of a steading, amongst straw or other highly inflammable material, is yet unknown on a farm. The nearest approach to these properties of any form of lantern I have seen is fig. 58. 1107.

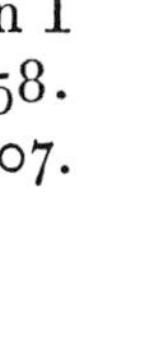

Fig. 58

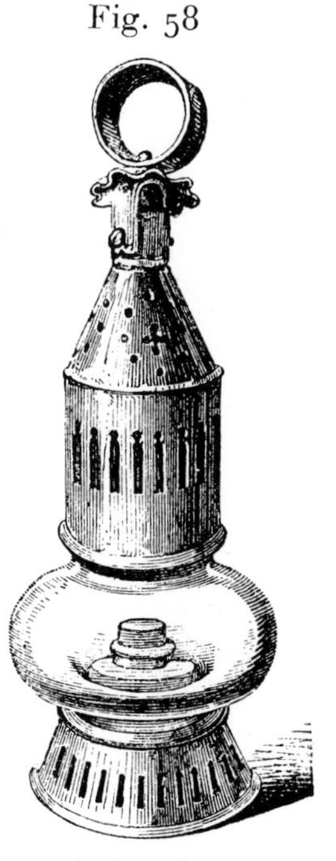

Safe farm-lantern.

Fig. 59

Lever turnip-slicer for cattle.

a b Sole in 2 pieces, connected by an iron strap *a c* on each side, and supported on 4 legs, 2 feet high.
d e Lever 4 feet long, jointed at *d*.
m Block of wood connected with the lever, and studded with iron knobs to prevent the turnips slipping.
f g 8 Cutter-blocks of cast iron, forming a hollow cradle for turnips.

The best straw-cutter is made by Messrs Richmond and Chandler of Salford, Manchester. It is in perspective in fig. 61. The leading peculiarity of this cutter is the toothed rollers, which are self-feeding and not liable to choke. To admit of the rise and fall of the feeding roller, according to the thickness of the layer of straw passing through, a swing-joint is provided to the centre shaft of the machine. The width of the feeding-mouth is 9 inches, rising from 1½ inch to 4 inches. The form of the knives is that of a differential scroll, and gives a continuous and uniform cut during the evolution of the fly-wheel. The price of the machine, whether for hand or power, is £7 highly finished. The cost of a pulley when it is driven by power is 9s.; change-wheels, to vary the length of the cut, 6s. 6d. per pair.

1126.

There are several machines for bruising linseed into meal, though, from its oleaginous nature, the rollers are apt to clog and get out of working order. A simple and cheap machine for the purpose, by Mr A. Dean, Birmingham, driven by hand, costing £6, 5s., is fig. 62.

1154.

Grains used for cattle-food are bruised by hand or power machines. Fig. 63 is a hand corn-bruiser in perspective. This is a very efficient machine for bruising either oats or beans. From the different velocities of the two cylinders, the grooved one being the fastest, it produces a cutting as well as a bruising action, which renders its effects on the grain more perfect than simple pressure. It can be worked by one man, who will bruise 4 bushels of oats in an hour. The price of the machine is £6, 10s. When corn is desired to be merely flattened, and not reduced to the mealy state, it is necessary to use plain rollers, and these cannot be worked effectually but by power. 1206.

Fig. 60

Bentall's root-pulper.

a The hopper;
b Its grating.
c Shaft of the working barrel.
d Helical screw.
e Beams supporting the barrel and screw.
f Spur-wheel on shaft of screw.
g Pinion on shaft of barrel.
h Fly-wheel.
i Handle of fly-wheel.
k k Four legs supporting the beams.
l Stand for basket to receive the pulp

Fig. 61

Richmond and Chandler's straw and hay cutter.

a a Cast-iron framing.
b Cast-iron bed-plate.
c Fly-wheel.
d Handle on fly-wheel shaft.
e e Two cutting-knives attached to fly-wheel.
f Feeding-trough.
g Gearing, giving fast or slow motion to the straw.

Fig. 62

Linseed-bruiser.

a Hopper for the seed.
b Slide for regulating the feed.
c Spout for the meal.
d Handle of fly-wheel.
e Fly-wheel.
f Box containing crushing rollers.

Fig. 63

Hand corn-bruiser.

a a Frame.
b Case holding the bruising rollers.
c d Spur-wheels.
e Handle of fly-wheel.
f Screws for adjusting the rollers.
g Bearing of feeding roller.
h Fly-wheel.
i Feeding hopper.
k Spout for the bruised grain.

STABLES FOR FARM-HORSES.

Fig. 65 gives a view of the particulars of a *stall for work-horses*, fitted up with wooden travis-posts, which is yet the common method. 1293.

Fig. 64 shows the cast-iron hind-posts. 1294.

Fig. 64

Stall with cast-iron hind-posts.

The form of the corn-chest is more convenient, and takes up less room on the floor, when high and narrow than when low and broad, as in fig. 66, which is 5 feet long and 4½ feet high at the back above the feet. 1306.

TREATMENT OF FARM-HORSES.

When 8 P.M. arrives, the steward, provided with light in the lantern, fig. 58, summons the men to the stable to give the horses a grooming for the night, and their suppers. The sound of a horn or the ring of a bell are the usual calls on the occasion. Lights are placed at convenient distances against the wall of the stable, to let the men see to groom the horses; and the best consist of tallow candles in glass lanterns, except when there is gas. The grooming consists first in currying the horse with the curry-comb *b*, fig. 68, to free him of the dirt adhering to the hair, and which, being now dry, is easily removed. A wisping of straw removes the roughest of the dirt loosened by the curry-comb. The legs ought to be thoroughly wisped—not only to make them clean, but to dry up any moisture that may have been left in the evening; and

Fig. 66

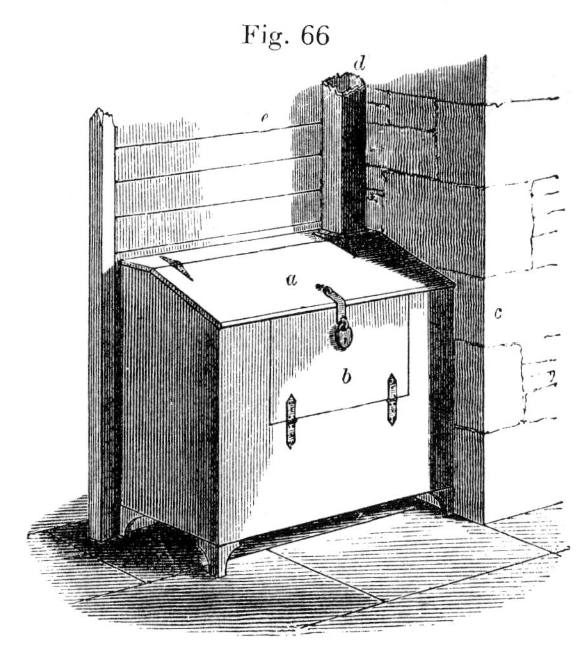

Corn-chest for work-horses.

Fig. 65

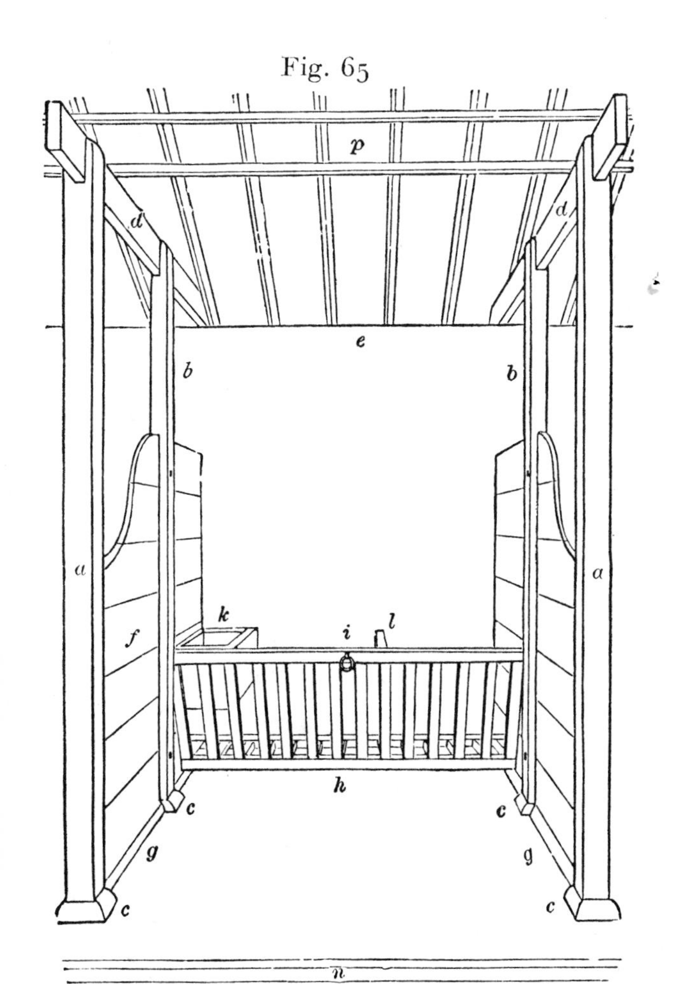

Stall for a work-horse stable.

a a Hind-posts.
b b Head-posts.
c c Stone blocks for head-posts.
d d Battens from wall to wall *e*.
f f Travis-boards.
g g Curb-stones for travis-boards.
h Sparred bottom of hay-rack.
i Ring for stall-collar.
k Corn-manger.
l Bar across hay-rack.
m Causeway in the stall.
n Stone gutter for urine.
o Causeway of roadway.
p Two spars from batten to batten for fodder.

Fig. 67

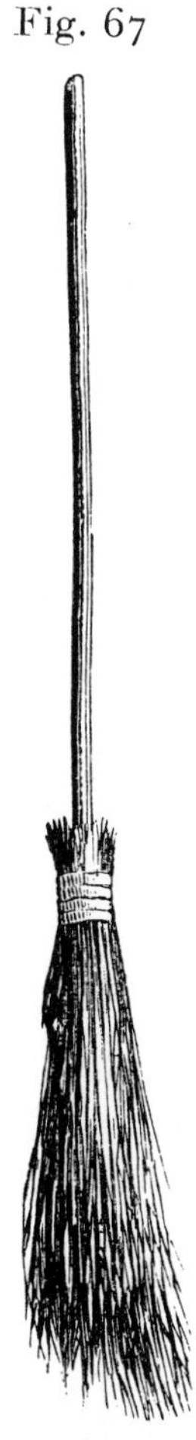

Birch broom for stables.

at this time the feet should be picked clean, by the foot-picker *a*, of any dirt adhering between the shoe and foot. The brush *c* is then used, to remove the remaining and finer portions of dust from the hair, and it is cleared from the brush by a few rasps along the curry-comb. The wisping and brushing, if done with some force and dexterity, with a combing of the tail and mane with the comb *d*, should render the horse pretty clean; but

Fig. 69

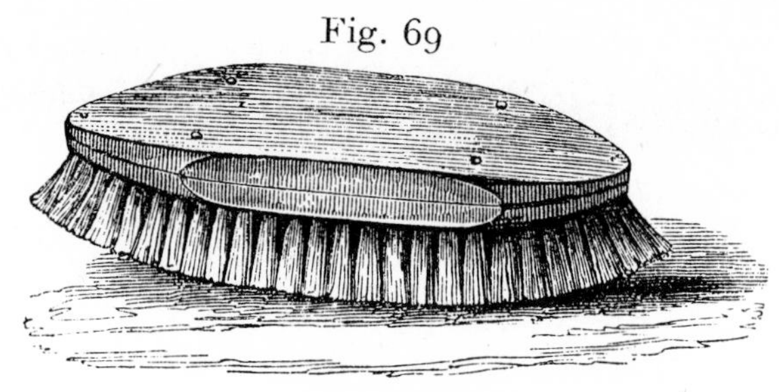

Water-brush.

Fig. 68

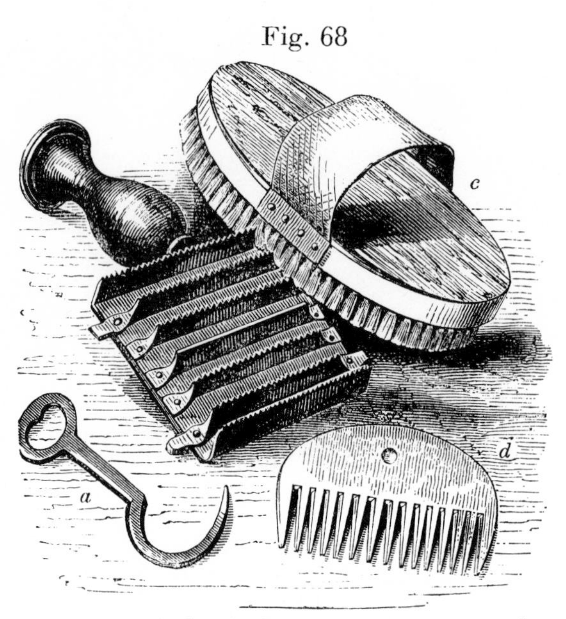

Curry-comb, brush, foot-picker, and mane-comb.

there are more ways than one of grooming a horse, as may be witnessed by the skimming and careless way in which some ploughmen do it. It is true that the rough coat of a farm-horse in winter is not easily cleaned, and especially in a work-stable where much dust floats about and no horse-clothes are in use; but, rough as it is, it should be *clean* if not *sleek;* and it is the duty of the steward to ascertain whether the grooming has been efficiently done. A slap of the hand upon the horse will soon let be known the existence of loose dust in the hair. Attendance at this time will give the student an insight into the manner in which farm-horses ought to be cleaned and fed and generally treated in the stable. 1317.

For washing the legs and heels of a horse there is nothing like a water-brush, fig. 69. 1318.

The straw of the bedding is then shaken up with a *stable fork*, fig. 70, which is most handy for shaking up straw when about 5 feet in length, and the prongs least dangerous for the legs of horses when blunt. The prongs terminate in a tine driven into a hooped ash shaft. This mode of mounting a fork is better than with socket and nail, which are apt to become loose and catch the straw. Fig. 71 is a steel-pronged fork of Lincolnshire, and is an excellent instrument for working amongst straw. 1319.

Fig. 70

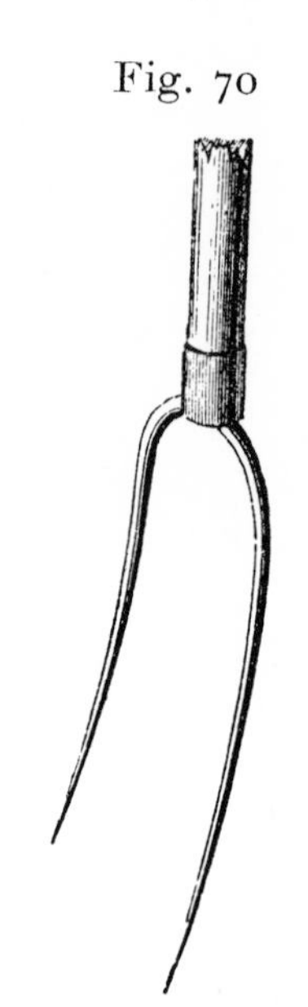

Common straw-fork.

Fig. 71

Lincolnshire steel straw-fork.

That horses will thrive on bruised *whins* or *furze*, I had considerable experience in the winter of 1826, after the summer heat had burned up the straw of all sorts of grain on light soil. Old whins, growing in a fir plantation, supplied young shoots from 1 foot to 3 feet in length, which were cut by a field-worker with a hook, and led to the steading, where it was bruised with a rammer, fig. 72. 1347.

Fig. 72

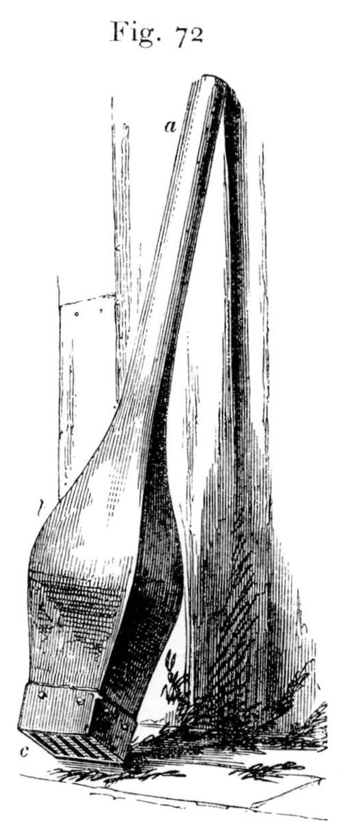

Hand whin-bruiser.

Young work-horses are always docked before being put to grass. *Docking* consists of amputating the last 6 joints of the tail, the object being to prevent its long point being injured when the horse works in the tilt-cart. The operation is simple, and is effected by the docking-iron, fig. 73. The horse's tail is prepared by clipping away the hair up to the sixth joint. That *joint* is laid carefully in the circular notch, and the cutting-plate is brought forcibly upon the joint until the two handles meet. The wound is dressed with tar, and bound up for a time with a pledget of tow. 1357.

Fig. 73

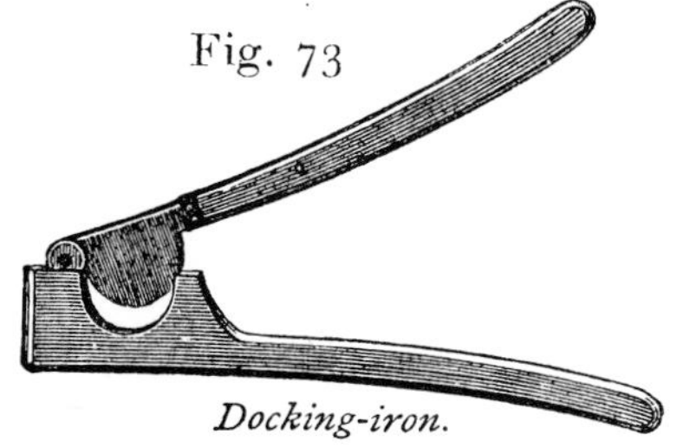

Docking-iron.

"In the horse and cattle, sheep and dog, *bleeding*, from its greater facility and rapidity," says Professor Dick, "is best performed in the jugular or neck vein, though it may also be satisfactorily performed in the *plate* and *saphena* veins, the former coming from the inside of the arm, and running up directly in front of it to the jugular; the latter, or thigh-vein, running across the inside of that limb. Either the fleam or lancet may be used. 1358.

Fig. 74

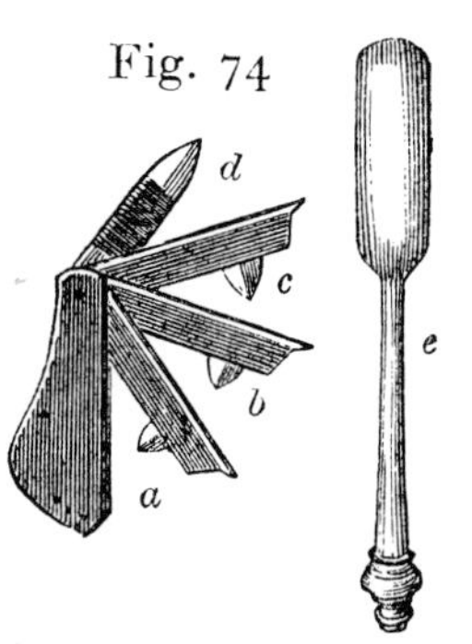

Fleams and blooding-stick.

a Fleam for young animals.
b Fleam for the horse.
c Fleam for cattle.
d Lancet.
e Blooding-stick.

To the *horse*, physic is usually administered in the form of a bolus or *ball;* to *cattle* by drinking or *drenching*, though for both either way may be employed. A ball is conveniently made of linseed-meal, molasses, and the active ingredient, whether purgative, diuretic, or cordial; it should be softish, and about the size of a pullet's egg. In administering it, the operator stands before the horse, which is generally unbound, and its head turned in the stall, with a halter on it. An assistant stands on the near side of the horse to steady its head, and keep it from rising too high; sometimes he holds the mouth, and grooms generally need such aid. The operator seizes the horse's tongue in his left hand, draws it a little out to one side towards himself, and places his little finger fast upon the under jaw where are no teeth; with his right hand he carries the ball smartly along the roof of the mouth, and leaves it at the root of the tongue; releases the tongue, the mouth is closed, and the head is held up, till the ball is seen descending the gullet on the left side. When loath to swallow, a little water may be offered, and it will carry the ball before it. A hot, troublesome horse should be sent at once to a veterinary surgeon. Instruments should be avoided in him, and adding croton farina to the mash often answers the purpose."

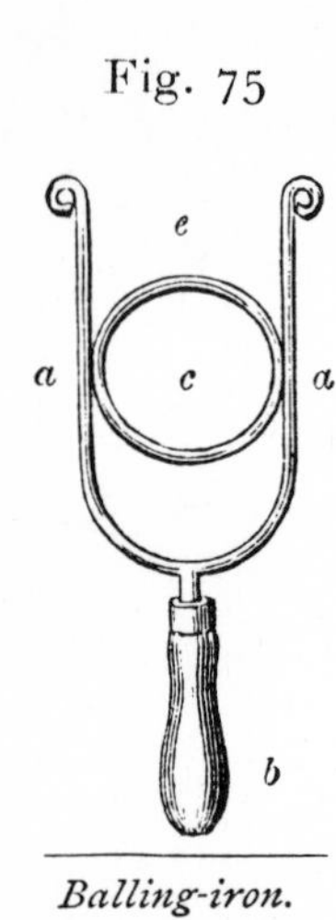

Fig. 75

Balling-iron.

The balling-iron, fig. 75, admits the hand freely into the mouth to administer a ball; *a a*, a branched rod of iron, is fixed to a hooped handle *b* by means of a tine, and the circular ring *c* of the same description of iron is fixed between the branches. The instrument is used by inserting it by the handle in a horizontal position into the horse's mouth, and on turning down the handle, the circular ring, acting on the inside of the mouth, opens it, the lower jaw passing into the opening *d*, while the upper rests on the ring *e*. The hand, with the ball, is introduced through the ring *c*. In case of a refractory horse, the ball-syringe, fig. 76, may be used with the balling-iron. 1362.

Fig. 76

Ball-syringe.

"*Injections*, though easily administered by means of the old ox-bladder and pipe, are still more conveniently given with Read's stomach-pump, fig. 78, or with the clyster-funnel, fig. 72. The end of the pipe of the instrument is

Fig. 77

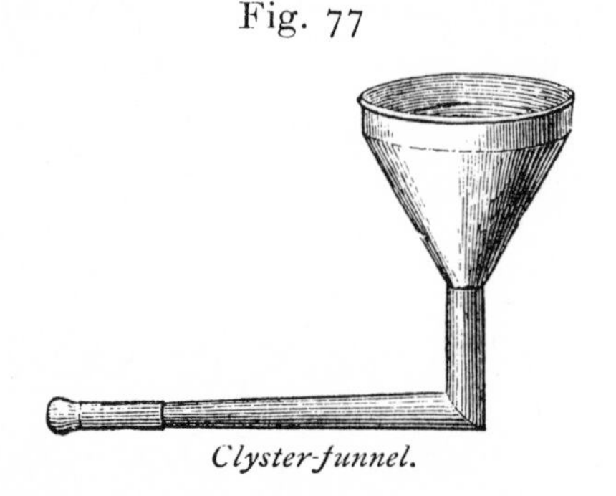
Clyster-funnel.

introduced into the anus of the horse some distance, and the injection, on being poured into the funnel, finds its way into the intestines by gravity. For laxative clysters for the horse or cow, from 1 gallon to 12 pints imperial of warm water or gruel, at the temperature of 96° Fahr., with a couple of handfuls of salt or 2 oz. of soft soap, prove most useful. 1370.

Fig. 78

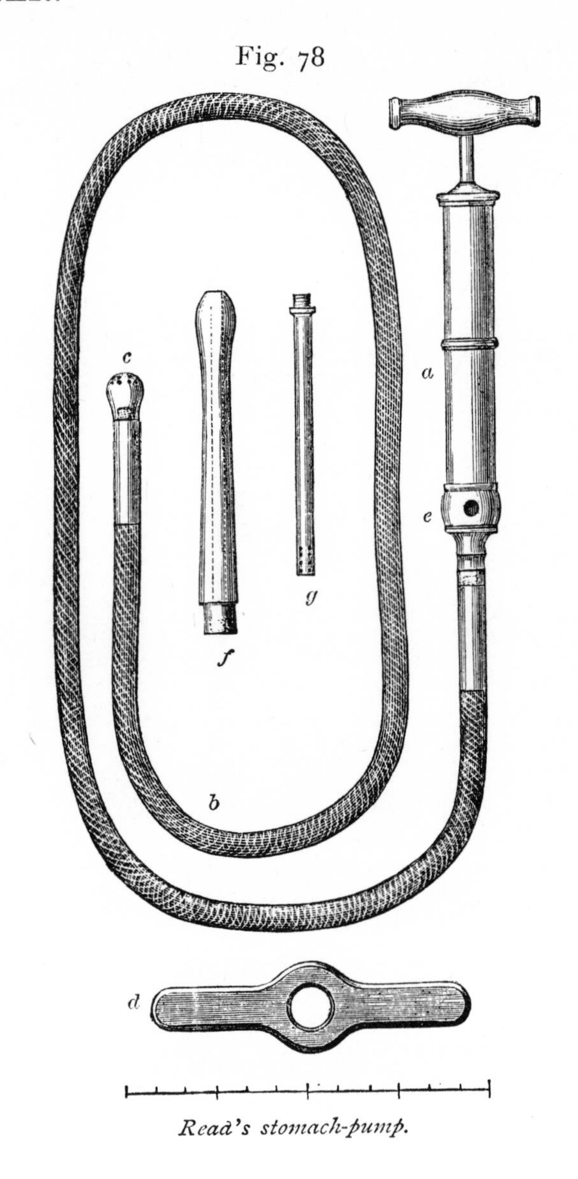

Read's stomach-pump.

FEEDING SWINE.

The older pigs have the liberty of the large courts, amongst the cattle, where they make their litter in the open court when the weather is mild, and in the shed when cold. Though thus left at liberty, they should not be neglected of food, as is too often the case. They should have sliced turnips given them every day, in troughs, as also water. Pigs, when not supplied with a sufficiency of food, will leap into the cattle-troughs and help themselves to turnips; but the dirty practice should not be tolerated, and it can only arise from their keeper neglecting to give them food. The cattle-man attends upon those pigs, and should give them turnips and water at regular times. 1412.

I have seen in England a convenient pigs' trough adapted for standing in the middle of a court. It consists of cast iron in one entire piece, as in perspective, fig. 79. The divisions have a convexity on the upper edge, to prevent food being dashed from one compartment into the other. This trough stands upon the top of the litter, is not easily overturned—the cattle cannot hurt themselves upon it, while it is easily pushed about to the most convenient spot for it to stand.

1413.

Fig. 79

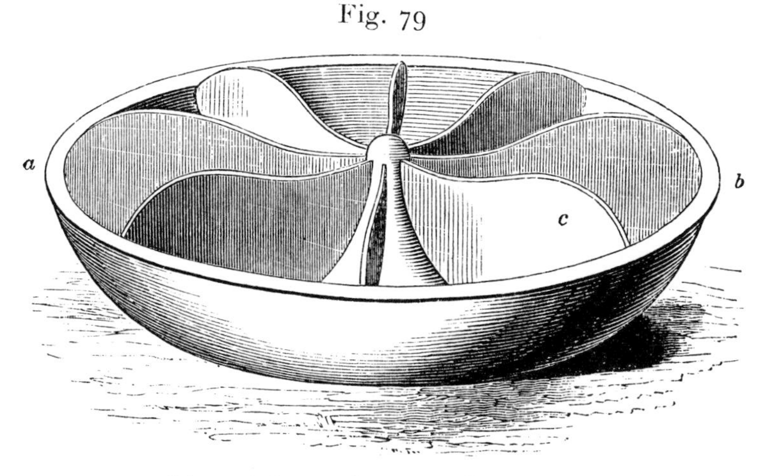

Ring pigs' trough, to stand in a court.

a b Hollow hemispherical trough, 30 inches diameter.
c Eight subdivisions within it, 9 inches high, converging and meeting at a central pillar.

Fig. 80

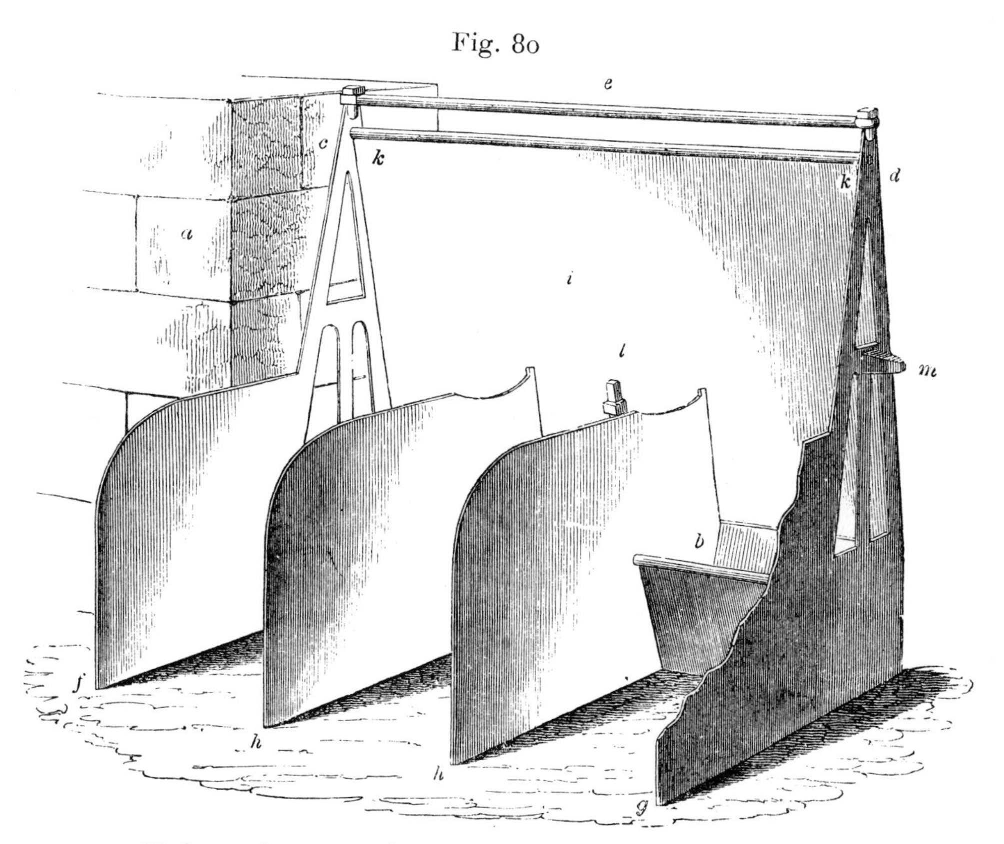

Pigs' troughs, to stand in an opening of the outer wall of a sty.

a Wall of court at the trough.
b Trough, 20 inches by 16, and 9 inches deep.
c d Ends of trough, 3½ feet high.
e Stretcher-bolt connecting the ends.
f g Lower divisions of troughs.
h h Intermediate divisions.
i Swing-door.
k k Pivots in which the swing-door is jointed.
l Bolt in swing-door to shut off and on the troughs.
m Dowel to secure the trough into the wall.

ACCOMMODATION FOR CORN

[Stephens' barn was designed to house a threshing machine in the upper level which received the unthreshed crop from the stackyard behind it and delivered the grain and straw on the lower level.]

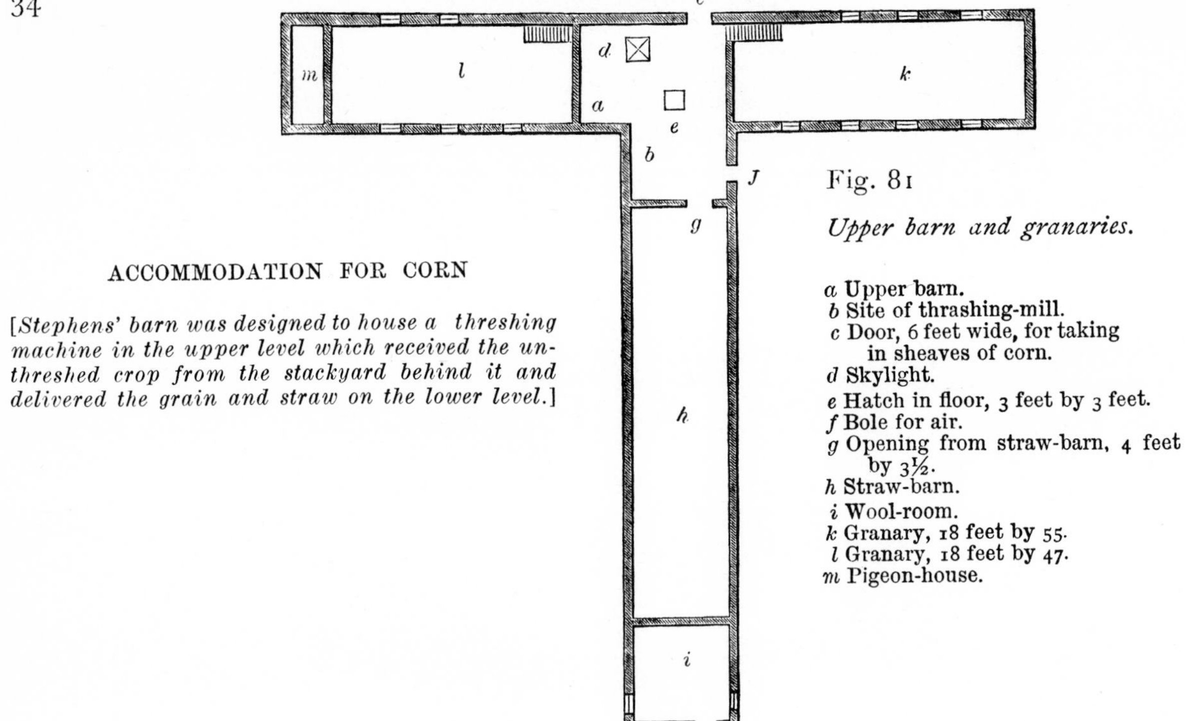

Fig. 81

Upper barn and granaries.

a Upper barn.
b Site of thrashing-mill.
c Door, 6 feet wide, for taking in sheaves of corn.
d Skylight.
e Hatch in floor, 3 feet by 3 feet.
f Bole for air.
g Opening from straw-barn, 4 feet by 3½.
h Straw-barn.
i Wool-room.
k Granary, 18 feet by 55.
l Granary, 18 feet by 47.
m Pigeon-house.

Fig. 82

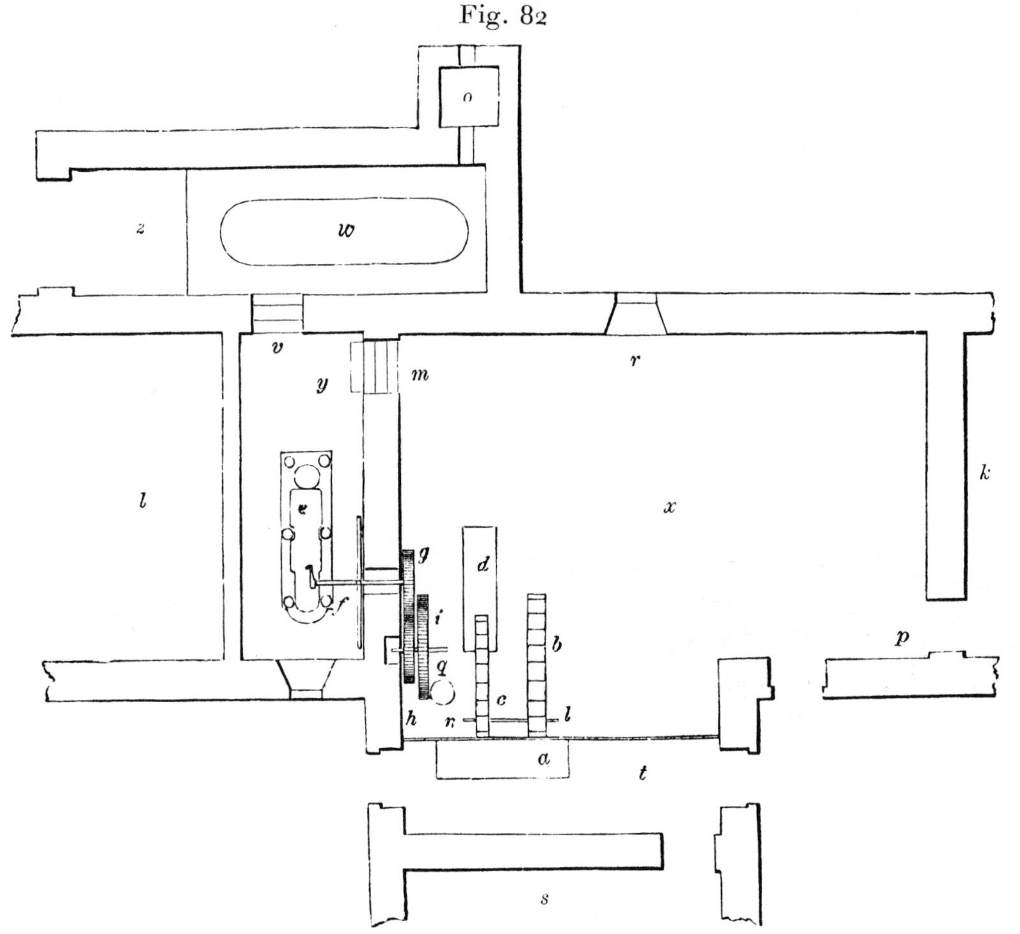

Arrangement on the ground-floor with the corn-barn.

x Corn-barn.
t Chaff-house.
s Straw-barn.
y Engine-house.
w Boiler-house, 25 feet by 9.
z Coal-store, 25 feet by 5.
a First fanner.
b Elevator from second spout.
c Elevator from first spout.
d Second fanner supplied by the elevator *c*.
e Steam-engine.
f Main shaft carrying fly-wheel.
g h Intermediate spur-wheels.
i Great spur-wheel.
q Hummeller.
m Door from corn-barn to engine-house. Here also stair to granary, *l*.
o Chimney-stalk, 6 feet square, 50 feet high.
p Stair to granary, *k*.
r Window in corn-barn.
v Steps to boiler and furnace-house.

Fig. 83

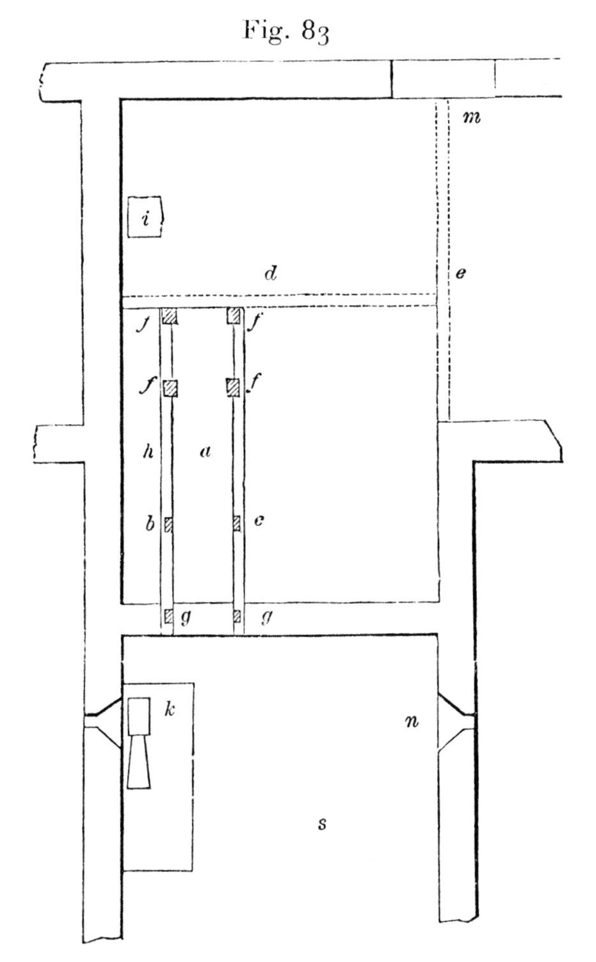

Arrangement on the upper barn-floor.

a Space for thrashing-machine.
b c Foundation-beams of the thrashing-machine.
d e Beams supporting the foundation-beams.
f Posts for framework of drum.
b c, g g Posts of framework of shakers.
f f h b Space of driving gearing.
i Corn-bruiser.
k Straw-cutter.
s Straw-barn.
m Door by gangway to stackyard.
n Bole for air.

Fig. 84

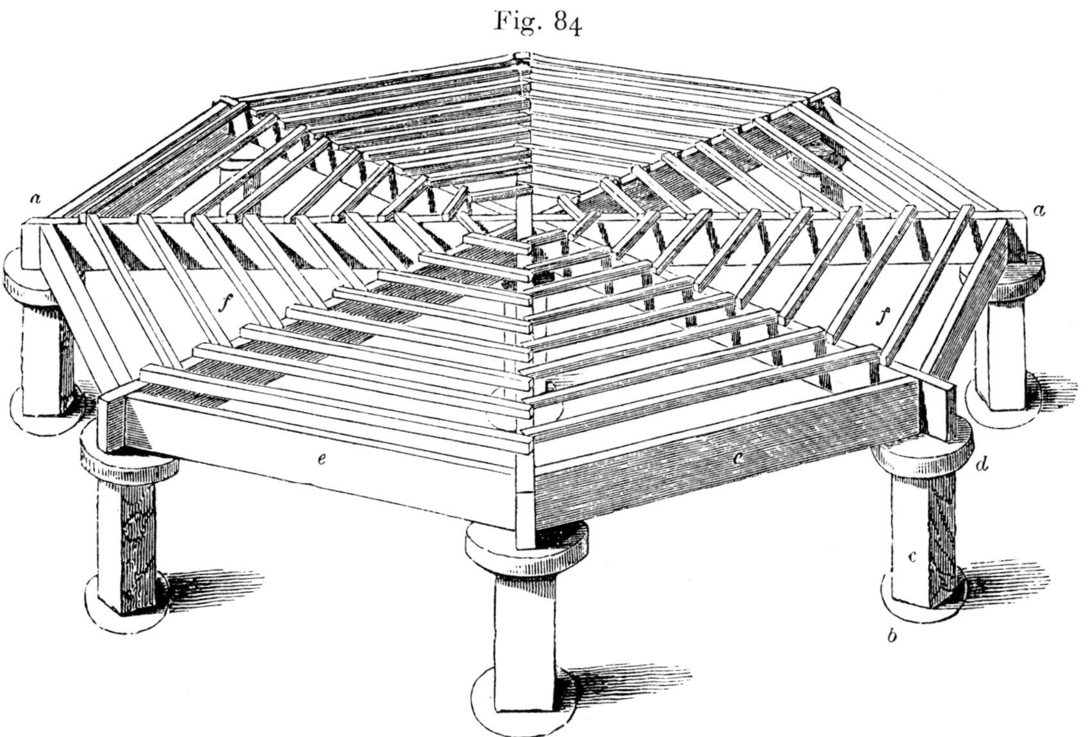

Wooden stathel for stacks.

a a Plank of Scots fir or larch, 15 feet in length.
b Stone flag sunk in the ground.
c Upright stone support, 18 inches high and 8 inches square, 8 in number, and one in the centre.
d Stone bonnet, at least 2 inches thick.
a Half-scantling, 7½ feet long, 9 inches deep, 2½ inches thick, placed on each bonnet.
e e Bearers, 9 inches deep, 2 inches thick from bonnet to bonnet.
f f Fillets of wood, nailed up on the scantlings.

Fig. 85

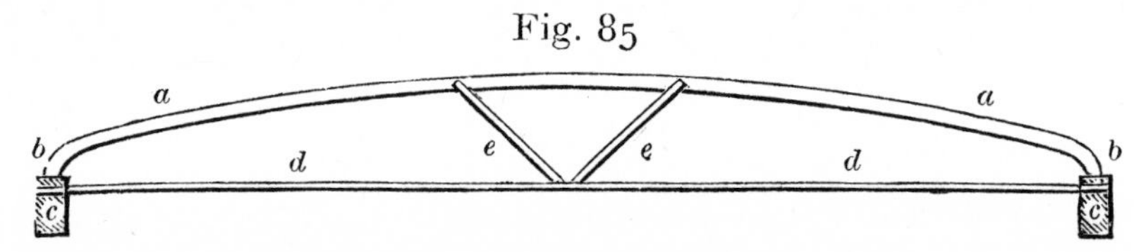

Truss for a galvanised corrugated iron roof.

a a Covered rib or rafter.
b b Shoes bolted to the beams.
c c Beams.
d d Tie-rod.
e e Struts of wrought-iron.

Fig. 86

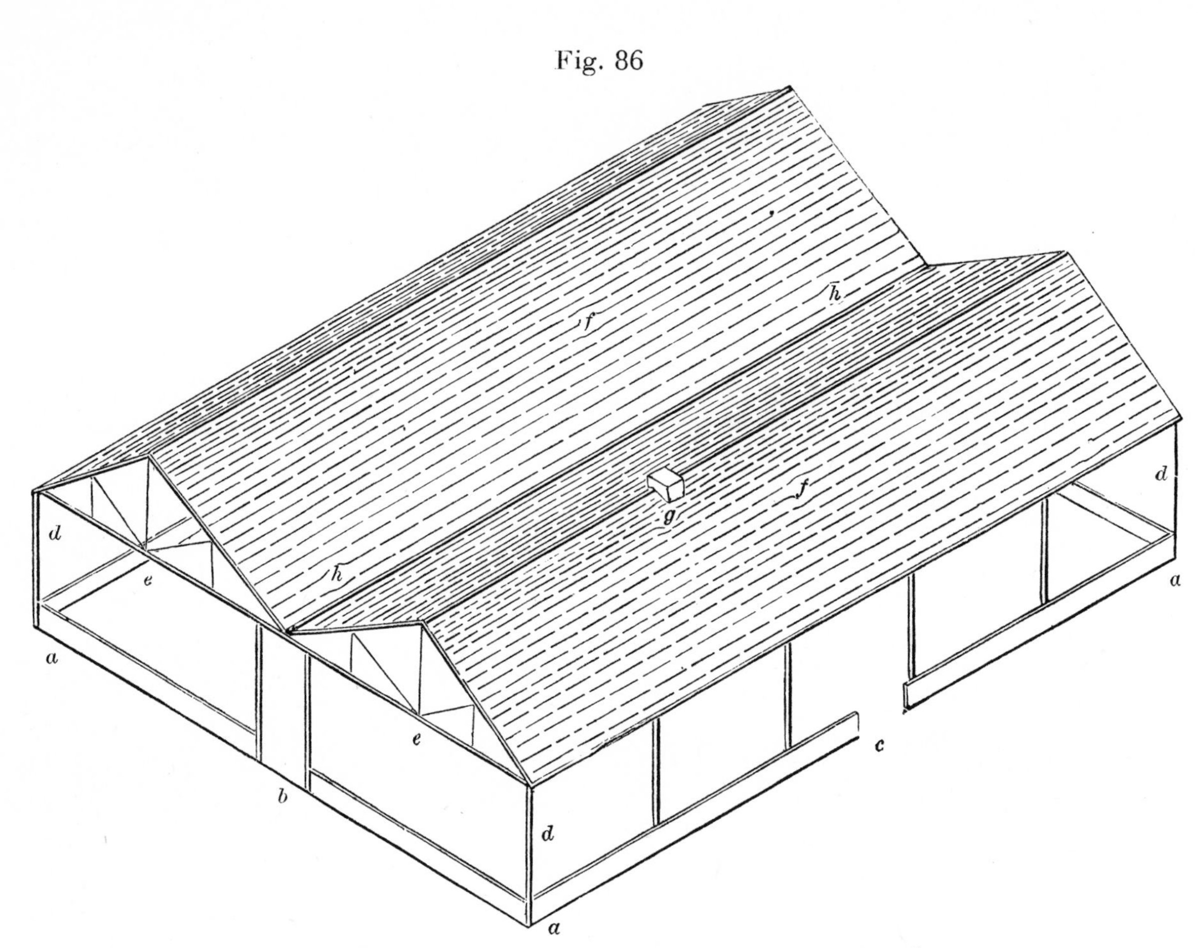

Isometrical perspective of an iron-roof covered stackyard.

a a Stackyard wall, 3½ feet high.
b Cart entrance, 32 feet high, 12 feet wide.
c Outlet to upper barn.
d d Cast-iron hollow pillars, 32 feet high.
e e Iron bracings supporting roof.
f f Roof of galvanised iron.
g Vent in any number.
h h Valleys of roof, along which rain-water runs to hollow pillars.

THRASHING AND WINNOWING CORN.

The thrashing-machine is set in motion by different kinds of power,—by steam, by horse-strength, by the wind, and by water. Of these, wind power is getting more and more out of use in driving farm machinery, on account of the great uncertainty attending the motions of so fickle an element, in so variable a a climate as ours; and every day, as the management of the steam-engine is more and more understood, it is becoming more in use on farms. Where water is sufficiently abundant, it is the simplest as well as the cheapest of motive powers, and is always preferred to all others; but where the supply is insufficient, although it may be ample enough for a time in winter, it partakes of the disadvantages attending wind—it may be insufficient at the time it is most wanted. Experience has abundantly proved that thrashing-machines dependent on water derived chiefly from the drainage of the surface of the ground, frequently suffer from a short supply in autumn, and late in spring, or early in summer, thereby creating inconvenience for the want of straw in the end of autumn, and the want of seed or horse-corn in the end of spring. Wherever such casualties are likely to happen, it is better to adopt a steam-engine at once. Although coal should be distant and dear, for all that a steam-engine requires, a steam-engine should supersede horses. 1519.

Until of late years the thrashing-machine was in most cases impelled by horses moving in a circular course; and as this power continues to be employed on the smaller class of farms, it is still of that importance to demand being here brought under notice. *Horse-wheels* are of various construction, as *under-foot* and *over-head;* the under-foot being chiefly used where small powers are required, and the over-head where four horses and upwards are employed. In general, in the under-foot wheel, the horses draw by means of trace-chains and swing-tree. In the over-head wheel, of old construction, we also find occasionally the same method of yoking practised; but in all modern over-head wheels the horses draw by a *yoke* descending over their back, from a horizontal beam placed over-head. 1531.

Fig. 87

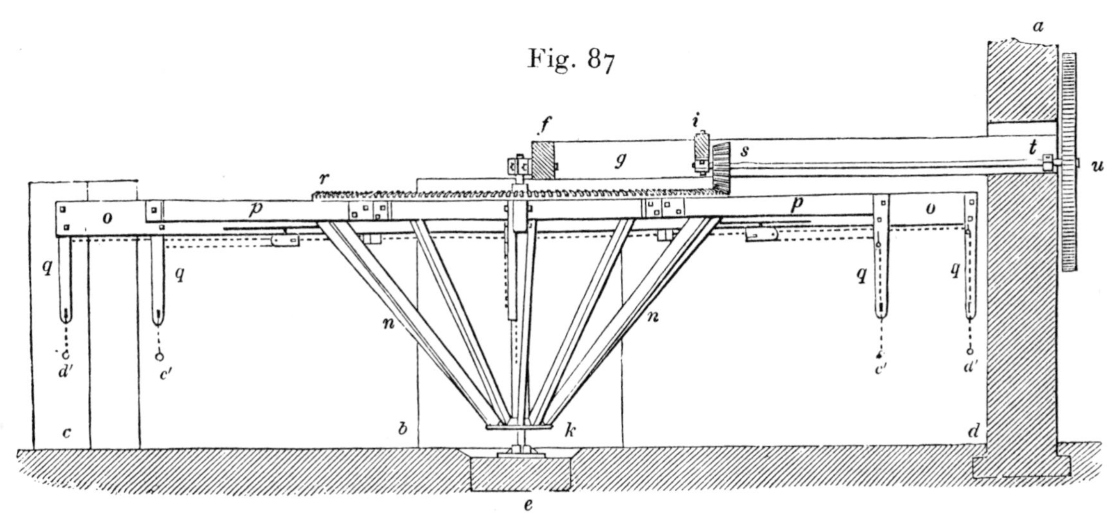

Horse-wheel for a Scotch thrashing-machine.

a Barn-wall.
b One of two main pillars.
c One of two minor pillars.
d Floor or horse-walk.
e Stone block supporting footstep of horse-wheel.
f Collar-beam.
g Shears framed into the collar-beam.
i Cast-iron bridge.
k Central shaft.
o o Horse-beams.
n n Diagonals.
p p Horizontal braces.
q q Yoke-bars.
r Cast-iron wheel.
s Horse-wheel pinion.
s t Lying-shaft.
u Spur-wheel.

Fig. 88

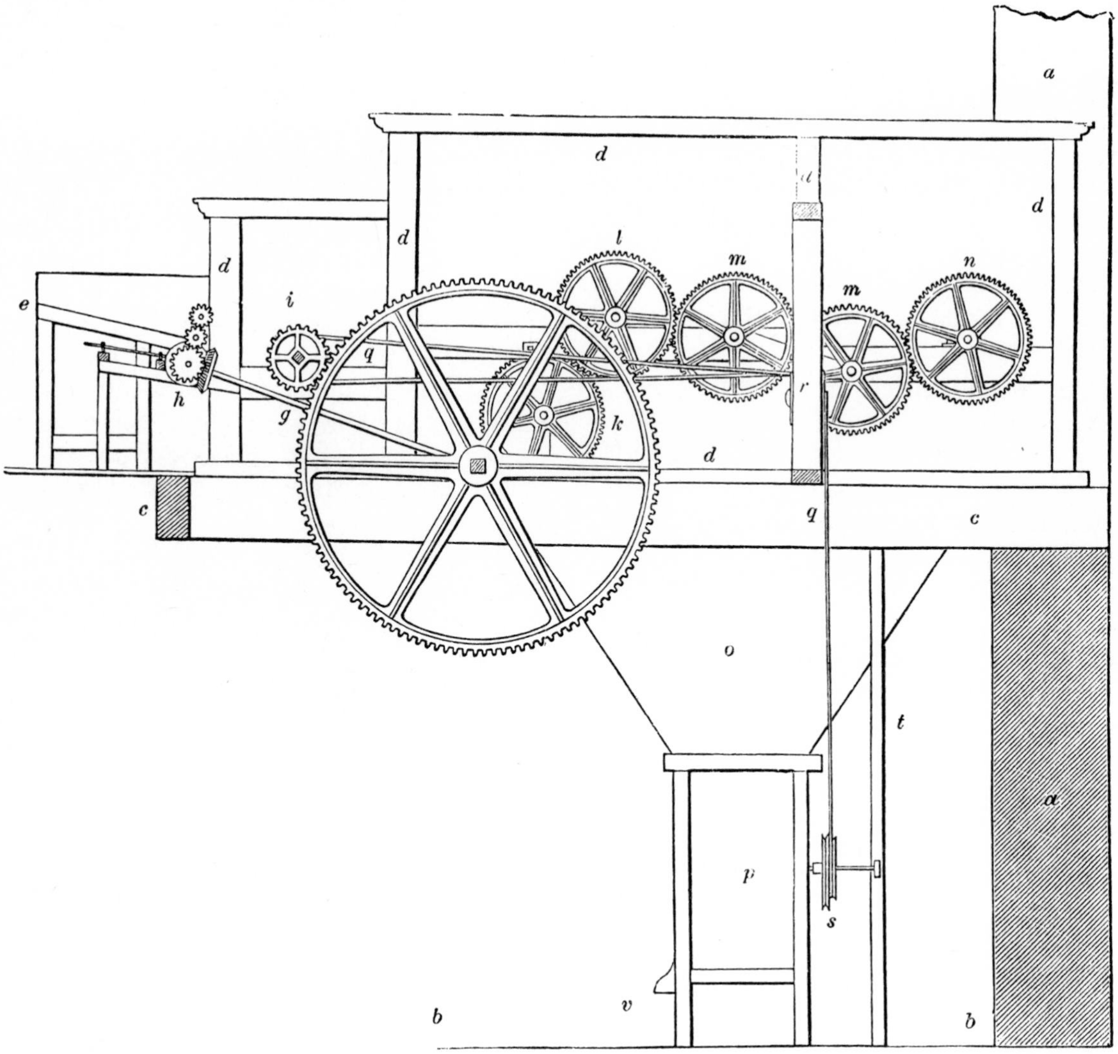

Elevation of a Scotch thrashing-machine.

a a Barn-wall.
b b Floor.
c c Foundation beams.
d Different parts of framework.
e Feeding-board.
f Great spur-wheel, 50 rotations.
g Small inclined shaft.
h Feeding-gear, moving 45 to 50, or 65 to 70, rotations per minute.
i Pinion on drum-shaft, 360 revolutions.
k Intermediate wheel.
l Wheel of the first shaker.
m m Intermediate wheels.
n Wheel of the second shaker.
o Hopper.
p Fanner.
v Spout for corn.
q q Double rope of fanner.
s Sheave on shaft of fans.
t Upright post to support sheave of fanner.

A method of equalising the resistance to the shoulders of each individual horse has been long practised, and which, from its simplicity as well as its beneficial effects upon the horses, is deserving of general adoption. Fig. 90 shows the application of this to the horse-beam. The advantages of this mode of yoking will at once be obvious; for suppose that, from inadvertence, the horse may have been unequally yoked, whenever he exerts his force, the chain that had been yoked short—suppose it to be the left shoulder—will immediately pull down the end of the lever to which it is hooked, and so bring the longer chain to bear with equal resistance upon the right shoulder.

1536.

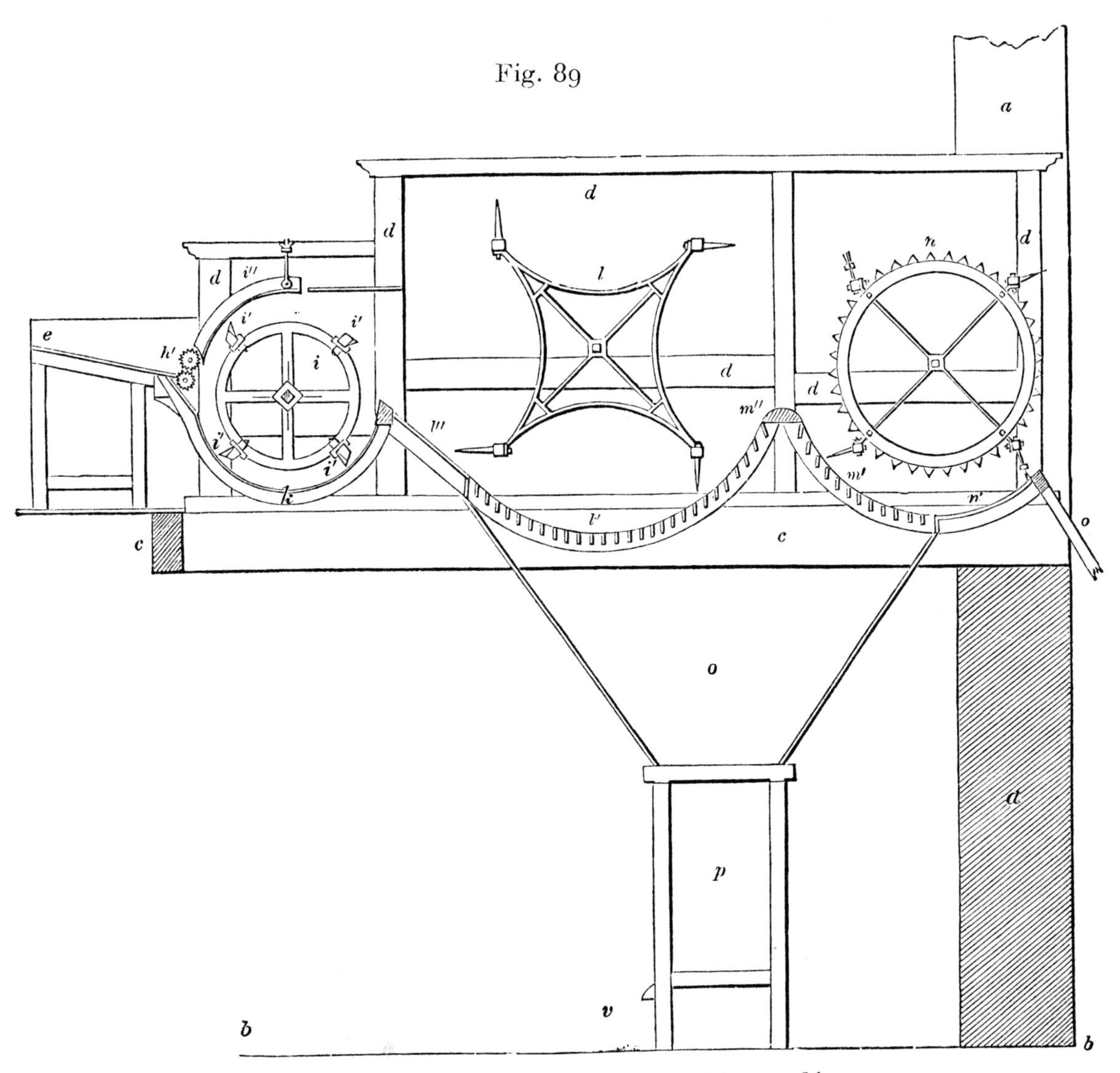

Longitudinal section of a Scotch thrashing-machine.

a a Barn-wall.
b b Floor.
c c Beam.
d Framework.
e Feeding-board.
i Drum.
k Drum-case.
l First shaker.
m m First shaker screen.
n Second shaker.
o Hopper.
p Fanner.
v Corn-spout.
o' Straw-screen.
h' Feeding-rollers.
i' Drum-beaters and cover.
n' Second shaker screen and board.

Fig. 90

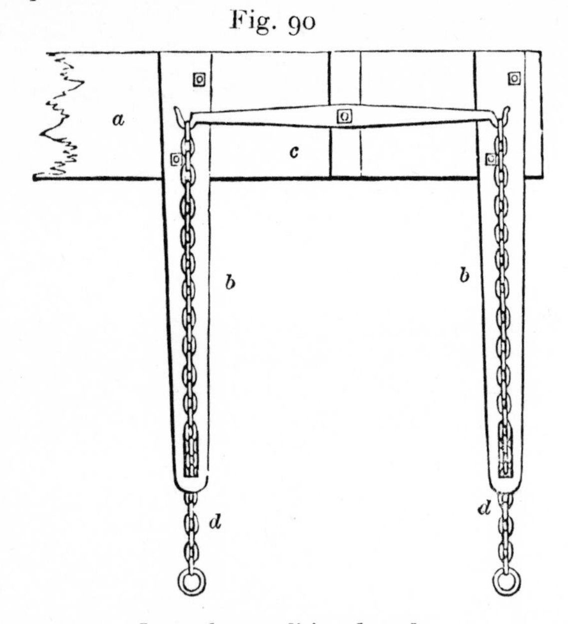

Lever for equalising draught.

a Part of horse-beam. *c* Lever.
b b Yoke-trees. *d d* Draught-chains.

Water, when it can be commanded, is the cheapest and most uniform of all powers; and on many farms it might be commanded by carefully collecting and storing in a dam. *Water-wheels* have been commonly treated as of two kinds; but, with great deference, I conceive they may be classed under two heads. The *under-shot* or *open float-board* wheel, which can only be advantageously employed where the supply of water is considerable and the fall low; it can therefore rarely answer for farm purposes, and need not be discussed. The second is the *bucket*-wheel, which may be *over-shot* or *breast*, according to the height of the fall. It is this wheel that is adopted in all cases where water is scarce or valuable, and the fall amounting to 6 or 7 feet or more, though it is sometimes employed

Fig. 91

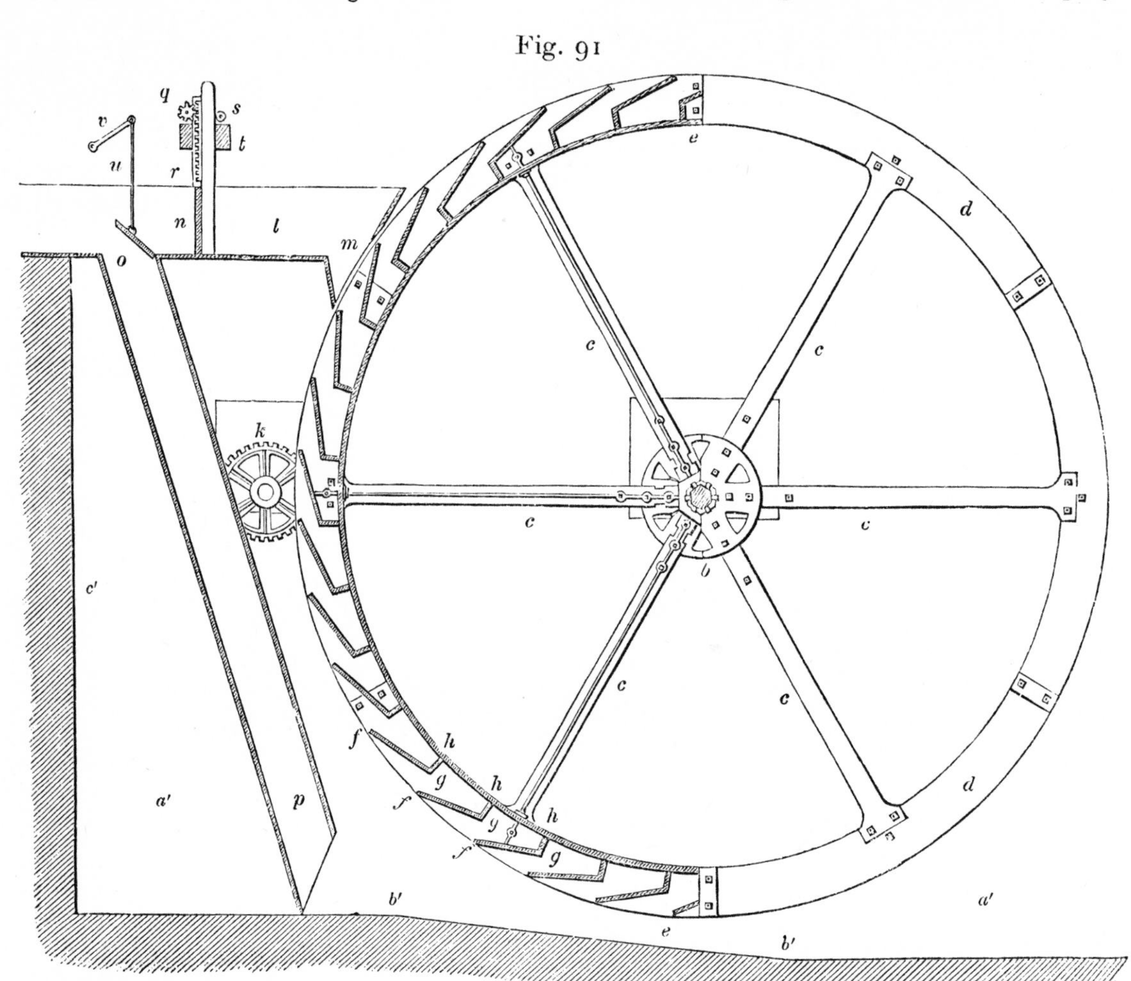

Section and elevation of a bucket water-wheel.

a′ a′ Barn-wall.
b′ b′ Sole of ark.
b Eye-flanges.
c Arms.
d d Shrouding.
e e Grooves for securing the buckets.
f f Pitch of the buckets.
f g Front of bucket.
g h Bottom of bucket.
k Pinion.
l Trough.
m Spout.
n Regulating-sluice.
q Pinion.
r Sluice-stem.
s Friction-roller.
t Cross-head.
o Trap-sluice.
o p Spout.
u Connecting rod.
v Crank-lever.

with even less fall than 6 feet. It is the most effective mode of employing water, except where the fall is excessively high, or exceeding 50 feet, when, in such cases, it is applied to motive machines that will rarely be employed for agricultural purposes. 1538.

Portable thrashing-machines are now very common in England. From one extreme of using the flail only, to the other of employing the portable thrashing-machine, the farmers of England have gone in separating their corn from its straw. They seem to have ignored a fixed thrashing-machine, which has long been in use in Scotland. But in proceeding thus, they have not probably acted so much upon their own convictions of the superiority of portable thrashers, as upon the persuasions of their inventors—the implement-makers—who, being naturally attracted by the ingenuity and usefulness of the locomotive, might wish to apply it to the thrashing of grain, instead of adopting and propagating the old stationary steam-engine for the purpose. The locomotive is well adapted to steam-ploughing, and indeed that operation cannot be carried on without it; but for thrashing machinery, whether English or Scotch, there seems nothing so well suited for it as the stationary steam-engine. I do not think that the English portable thrashing-machine will ever become a favourite in Scotland, and in instances where it has been tried there, it has not given the satisfaction that was expected of it. 1546.

Fig. 92

Garrett's portable combined thrashing-machine in perspective.

The first preparation for *thrashing* corn—that is, separating the grain from the straw by the thrashing-machine or the flail—is taking in the stack to be thrashed, and storing it in the upper or thrashing barn. 1548.

Fig. 93

Casting down a stack.

a Barn-sheet spread.
b Stack.
c Stack-caster.
d Row of sheaves on side of sheet.
e Corn-barrow being filled.
f Field-worker filling the barrow.
g Field-worker helping to fill barrows.
h Field-barrow.
i Field-worker wheeling away filled barrow.
k Sheaf of corn being thrown down.
l Sheaves on the stack.

Fig. 94

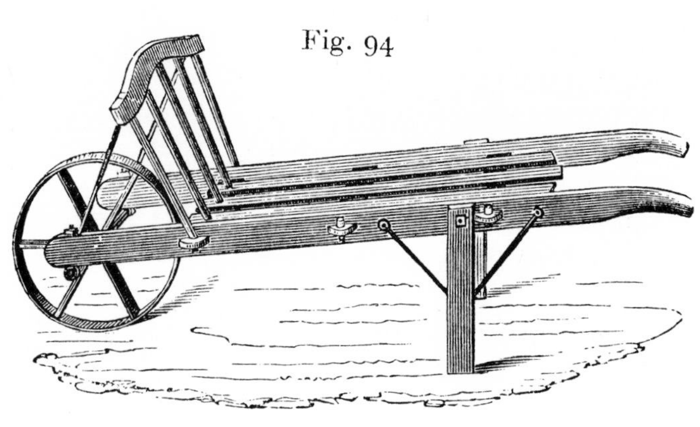

Corn-barrow.

Ladders are most useful implements about a farm-steading. They are best formed of tapering Norway pine spars, sawn up the middle. A useful form of ladder for farm purposes is in fig. 95, where the rounded form of the Norway spar, divided in two, is placed outmost, though it is as often placed inmost. 1549.

The steward feeds in the corn into, and has the sole control of, the mill. Two women are in the upper barn—one to bring forward the sheaves, the other to loosen their bands and place them, one by one, with the band of the sheaf laid lengthwise, as required, upon the table of the feeding-in board. Other two women are in the corn-barn below, one to take away the corn as it comes from the spout, and riddle it in a bin in one corner or side of the barn. The other takes away the roughs, or coarse corn, from the other spout, and riddles it in a heap by itself, throwing the skimmings of the riddlings on a chaff-sheet, which she carries to the upper barn, to be again put through the mill. 1554.

Fig. 95

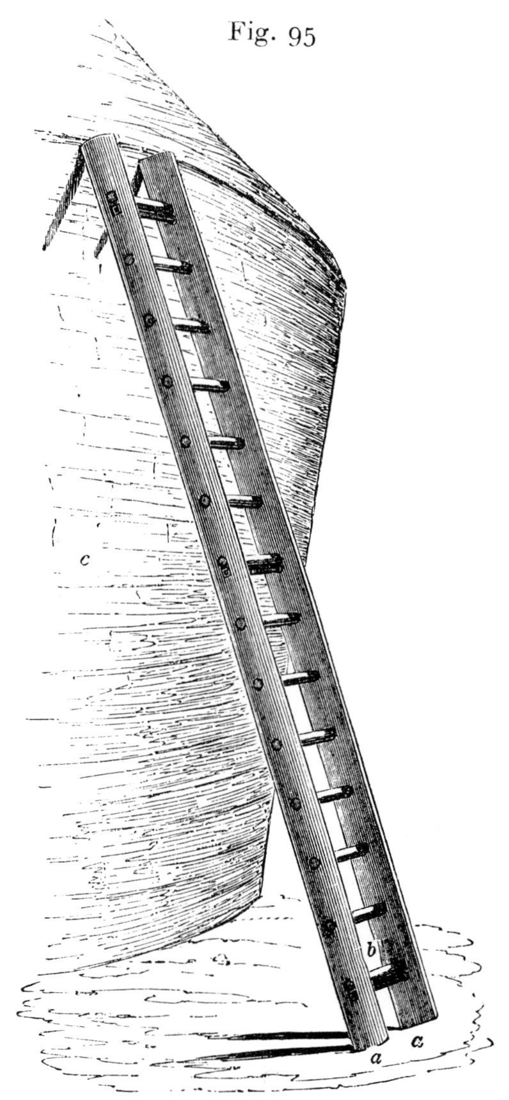

Ladder, 15 *feet long.*

a a Spars of ladder. *c* Stack.
b Steps of ladder.

Fig. 96

Feeding in sheaves into the thrashing-machine in the upper barn.

a Sheaves mowed up from the stackyard.
b Rake.
c Refuse on floor.
d Feeder-in of corn.
e Feeding-in board.
f Field-worker loosening sheaves.
g Field-worker bringing forward sheaves from the mow.
h Wecht.
i Broom.

Fig. 97

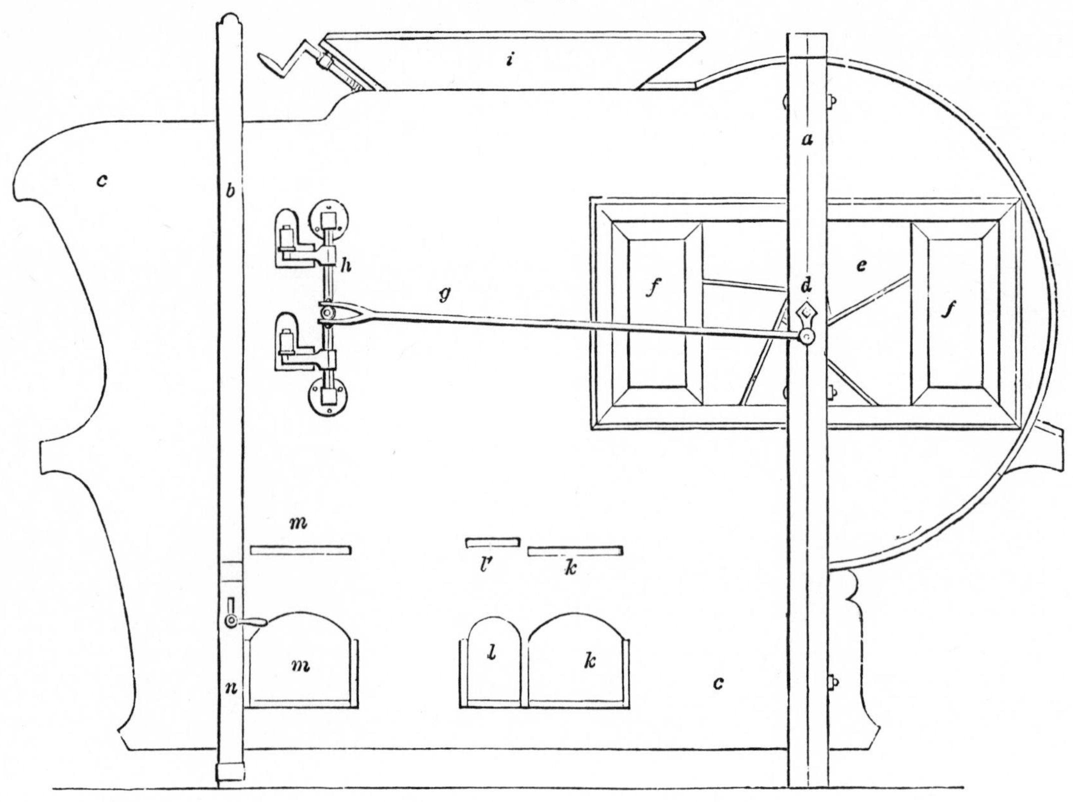

Elevation of the dressing-fanner.

a Fore framing, made in halves.
b Back frame, made single.
c Side-boarding.
d Crank on fan-spindle.
e Arms of fans.
f f Sliding-panels on air-port.
g Connecting-rod.
h Bell-crank spindle.
i Hopper for undressed corn.
k l m Spouts for first, second, and light grain.
k' l' m' Sliders upon spouts for the opposite side.
n Slot-bar for adjusting the fanner to the floor.

The next process with corn is the *winnowing*—that is, making it clean for the market—and this process is conducted in the corn-barn. The first thing to be done towards preparing the thrashed heap of corn for the market, is passing the roughs of wheat or oats through the blower. This machine is set with its tail at the barn-door, that the chaff may be blown away from it. The steward drives it, one woman fills the hopper with the roughs; and as they do not pass easily through the hopper, another woman stands upon the stool belonging to the barn, and pushes them with her hand towards the feeding-roller, while the other two women riddle the corn upon the new-thrashed heap. The riddlings of the roughs, and all the light corn, are put past for the fowls in the light-corn bin. 1563.

Before proceeding to describe the winnowing of corn, it is right to give some idea of the machines employed to winnow it. They are named *blowers* or *fanners*, because they blow away the filth from the corn by means of fans. When cleaning-fanners are fixed to one spot, and are connected with elevators, they are generally of large dimensions, and of more complicated construction than when made to be moved about in the barn. 1564.

The finishing-fanner or duster is a fanner of simpler construction than fig. 97, although as regards the blast it is constructed on the same principle. In operating with this fanner, the grain is taken from the hopper by the revolution of the feeding-roller; and as it falls perpendicularly in

Fig. 98

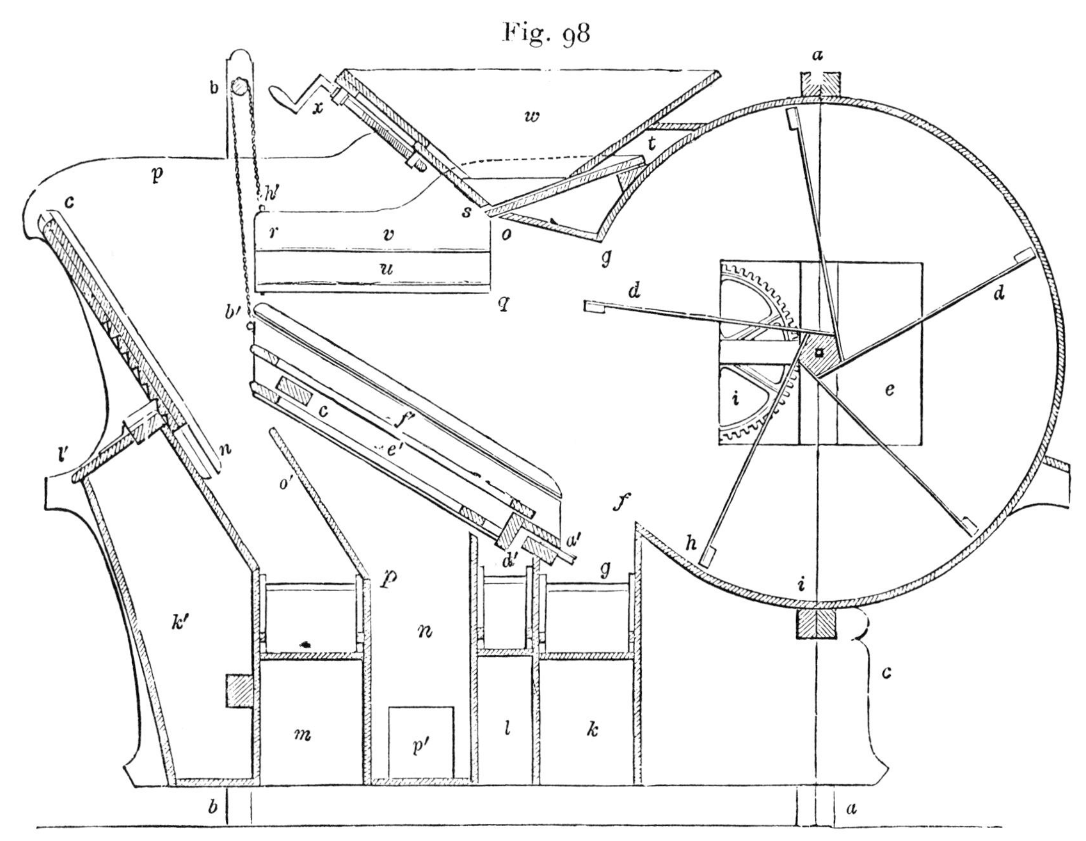

Longitudinal section of the dressing-fanner, with riddles and sieves.

a Fore framing, in halves.
b Back-framing, single.
c c Side-boarding.
d Arms of fans.
e Air-port of fans.
f g Space for discharge of air.
g o Funnel-board for the air.
s t Shoe.
q r s Riddle-frame.
u v Riddles, upper and lower.
w Hopper for corn.
s Sluice.
x Screw-winch to regulate feed.
a' b' Sieve-frame.
e' f' Sieves, upper and lower.
b' h' Chains supporting riddle-frame.
b Stretcher-rod across fanners.
i Toothed wheel acting on a pinion on fan-spindle, and moved by winch-handle.
k' Locker for spare riddles.
l' Lid of locker.
c n Slider for catching light corn.

a thin sheet, is intercepted by the blast under the most favourable circumstances. All such chaff and dust as yet remain amongst it are blown over the sliders; the light grain that may have remained is separated over the sole, and falls down the spout; the remainder runs down the sole, and in passing over the sieve, should any small seeds yet remain, they are intercepted, and fall through it, while the best corn passes on, and is delivered at the end spout. 1565.

The barn implements required in connection with the fanners to clean the corn for the market must also be first described. The most complete implements for separating heavy articles from corn of any kind are *riddles.* They are formed either entirely of wood, or partly of wood and wire. Wood riddles have long been in use, though I believe, in the hands of a skilful riddler, the wire riddle makes the best work. The wood riddles are made of fir or willow, but American elm is the best. The wire riddles have hitherto been made of iron wire, on account, perhaps, of its cheapness; but I should suppose that copper wire would make a better and more durable riddle. A riddle, whether of wood or wire, consists of a bottom of open mesh-work, and of a cylindrical rim of wood, the diameter of which is usually 23 or 24 inches, and its depth 3 inches. Rims are made either of fir, or oak, or beech, the last being most used. In fir rims, the wooden withes of the bottom are passed through slits, thereby endangering the splitting of the rim all round, which they not unfrequently do; but in the oak rim the withes are passed through bored holes, which never split. There is little danger of wire splitting the rims of any sort of wood. The following figures of riddles are portions only of the bottom of each kind, but the meshes are at full sizes. 1567.

Fig. 99

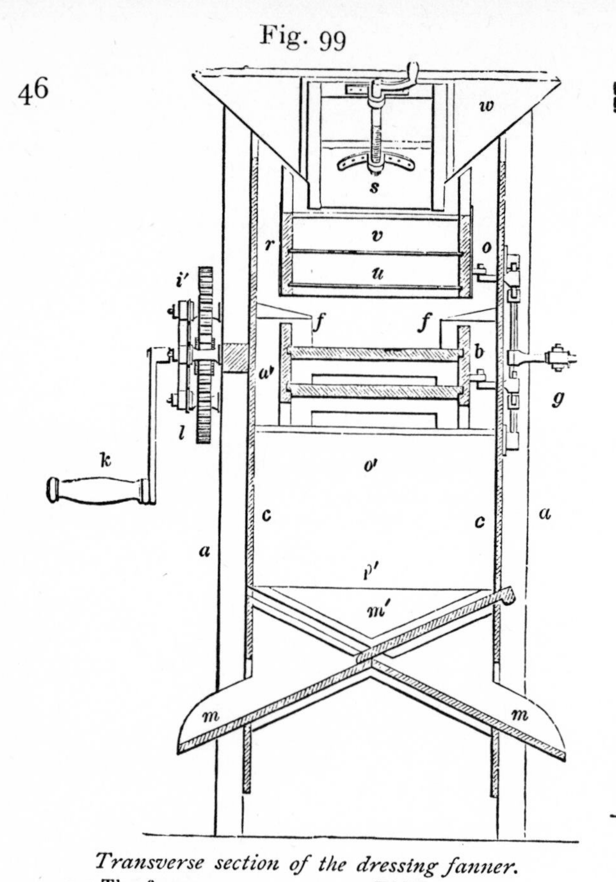

Transverse section of the dressing fanner.

a a The frames.
c c Side-boardings.
m m Light spouts.
m' Sliders to change direction of discharge.
o' p' Sloping division.
a' b Sieve-frames with sieves.
f f Flaunch-boards.
r o Riddle-frames.
u v Riddles.
w Hopper.
s Sluice.
g End of connecting-rod.
b o Attachments of riddle-frames with bell-crank.
i' Toothed wheel.
k Winch-handle.
l Framework.

Fig. 100

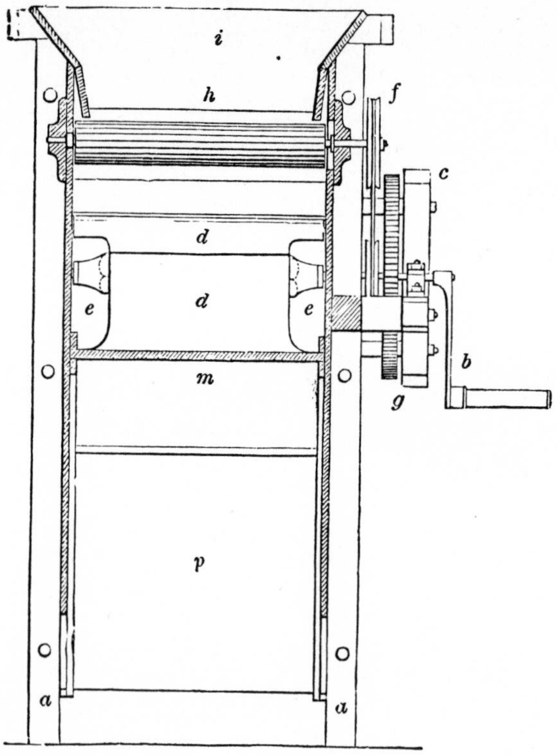

Transverse section of the finishing-fanner or duster.

a a Frames.
b Winch-handle.
c Wheel-framing.
g Wheel.
f Pulley of feeding-roller.
h Feeding-roller.
i Hopper.
m The sole.
p Division under the sole.
d d Arms of fans.
e e Axle of fans.

Fig. 101

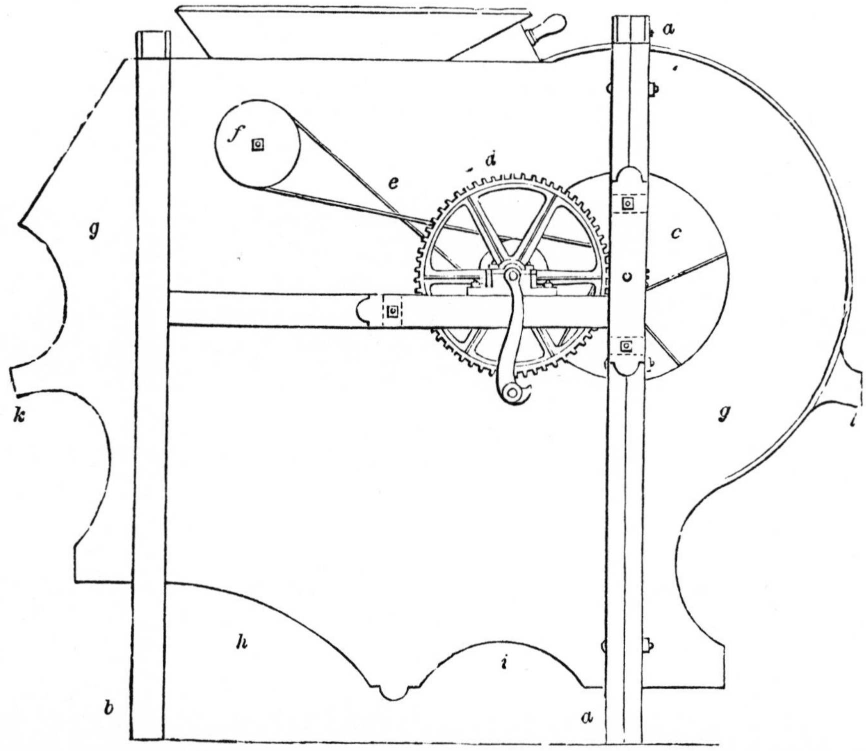

Elevation of the finishing-fanner or duster.

a a Frame, in halves.
b b Frame, single.
c Air-port.
d Wheel and pinion.
e Cross-belt between wheel and pulley.
f Pulley on axle of feeding-roller.
g g Side-boarding.
h i Boarding cut away to give access to light corn and seeds.
k l Handles to carry the fanner.

Fig. 102

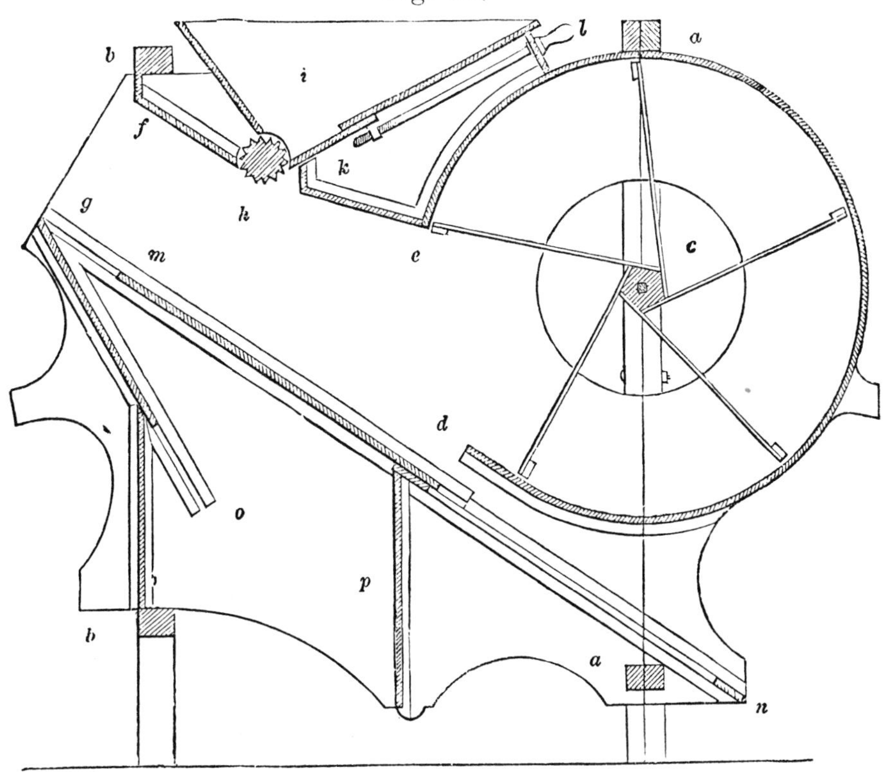

Longitudinal section of the finishing-fanner or duster.

a a b b Cross-rails of the frames.
c Air-port.
d e f g Open funnel for the air.
h Feeding-roller.
i Hopper.
k Slider of hopper.
l Adjusting-screw.
m d Solid sole of funnel.
d n Wire-sieve for good corn.
n End spout.
m d, g o Slides up and down for chaff and light corn.
p Division between light corn and seeds.

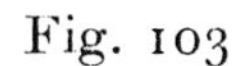
Fig. 103

Winnowing corn.

a Fanner.
b Driver.
c Woman feeding the hopper.
d Woman taking up corn.
e e Women riddlers.
f Corn-basket.
g Wooden shovel.
h Besom.
i Light corn.
k Chaff.

Fig. 104

Wooden wheat-riddle.

Fig. 105

Wooden barley-riddle.

Fig. 106

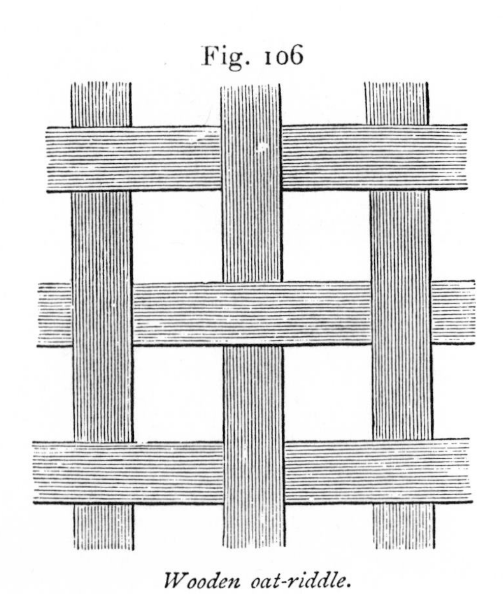

Wooden oat-riddle.

Fig. 107

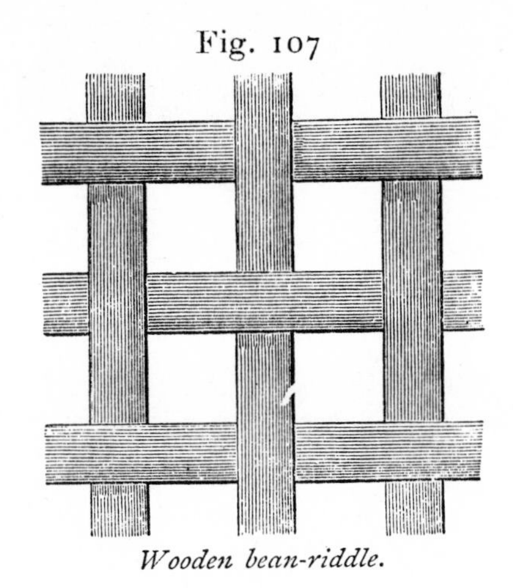

Wooden bean-riddle.

Fig. 108

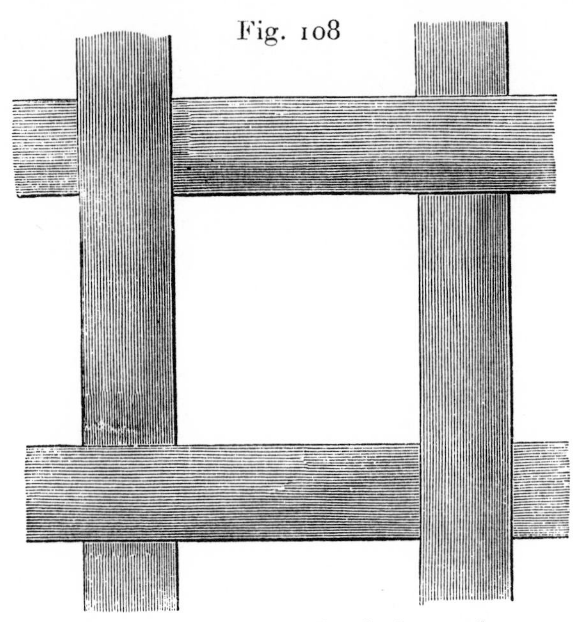

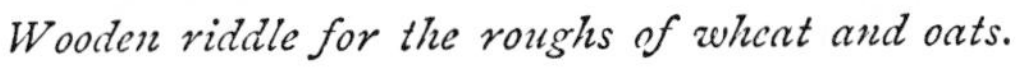

Wooden riddle for the roughs of wheat and oats.

Fig. 109

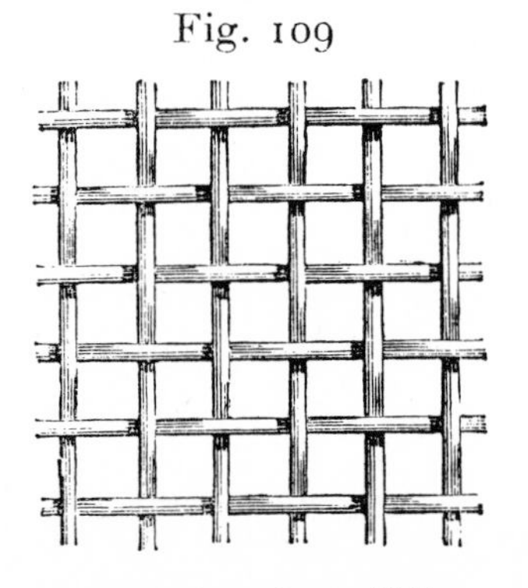

Iron-wire wheat-riddle.

Fig. 110

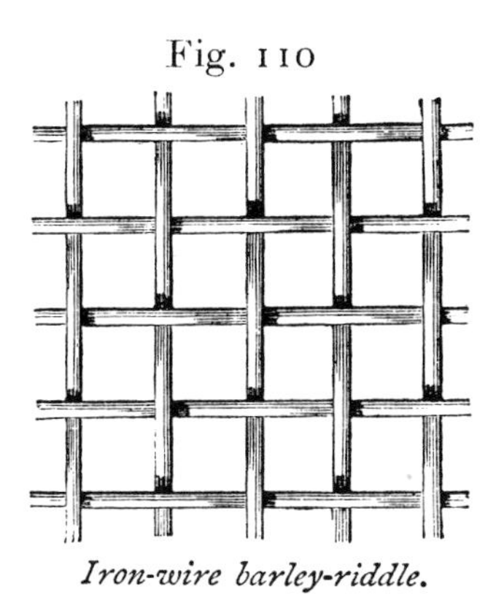

Iron-wire barley-riddle.

Fig. 111

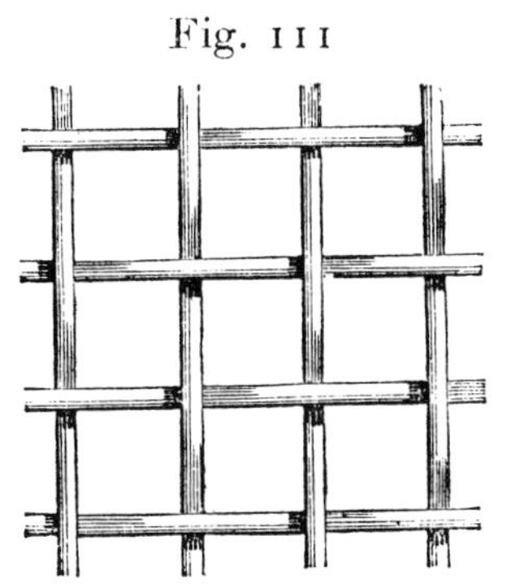

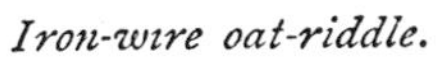

Iron-wire oat-riddle.

Fig. 112

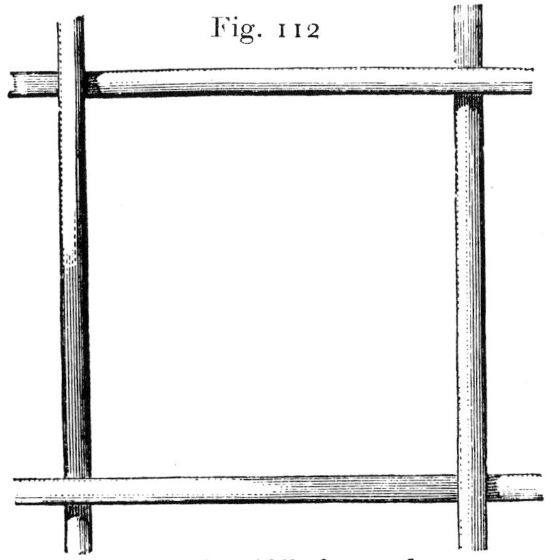

Iron-wire riddle for roughs.

Fig. 113

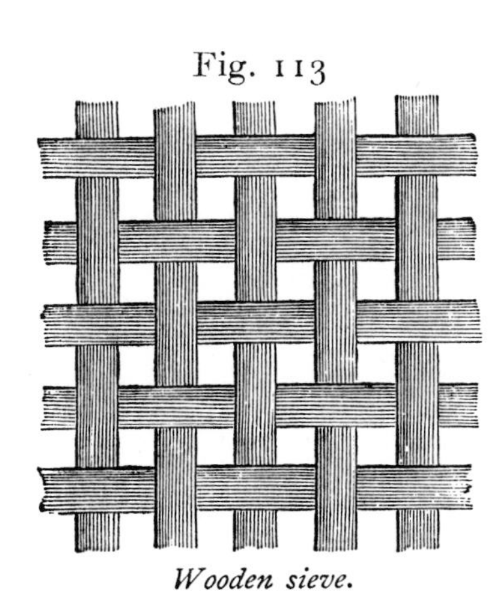

Wooden sieve.

Fig. 114

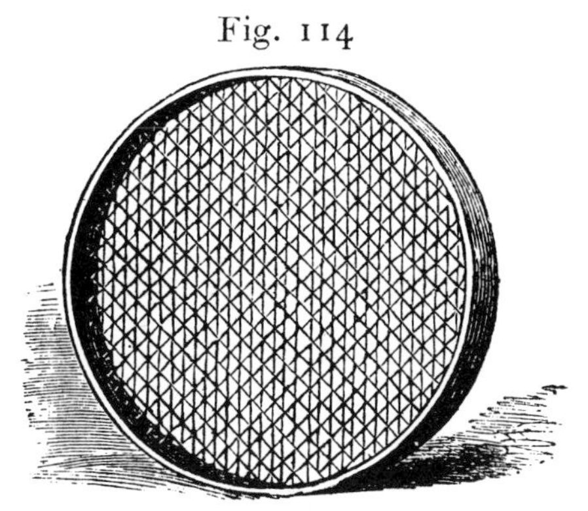

Triangular-meshed iron-wire sieve.

Fig. 115

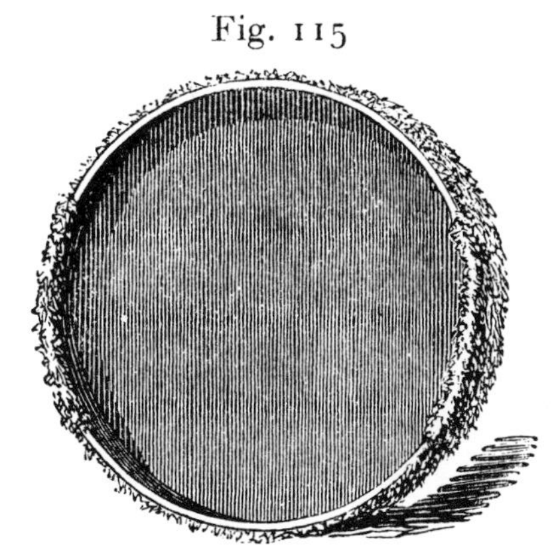

Wecht of skin.

Fig. 116

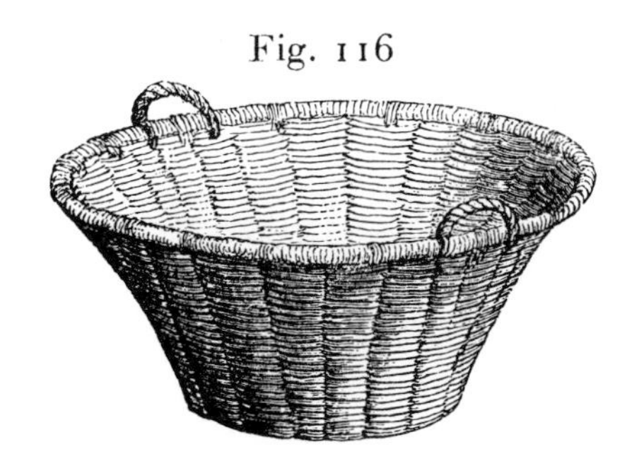

Corn-basket of wicker-work.

Fig. 117

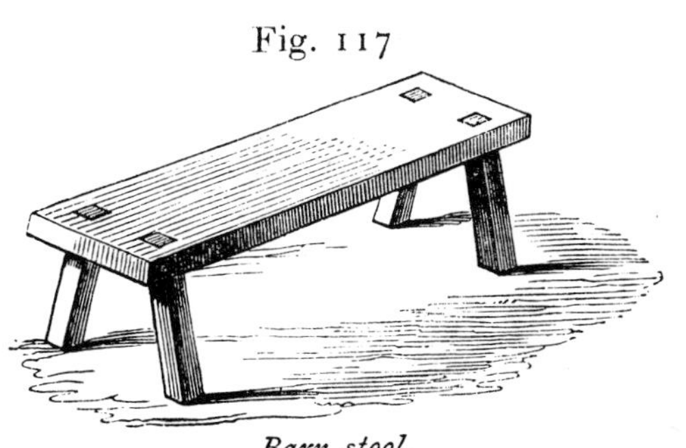

Barn stool.

Wechts or *maunds* for taking up corn from the bin or floor, of the form of fig. 115, are made either of withes or of skin, attached to a rim of wood; one of fir withes, with a rim of oak. A young calf's skin with the hair on, or sheep's skin without the wool, tacked to the rim in a wet state, after becoming dry and hard, makes a better and more durable wecht than wood. Wechts should be made of different sizes; two as large as two fulls will fill the bushel with ease; and others of smaller diameter, and less depth of rim, to take up the corn from the fanner, to give to the riddlers. Baskets of close and beautiful wicker-work, such as fig. 116, are used in barns in parts of England instead of wechts. 1569.

A strong four-legged *stool*, 2½ feet long, 9 inches broad, and 9 inches high, fig. 117, made of ash, is useful in a barn, to allow the women to reach the hopper of the fanner easily. For want of a stool the inverted bushel is taken to stand upon, much to its injury. 1570.

A couple of wooden *scoops*, such as fig. 118, to shovel up the corn in heaps, are indispensable implements in a corn-barn. The scoop is 3 feet 3 inches in height, with a head like a common spade; a helve 18 inches in length, and the blade 14 inches wide and 16 inches long. The blade, helve, and handle are of one piece of wood, of plane-tree, the belly of the blade being a little hollowed out, and its back thinned away to the sides and face. This is a convenient size of scoop for women's use, and they have most occasion to use it, and it is light. In granaries in towns, scoops are made longer, with a handle of a separate piece of ash, and are clumsy implements when made of more than one piece of wood. A wooden scoop does not injure a floor so much as an iron spade, and better retains the corn upon its face in the act of shovelling. 1572.

Fig. 118

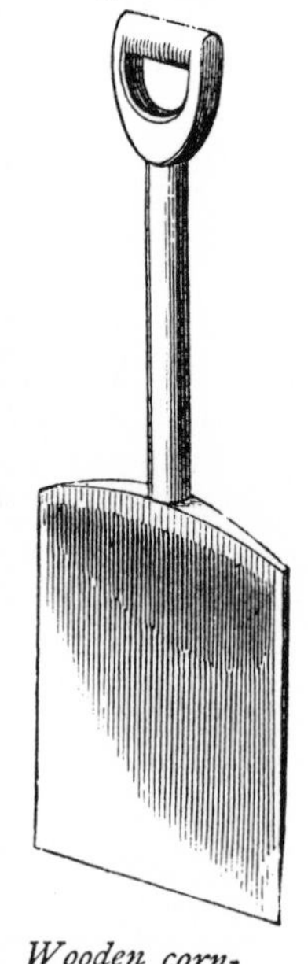

Wooden corn-scoop.

Before proceeding to measure up grain, it is requisite to describe the implements used in measuring. Corn is now invariably measured by the imperial bushel, fig. 119. It is of cooper-work, made of oak and hooped with iron; and, according to the Weights and Measures Act, must be stamped by competent authority before it can be legally used; and having been declared the standard measure of capacity in the country for dry measure, it forms the basis of all contracts dependent on measures of capacity when otherwise indefinitely expressed (5th Geo. IV., c. 74, sec. 15). The bushel must contain just 2218.19 cubic inches, though its form may vary.

Fig. 119

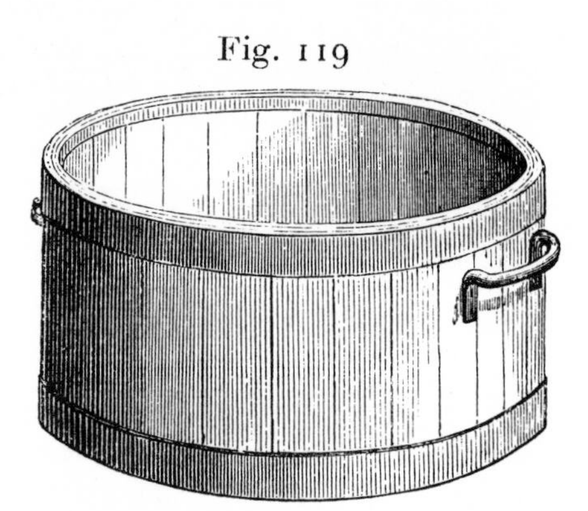

Imperial bushel of a convenient form.

In connection with the bushel is the *strike* for sweeping off the superfluous corn above the edge of the bushel. It is made of two forms; one a flat piece of wood, fig. 120, the other a roller. The Weights and Measures Act prescribes that the strike shall be round, of light wood, 2 inches in diameter; but he who

Fig. 120

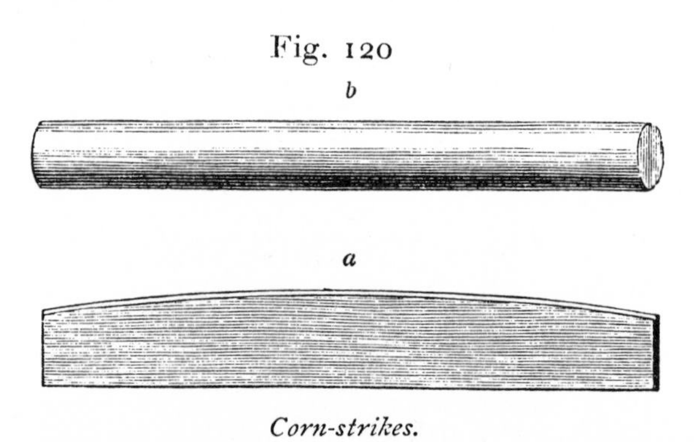

Corn-strikes.

a Flat corn-strike. *b* Cylindrical corn-strike.

drew up the Act must have had little experience of using one. If the object of striking corn in a bushel be to separate one stratum of grains from another, the *sharp* edge of the flat strike is best fitted for the purpose. 1577.

Wheat and oats are dressed clean by the fanner; but it is otherwise, at times, with barley. When barley has not been thoroughly ripened, the awns are broken off at a distance from the grain by the thrashing-machine; and as the part left must be got rid of before the corn can be clean dressed, a *hummeller* is used for the purpose. 1580.

Fig. 121

Measuring up corn in the corn-barn.

a Measurer of corn.
b Bushel.
c c Women filling bushel.
d d Women holding the sack.
e Sack being filled.
f Sack-barrow.
g Filled sacks.
h Empty sacks.
i Heap of corn.
k Wooden shovel.
l Besom.

Fig. 122 is a perspective view of a compact and well-constructed *hand* hummeller, manufactured by Ransome & Sims, Ipswich. The machine stands about 4 feet high, and has a central vertical shaft which carries on its periphery a series of wrought-iron pins which pass between the spaces formed by pins placed in the interior periphery of the outer cylinder, the diameter of which is 16 inches, and height 6¼ inches. The barley is put into the hopper, and is delivered hummelled by the spout.* In the smaller class of farms, *hand - hummellers* are used of various forms, retaining one principle of construction and of effect. They are round, square, and oblong, consisting of a number of parallel bars of iron, placed in a frame. Fig. 124 is a square hummeller in perspective. 1581.

Fig. 122

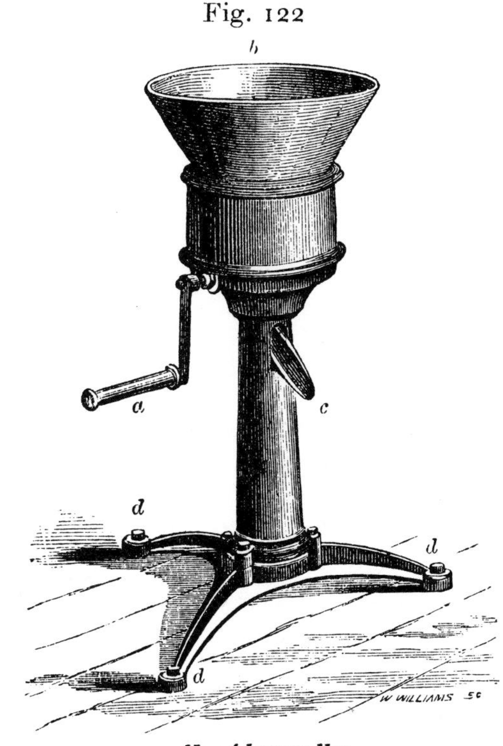

Hand-hummeller.

a Handle.
b Hopper, 22½ inches by 9.
c Delivery-spout.
d d Bolts to fix it to the floor.

* *Book of Farm Impl.*, 393.

Fig. 123

Filled sacks on the barn-floor properly arranged.

a First sack set in a corner.
b c Second and third sacks in the first row.
d First sack in second row set in the hollow between *a* and *b*.
e f Second and third sacks of second row.
g h Bottom of ill-filled sack.
d Well-filled sack.
d e f Sacks with folded mouths.
a b c Sacks with tied mouths.

Fig. 124

Fig. 125

Fig. 126

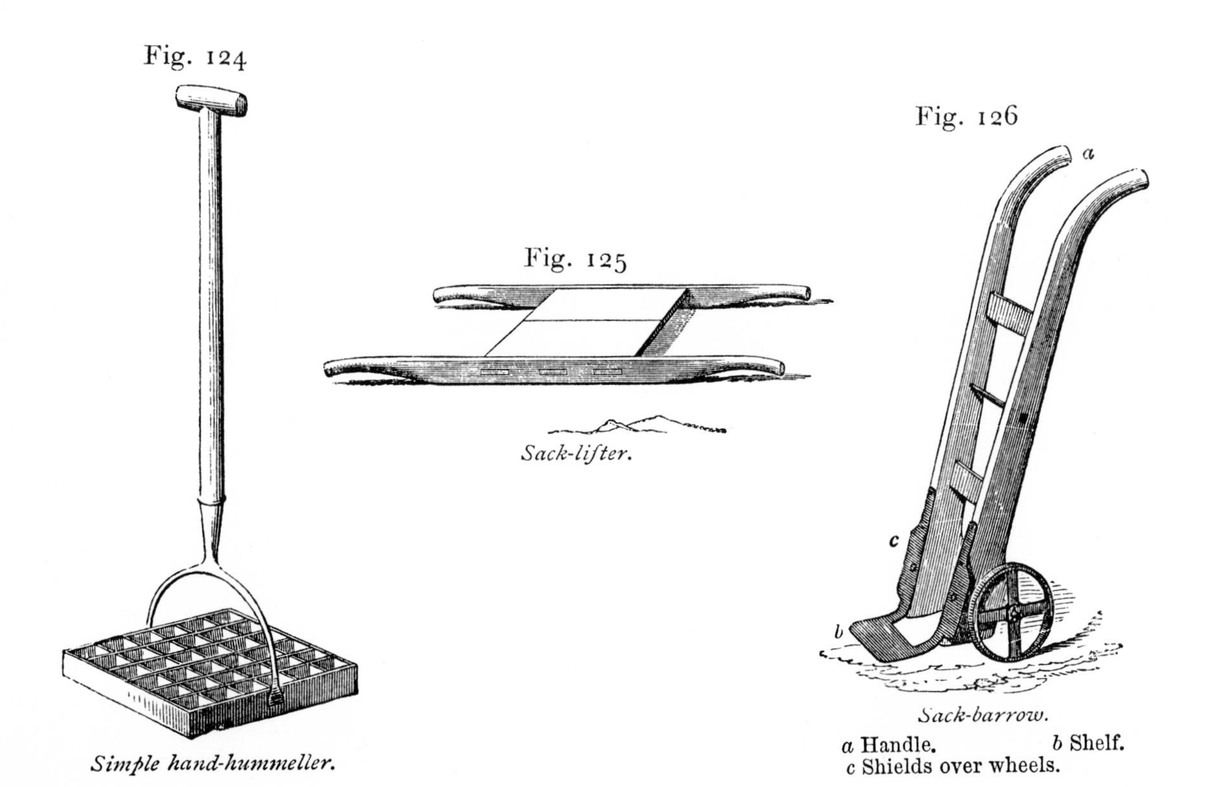

Simple hand-hummeller.

Sack-lifter.

Sack-barrow.

a Handle. *b* Shelf.
c Shields over wheels.

Fig. 127

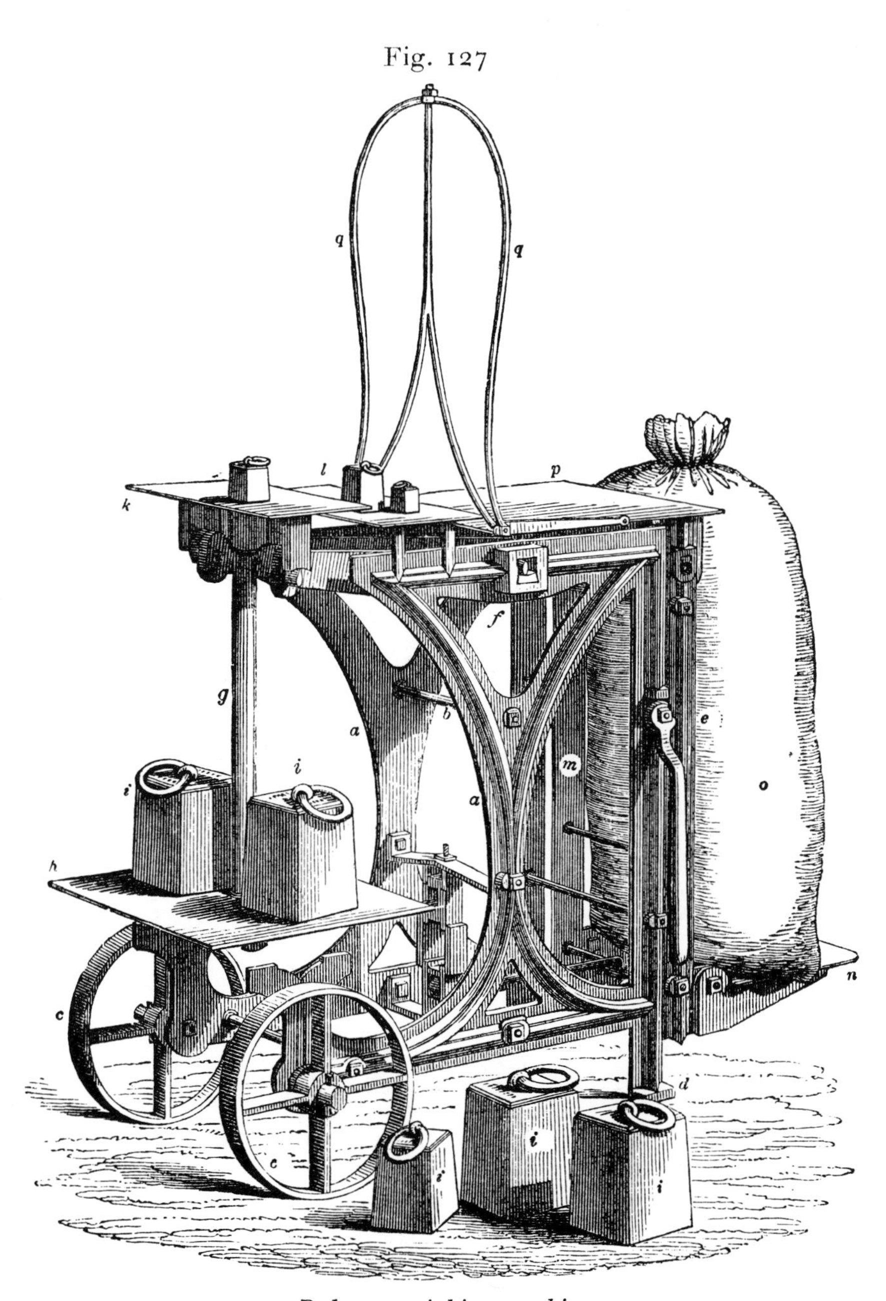

Balance weighing-machine.

a a Cast-iron framework.
b Cross-stretcher bolts.
c c Wheels.
d Feet.
e Folding handles.
f Double beam of cast-iron.
g Pillar.
h Shelf-plate.
i i Weights.
k Top scale
l Dead-plate for small weights.
m Framing.
n Shelf for sacks.
p Upper shelf or scale.
q q Light frame for supporting sacks when placed on the upper scale.

Fig. 128

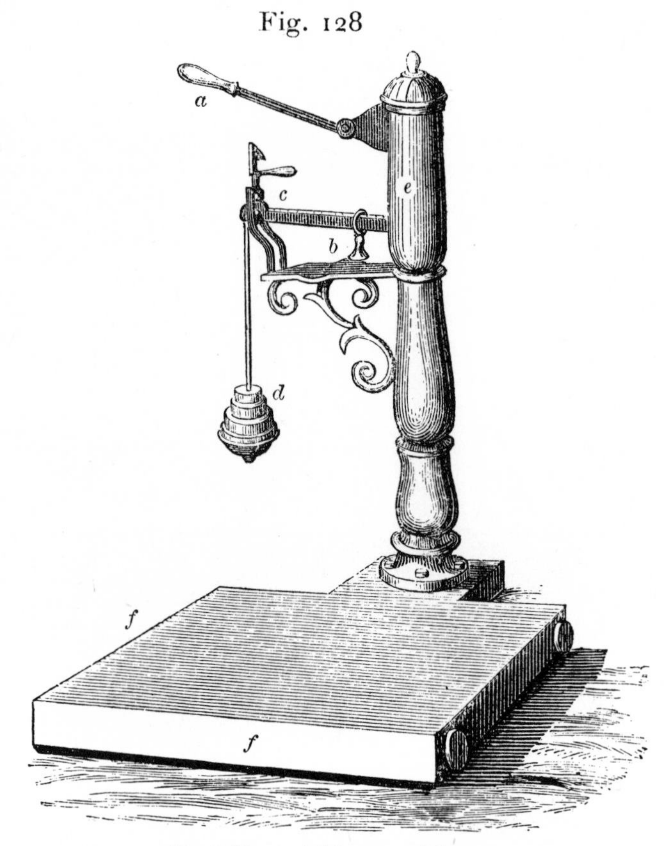

Portable weighing-machine.

a Lever. d Weight-plate. f f Platform.
c Balance. b Sliding-weight. e Standard.

TRANSPORT.

The tilt-cart is the most important vehicle of transport on the farm, and is employed for nine-tenths of all the purposes of carriage required in the multifarious operations throughout the year. It is employed to convey manure of all kinds; to convey stone and other materials for draining and other operations; leading home turnips and potatoes; and for carrying produce of all kinds to market. For some of these operations the tilt-cart is pre-eminently adapted, such as carrying and distributing of manures, or other matters that can be safely discharged by tilting. The dormant cart, on the other hand, is sufficiently commodious when substances have to be carried that require to be discharged from the cart by lifting, such as corn in bags, and many other articles requiring to be conveyed to and from the farm. Fig. 129 is a view in perspective of the common one-horse tilt or coup cart, of a simple and much approved construction. 1591.

Fig. 132 gives a perspective view of an English waggon manufactured by Crosskill, of Beverley. The length of the body over all is 10 feet, width 3 feet 10 inches, height of the front wheels 3 feet 4 inches, and that of the hind 4 feet 6 inches. The waggon is constructed either with a pole or shafts, and is provided with a brake easily regulated by a winch-wheel in front. The waggon has never yet found its way to a Scotch farm, as it possesses no decided advantage over the common cart. It is true that the waggon can convey a very heavy load, and it bears no stress upon the horse's back; but a horse draws a load all the better and the steadier by bearing a proportion of the load upon his back. Hay is the most bulky load of

Fig. 129

Single-horse tilt-cart.

a a Wheels. *b b* Body. *c* Bolsters. *d* Shafts. *e* Top sides.

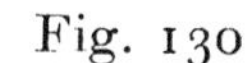
Fig. 130

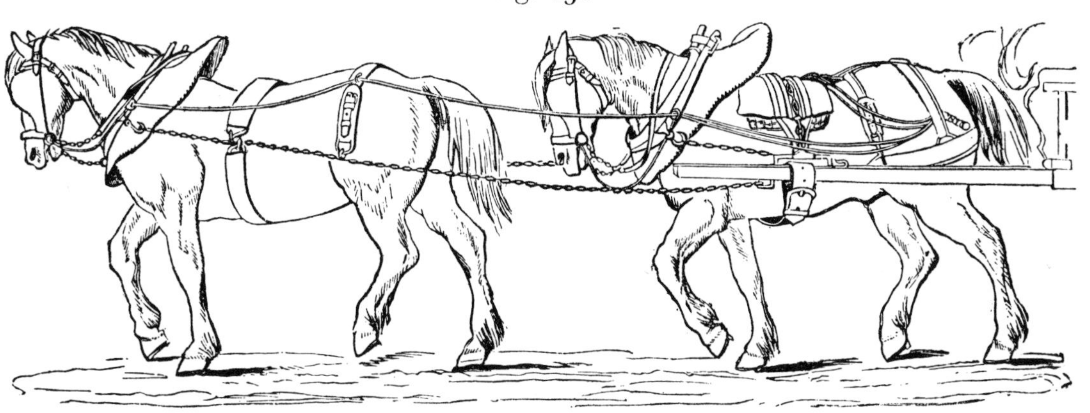

Scotch mode of yoking a double-horse cart.

Fig. 131

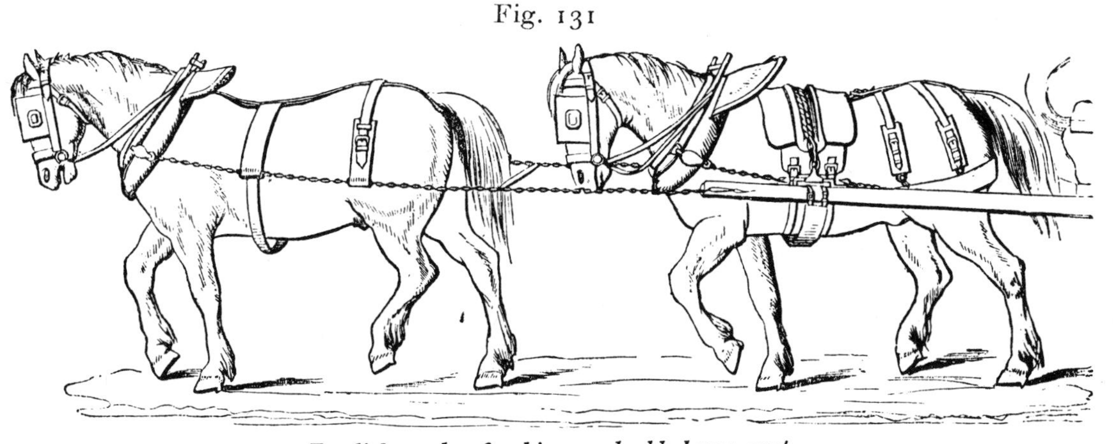

English mode of yoking a double-horse cart.

the farm, and yet one horse in a cart can draw 100 stones, or nearly a ton. On a comparison between a waggon and a cart, as a means of conveying all kinds of agricultural produce, it cannot be denied that the very appearance of the cart at once determines it to be the more handy and easily-managed machine. But, besides this, actual experiment has proved that the cart is more economical than the waggon in the ratio of 9 to 5. In trials at Grantham in 1850, 5 horses in 5 carts were matched against 10 horses in 5 waggons; the 5 carts beat the 5 waggons by 2 loads in the day's work.* 1596.

For a *liquid-manure cart*, a cask of 120 or 140 gallons contents will be found more economical in first cost than a rectangular tank; and as these machines can be only occasionally in operation, they will, if not very carefully attended to, become leaky while standing unoccupied. In this respect the cask will have a manifest advantage over the tank, for the tightening of a cask is an operation the most simple, by the act of driving up the hoops; while, in the case of the tank becoming leaky, no means of that kind can be resorted to, and the alternative is, either soaking

Fig. 132

English farm-waggon.

it in water till the wood has imbibed as much of the fluid as will expand its substance and close the leaks, or the vessel must be tightened by some more expensive process. As the more economical of the two, therefore, in point of expense, I have chosen the cask-mounted cart for the illustration. Fig. 134 is a representation in perspective of this cart, of the simplest and most convenient construction. 1718.

Fig. 133

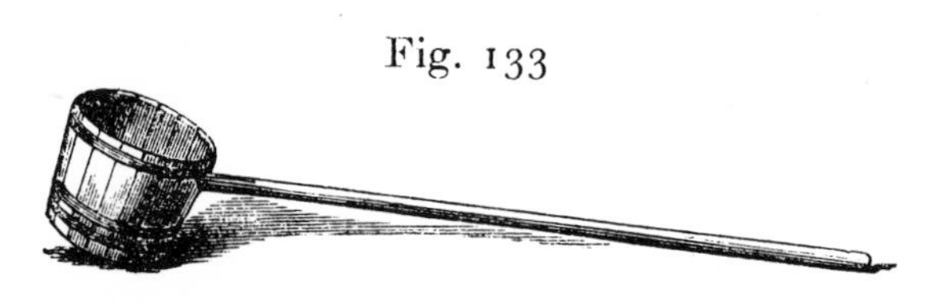

Scoop for filling a water-barrel.

* *Jour. Agric. Soc. Eng.*, xii. 617.

Fig. 134

Liquid-manure cart.

a a Shafts.
b b Wheels.
c Cask.
d Funnel or hopper.
e Distributor.
f Stem of distributor.
g Chain of flap.

Spring

Spring is a busy season on the farm. The cattle-man, besides continuing his attendance on the feeding cattle, has now the more delicate task of waiting on the cows at calving, and providing comfortable lairs for new-dropped calves. The dairymaid commences her labours, not in the peculiar avocations of the dairy, but in rearing calves—the support of a future herd—which, for a time, are indulged with every drop of milk the cows can yield. The farrows of pigs also claim a share of her solicitude. The shepherd, too, has his painful watchings, day and night, on the lambing ewes; 1746.

The condition of the fields demands attention as well as the reproduction of the stock. The day now affords as many hours for labour as are usually bestowed at any season in the field. The ploughmen, therefore, know no rest for at least twelve hours every day, from the time the harrows are yoked for the spring wheat until the turnips are sown. The turnip land, bared as the turnips are consumed by sheep, is now ridged up at once for spring wheat, should the weather be mild and the soil dry enough; or else cross-ploughed, and the ridging delayed until the barley-seed. The first sowing is the spring wheat, then the beans, the oats, and the barley. The fields containing the fallow land now receive a cross-furrow, in the order of the fallow crops—the potatoes first, then turnips, and lastly the bare fallow. 1747.

MILKING COWS.

A cow is generally easily led to the bull at a distance by a halter round the head. If she is known to have a fractious temper, it is better to put a holder in her nose than to allow her to run on the road and have to stop or turn her every short distance. A simple form of holder is in fig. 135, which has a joint that allows the two parts of the holder to meet, and to open so far asunder as to embrace the nostril of the animal. 1796.

Fig. 135

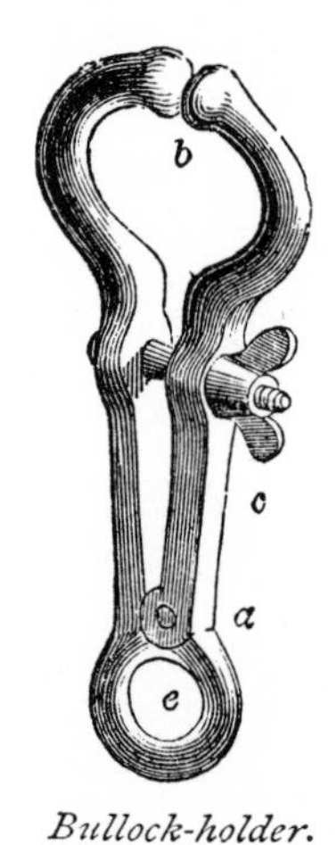

Bullock-holder.

a Joint.
b Knobbed points, meeting.
c Screw-nut.
e Ring for rein-rope.

Fig. 136

Milk-pail.

Fig. 137

Milking-stool.

SOWING SPRING WHEAT.

Fig. 138

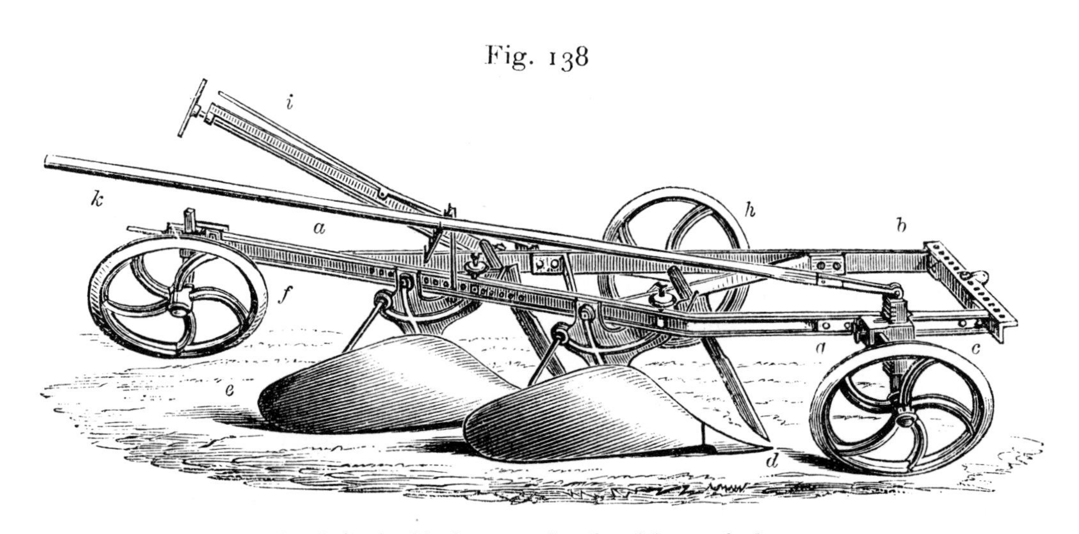

Fowler's double-furrow plough with single lever.

a to *b* Frame of wrought-iron flat bar.
a to *c* Frame of angle iron.
d Front plough fixed, with mould-board, coulter, and share.
e Hind plough, movable, with like mounting.
f g Inclined wheels with angular rims.
h Vertical wheel with angular rim.
i Handle and screw-rod.
k Lever for adjusting wheel *g*.
b c Cross or front bar acting as the bridle.

[*Stephens recommended a double furrow plough, made by John Fowler & Co of Leeds on Piries patent to speed up the rate of ploughing in preparation for Spring sowing.*]

Seed-*wheat* should be *pickled*—that is, subjected to preparation in a certain kind of liquor—before it is sown, in order to insure it against the attack of a fungal disease in the ensuing summer, called *smut*, which renders the grain comparatively worthless. 1838.

Wheat is pickled in this way: For some time—2 or 3 weeks—a tub is placed to receive chamber ley, and whenever ammonia is smelt therefrom, the ley is ready for use. It is better that the ammonia be strong, even to smart the eyes, and water added to dilute it, than that the ley be used fresh. This tub should be removed to the straw-barn, as also the wheat in sacks to be pickled, and part of the floor swept *clean*. Let two upright baskets be provided, each capable of holding easily about half a bushel of wheat, having upright handles above the rims. Pour the wheat into one basket from the sack, and dip the basketful of wheat into the tub of ley completely to cover the wheat, the upright handles protecting the hands from the ley. After

Fig. 139

Apparatus for pickling wheat.

a Sackful of wheat.
b Basket to receive the wheat from the sack.
c Tub of pickle.
d Basket of pickled wheat.
e Drainer for basket.
f Tub to receive draining of pickle from the basket.
g Heap of pickled wheat.
h Sacks for the pickled wheat.

remaining in the liquid for a few seconds, lift up the basket, so as to let the surplus liquid run from it into the tub again, and then place the basket upon the drainer on the empty tub, to drip still more liquid, until the other basket is filled with wheat and dipped in the ley tub. Then empty the dripped basket of its wheat on the floor; and as every basketful is emptied, let a person spread, by riddling through a wire wheat-riddle, fig. 109, a little slaked caustic lime upon the wet wheat to dry it. 1839.

The *rusky*, or seed-basket, fig. 140, is usually made of twisted straw in rows above each other, fastened together by withes of willow. It is provided with a couple of handles to admit the points of the fingers to pass, and the bottom should be flat. In the Border counties it is carried upon the head of the seed-carrier when full; in some counties in the arms, with the bottom edge supported upon the haunch. The seed is most easily poured into the sheet from the rusky on the head. 1843

Fig. 140

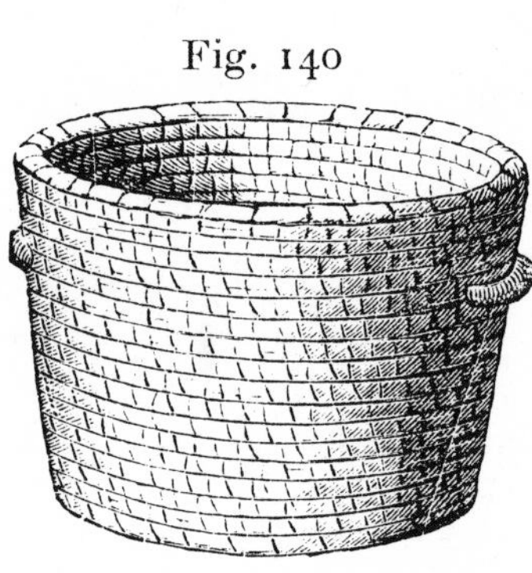

Seed-corn rusky.

Fig. 141 shows very correctly the manner in which a well-made sheet should be put on and held. A *basket* of wicker-work, such as fig. 142, is very common in England for sowing seed. It is suspended by a girth fastened to two loops on the rim of the basket, and passing round the back of the neck; the left hand holding the basket steady by the wooden stud on the other side of the rim.

Fig. 141

Sowing-sheet and hand-sowing corn.

Fig. 142

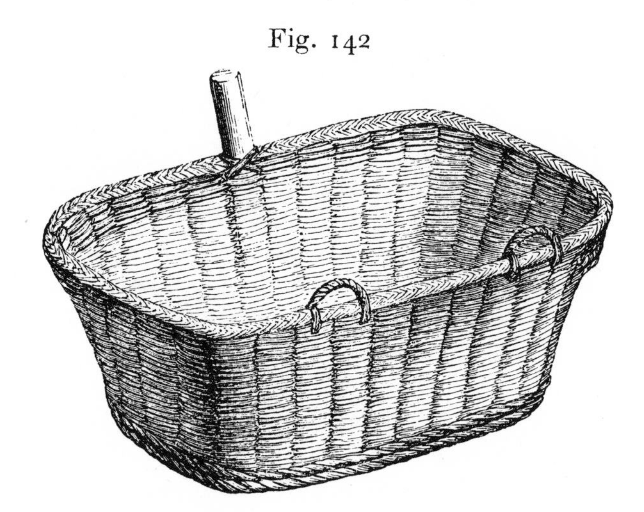

English sowing-basket.

Both these means for sowing seed are intended for the use of one hand only, but some sowers throw the seed with both hands, and then the implement must be made to suit the practice. Such a one is a basket, or box made of thin deal, the nearest side curved to suit the front of the sower's body; suspended by a girth fastened to loops on the nearest side, and passing round the back of the neck; a strap and buckle fastening the box round his body; and the further side suspended by straps slanting to the shoulders of the sower, and fastened to the strap behind his body. A more simple form of sowing-sheet for both hands is a linen semi-spheroidal bag, attached to a hoop of wood or of iron rod, formed to fit the sower's body, buckled round it, and suspended in front in the manner just described. Both hands are thus at liberty to cast the seed in, one handful after the other. 1844.

There are various forms of the *broadcast* sowing-machine. The one I have chosen for illustration exhibits the machine in the most perfect form, not only doing the work easily and well, but is so constructed that its long sowing-chest is divided into sections, the two end ones of which can be folded upon the central division, whereby the machine may pass through any field-gate without having to remove the sowing-chest. Fig. 143 is a view in perspective of the machine as at work. 1850.

Fig. 143

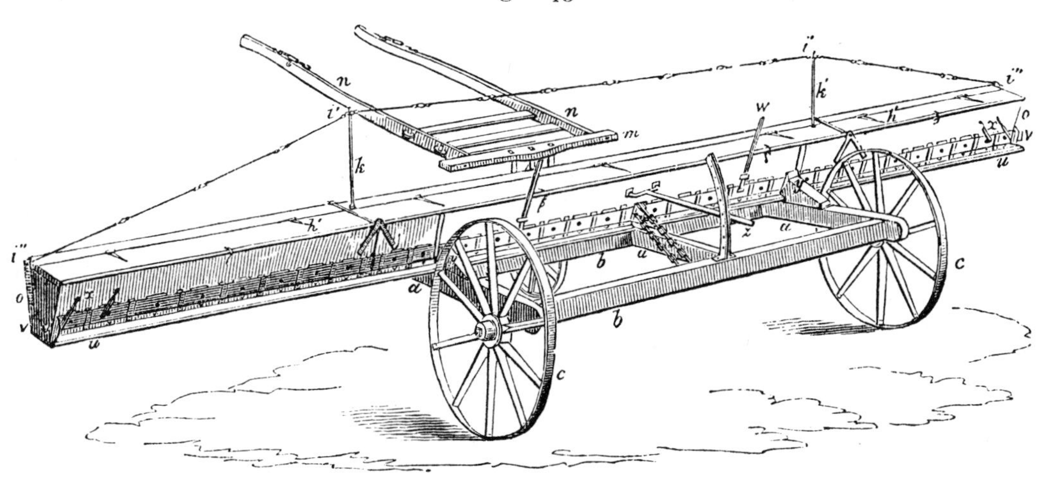

Broadcast sowing-machine.

a b b a Carriage.
c c Hind wheels.
b Front wheel.
n n Horse shafts.
m Splinter-bar.
o o Seed-chest.
i' i' i' i' Light tension-chain.
k k' Upright iron stanchions.
v v Adjusting screws.
x x Adjusting slides.
u u Apron.
z Adjusting quadrant.
w Lever.

The *common* or *East Lothian drill sowing-machine* is here taken to illustrate the principles of the drill-machine. Though it may be deficient in some points as compared with those of Berwickshire and Roxburghshire, yet its extreme simplicity and cheapness have brought it into very extensive adoption, not only in East Lothian, but in other districts where the drill system is followed. Fig. 144 is a view in perspective of this machine, having drills to sow 6 rows, which is the size most generally used, chiefly because it can be drawn by one horse; but also, in the event of its being employed along swelling ridges, its covering but a small breadth secures a nearly equal depth for the deposition of the seed, which cannot be easily done under the same circumstances if the machine is mounted with a greater number of coulters. But it follows from the peculiarity of structure, the coulters being permanently fixed in position for the depth to which they penetrate the soil, that the machine is best adapted for sowing across the ridges; and hence it is almost invariably worked in that direction, though, when worked in the direction of the ridge, the breadth covered by the machine is equal to nearly one-third of a 15-feet ridge. 1851.

Fig. 144

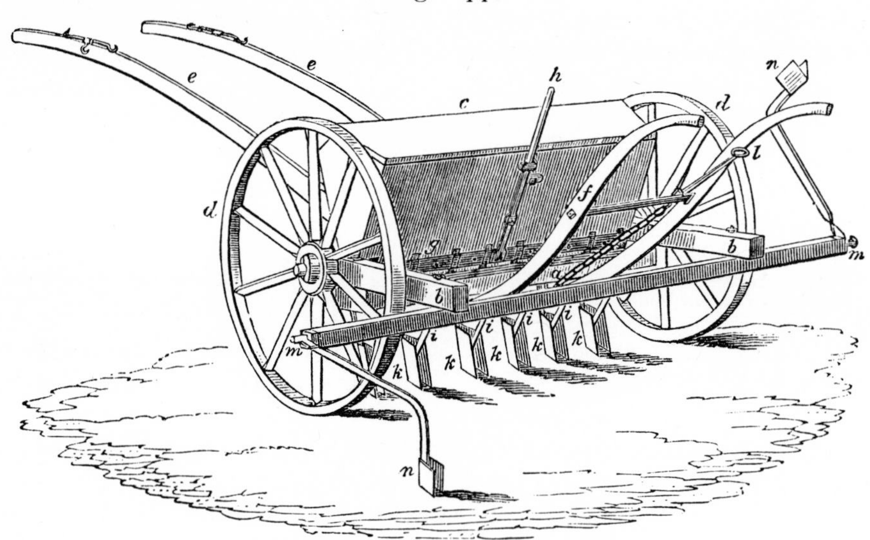

East Lothian grain drill-machine.

a Bed-plank.
b b Side-bars.
m m Bar.
c Seed-chest.
d d Wheels.
e e Horse-shafts.
k k Coulters.
i i Tubes.
n n Markers.
m n, m n Marking-rods.
f f Handles.
g Seed-orifices.
h Lever.
l Balance-chain.

Fig. 145

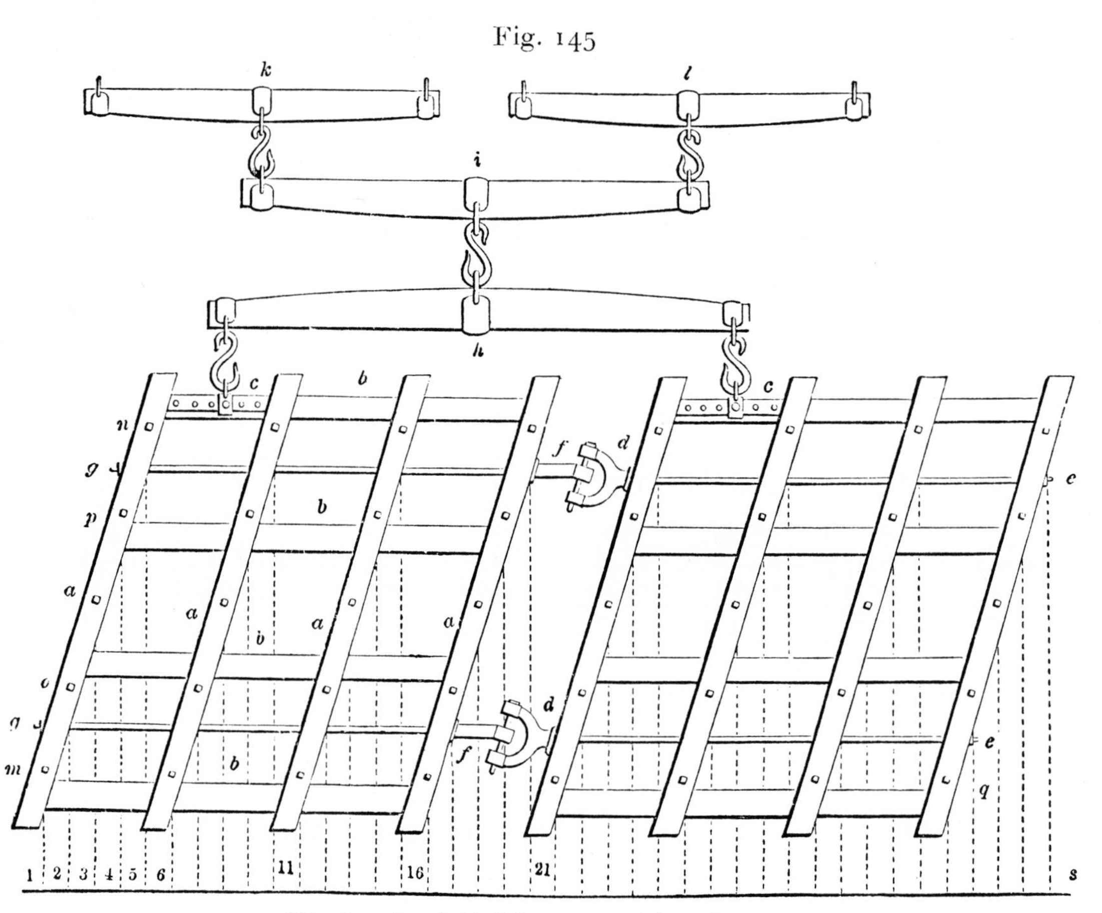

Wooden rhomboidal harrows, with swing-trees.

a a a a Four bulls.
b b b b Four slots.
c c Iron bars for yoking.
d d Double joints or hinges.
d e Bolts passing through the bulls.
e e Screw-nuts.
f g Bolts passing through the bulls.
g g Screw-nuts.
d f Loose joints.
f f Single joint.
h Master swing-tree.
i k l Common swing-trees.

The land, whether sown by hand or with any sort of machine, must be harrowed; but the order in time of using the harrows differs on the sort of machine used for sowing the grain. When the grain is sown by hand or with the broadcast machine, the harrow is used after the grain has been sown; but in sowing with drill-machines, the harrow is first used to put the land into the proper tilth for the machine. 1853.

Water-furrowing is making a slight plough-furrow in every open furrow, as a channel for rain-water to flow off the land. It may be executed lightly with a common plough and one horse, but better with a double mould-board plough and one horse; and as the single horse walks in the open furrow, the plough following obliterates his footmarks. The better water-furrowing by the double mould-board plough consists in the channel having equal sides; and the furrow-slice on each side being small, compared with the one furrow-slice of the common plough, on one side the water can run freely into the furrow. The plough simply goes up one open furrow and down another until the field is finished, the horse being *hied* at the turns into the open furrow. Water-furrowing finishes the work of the field. 1857.

Fig. 146

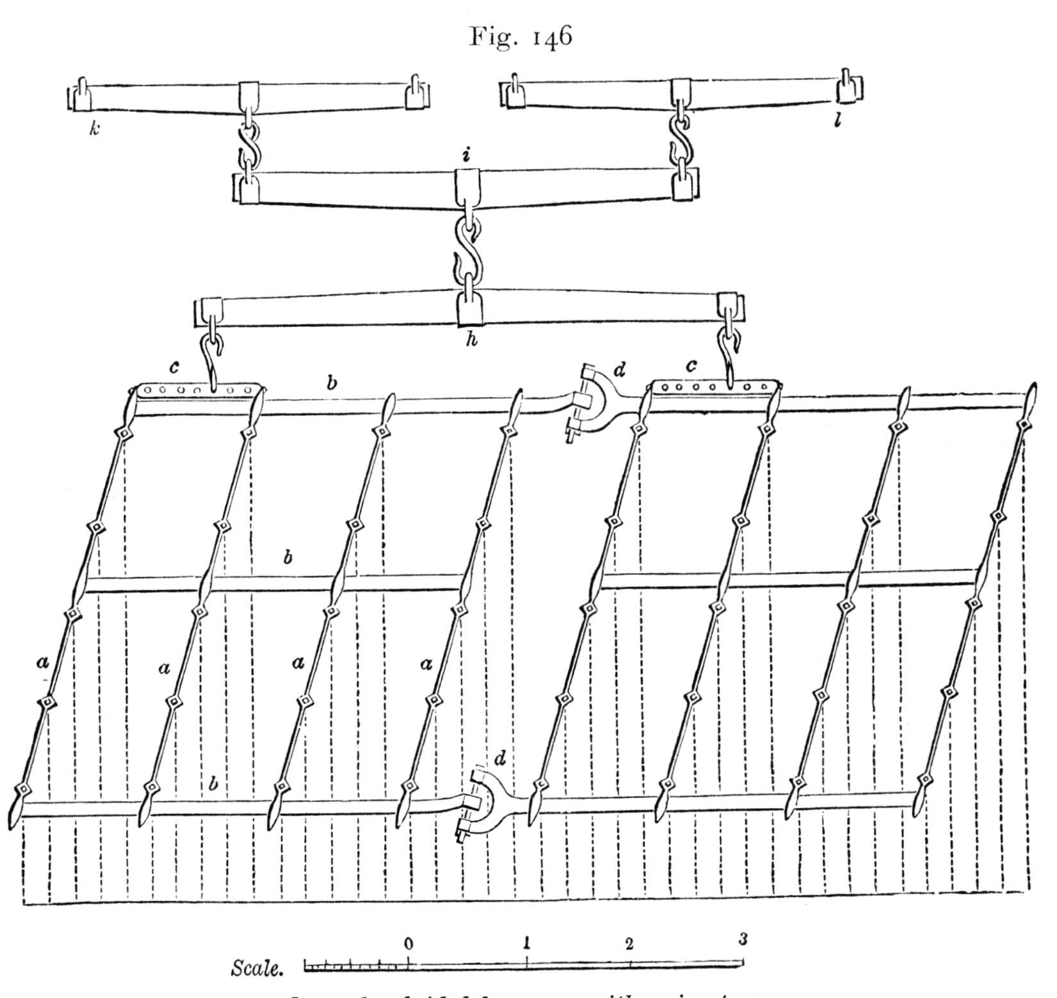

Iron rhomboidal harrows, with swing-trees.

a a a a Four bulls. *b b b* Three slots. *d d* Hinge-joints. *c c* Bars. *h* Master swing-tree. *i k l* Swing-trees.

Fig. 147

Sowing corn by hand, with the harrows in the field.

a Leading hand-sower.
b Second hand-sower.
c Elliptical form of the cast of seed.
d Open furrow between the 2 ridges.
e Field-worker for carrying seed to the sowers.
i Sack of seed-wheat,
f Leading pair of horses.
h Leading pair of harrows.
g Following-man with his pair of horses and harrows.

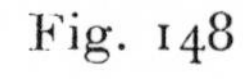

Fig. 148

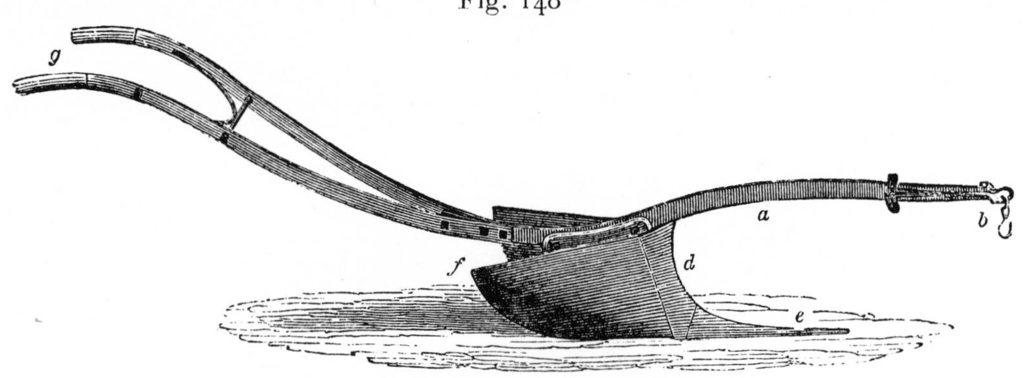

Water-furrowing and earthing-up double mould-board plough.

a Beam.
b Bridle.
d Breast.
e Share.
f Right and left mould-boards.
g Wood handles of the stilts.

Fig. 149

Presser-roller.

a a Rectangular frame.
b Pair of shafts.
c Cast-iron bracket.
d d Two pressing wheels.
e Light carriage-wheel.
f Iron stay-rod.
g Two iron scrapers.

Fig. 150

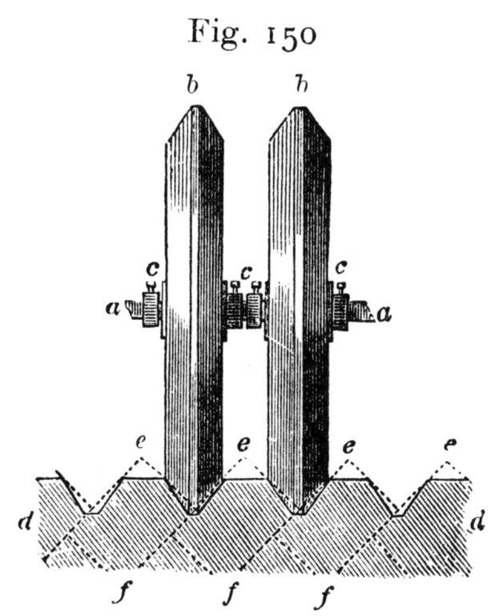

Action of the edge of presser-wheels.

a a Axle.
b b Two pressing-wheels.
c c c Square collars upon the axle.
d d Transverse section of ground being pressed.
e f Newly-ploughed lea, furrow-slices in dotted lines.

[*The pressure roller (furrow press) is used, Stephens says "To consolidate the soil in the lineal spaces in which the seeds of wheat are to have root". Hence it is only applicable in drill culture on loose soil, whether after ley or on bare land.*]

DRILLING UP LAND.

While the ploughing and sowing turnip-land with spring wheat is progressing in early spring, whenever the weather is favourable, preparation should be making for other early crops, the earliest being the bean and the pea. Beans and peas are usually cultivated on strong land; and as it cannot be worked in spring but when the weather is dry, unless it has been thoroughly drained, or rests upon a porous subsoil, it is not in every season that the bean and the pea can be cultivated. Beans and peas may also be cultivated in lighter and naturally dry soils, provided they are well manured. Whatever may be the state and quality of the soil, one mode of cultivating the bean and the pea is upon drills, in the same manner as the potato and the turnip.

1865.

In whichever state the surface may be, the drills are made of the same form, but in various ways. They are made by one landing of the common plough, when they are said to be *single;* or they are made with a bout of the plough, when they are called *double;* and both single and double drills are made either *towards* or *from* the *feering.* The ultimate form of the drills is apparently the same, but those made *from* the feering are the truest drills. Drills are also made by the double mould-broad plough, fig. 148.

1866.

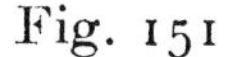
Fig. 151

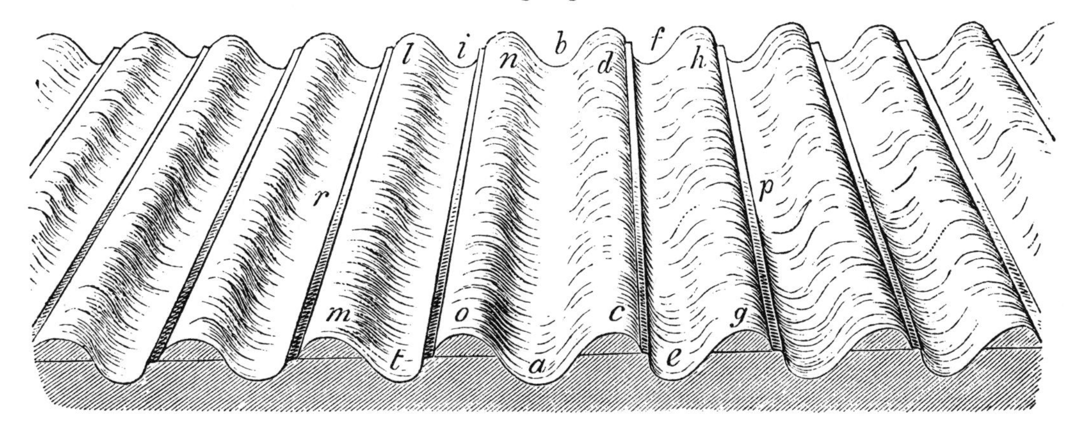

Mode of ploughing single drills.

a b Line of feering poles.
c d First furrow-slice laid over.
n o Second furrow-slice laid over.
g h and *l m* Successive similar furrow-slices.

SOWING BEANS.

As land is not likely to be sufficiently impressed by harrows for bean culture on the winter-furrow, recourse should be had at once to the grubber, which is an excellent implement for pulverising the surface of the soil. Fig. 152 is a view, in perspective, of Kirkwood's grubber.

1876.

Fig. 152

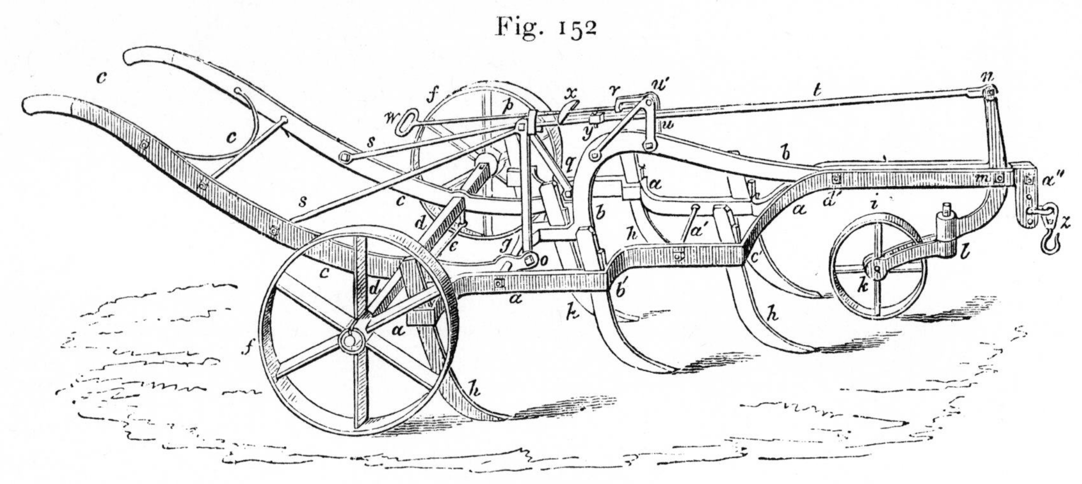

Kirkwood's grubber.

a a a Tine-frame.
d Double prolongation of frame.
e a' Bolts of frame.
a'' Muzzle at end of frame.
b b Beam.
r u' Bridle.
h h Tines, 7 in number.

d d Axle of carriage.
c c c c Handles or levers.
g Joint-rod of levers.
o Extremities of levers.
o p q Elevating apparatus.
s s Stays of elevating apparatus.
f f Hind wheels of carriage.
i Castor-wheel.

k l Shears of castor-wheel.
l n Crank-lever.
t Connecting-rod with crank-lever.
y' Nut or slide-box.
w x u Handle of connecting-rod.
p Prolonged screw-nut.
z Draught shackle and hook.

Fig. 153

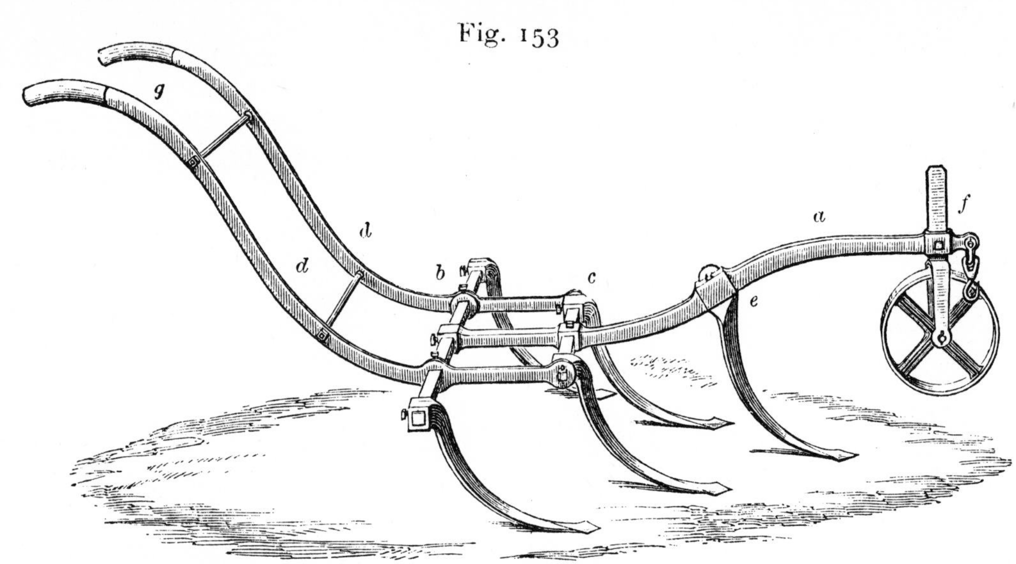

Tennant's grubber.

a Beam.
b Long square bar.
c Short square bar.
d d Stilts.
e Foremost tine.
f Wheel.
g Handles of stilts.

[*The seed is sewn in the furrows by means of a bean-barrow, and is then covered by splitting the drills with a plough.*]

1878. Up to this point I have taken for granted that the land was treated in the usual way; but should the stubble-land have been deep ploughed with the Tweeddale plough with 3 horses, the land in spring will require very little work, only grubbing, to be prepared for the manure by drilling—and the grubber need not be the complex Kirkwood's, but the simple Tennant's, which it will supersede.

Fig. 154

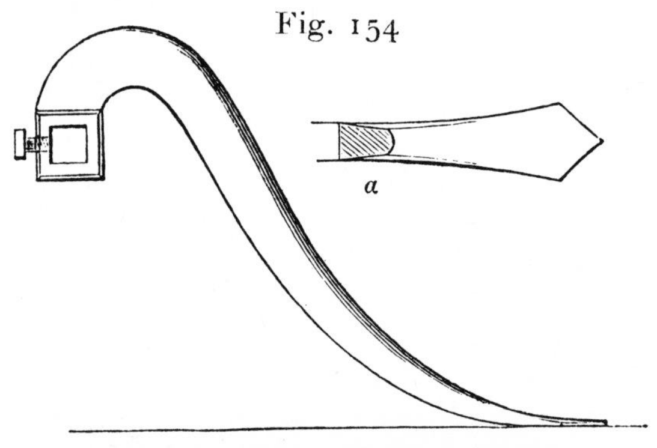

Swan-neck tine to Tennant's grubber.

a Finishing-point like Tennant's.

Fig. 155

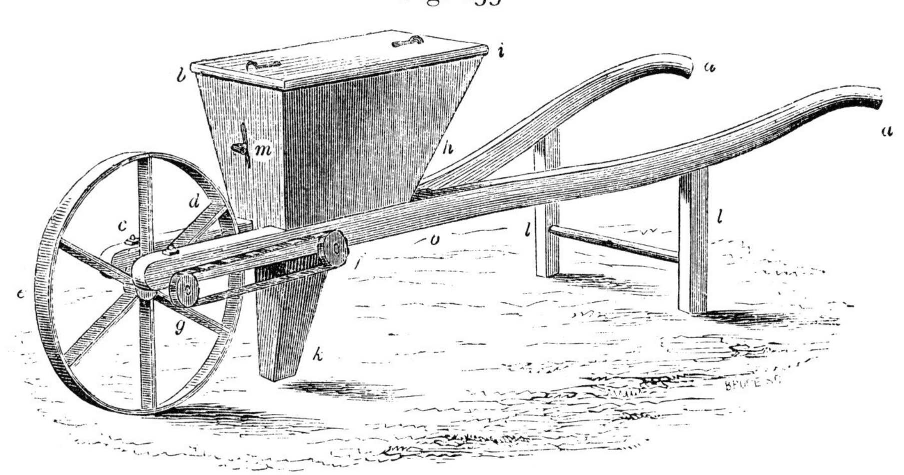

Bean-barrow.

a a b c Stilts and bed-frame.
d e Wheel.
f g Pitch-chain over 2 chain-wheels.
f Seed-cylinder on wheel-axle.
b d h i Seed-chest.
k Spout for seed.
l l Legs to support stilts.
m Pinching - screw to regulate the discharge of seed.

Fig. 156

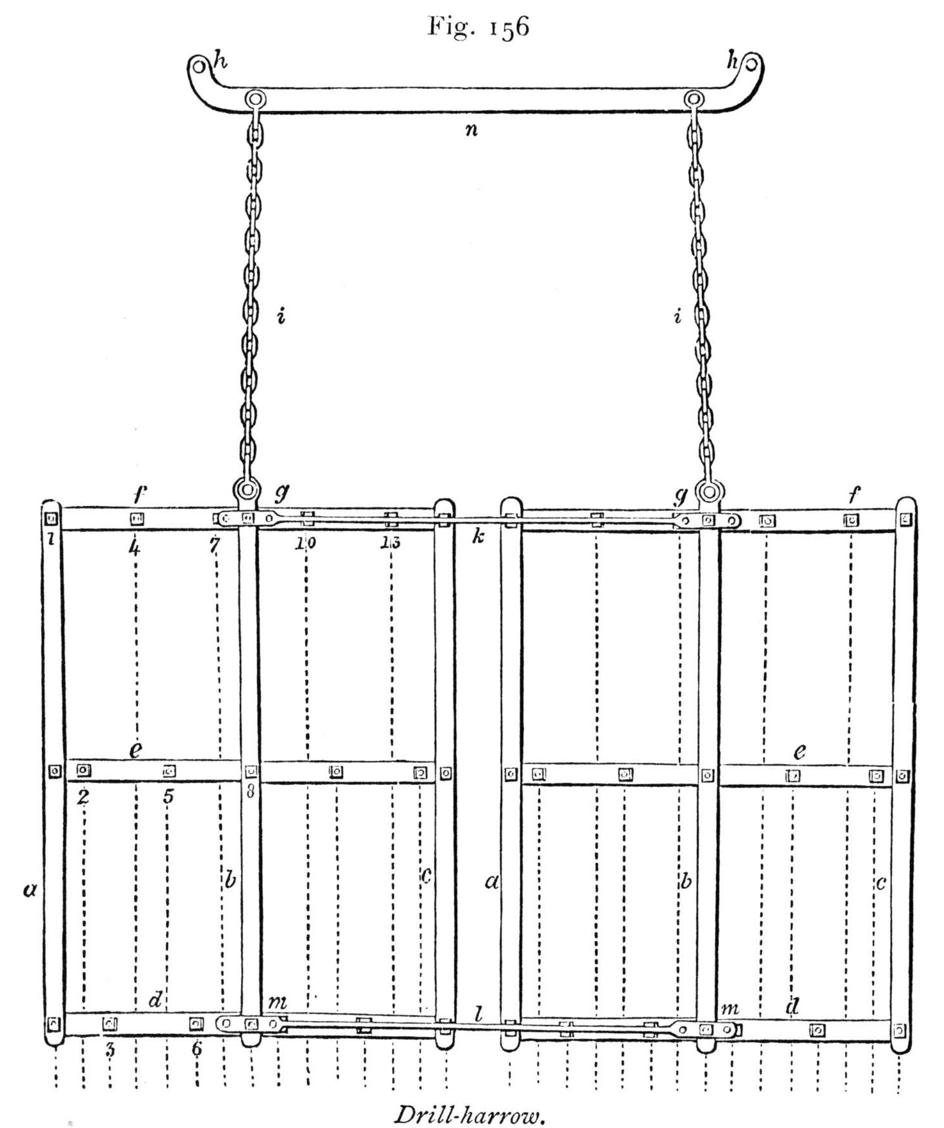

Drill-harrow.

a a c c Outside bulls.
k l Coupling-rods.
i i Draught-chains.
n Swing-tree.
h h Yoking points for hooks.
g m Middle bulls.
e e Middle bars.
f f Front bars.
d d Hind bars.

The common harrow, fig. 145, is often used to harrow down drills; but a better implement is the *drill-harrow*, of which fig. 156 is a geometrical plan of one of rectangular form. This harrow is worked in pairs; and, to render it applicable to its purpose, it is made of an arch form, partially embracing the curvature of the drill, and on this account is best fabricated of iron. 1883.

[*'Harrowing down' the drills is done to control the growth of weeds.*]

Fig. 157

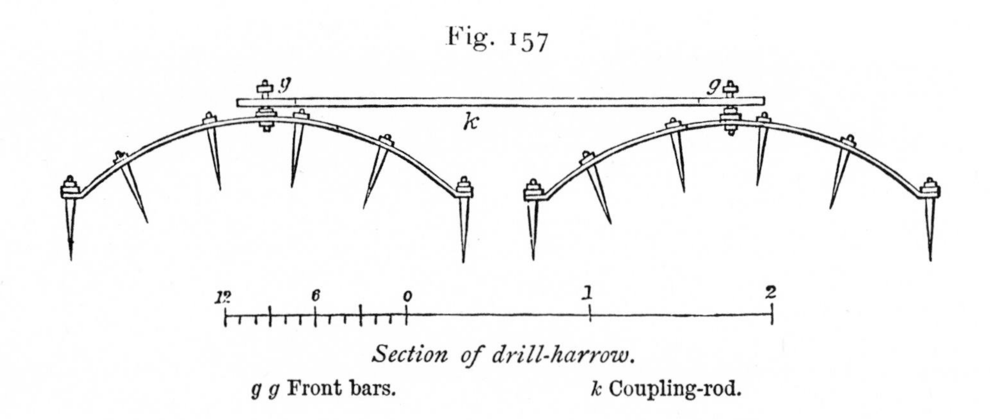

Section of drill-harrow.

g g Front bars. *k* Coupling-rod.

ROLLING LAND.

The rolling is always effected across the line of ridges, for otherwise the open furrows would not receive any benefit from it. Although the dividing of the cylinder into two parts facilitates the turning of the implement, it is not advisable to attempt to turn the roller sharp round, as part of the ground turned upon will be rubbed hard by the cylinders; and where young plants grow upon those parts, such as young clover, the probable effect would be to kill them. 1899.

Fig. 158

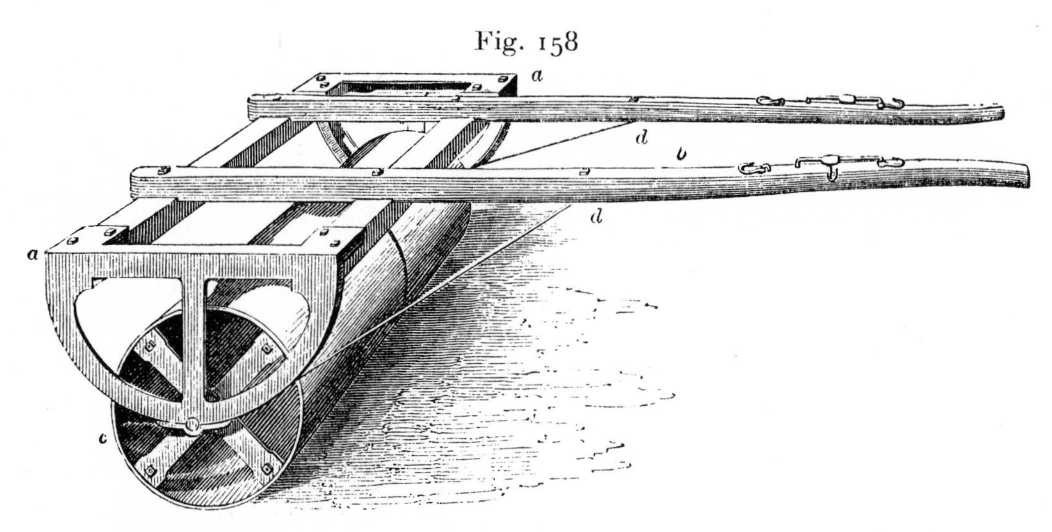

Cast-iron land-roller.

a Carriage-frame. *b* Horse-shafts. *c* Cylinder. *d d* Iron stays.

Crosskill's *clod-crusher* is the most efficient implement of its class. It is seen in perspective in fig. 159. The roller is 6 feet in length, and 30 inches in diameter; a cast-iron end frame, at each end of the roller, is bolted to a wooden

Fig. 159

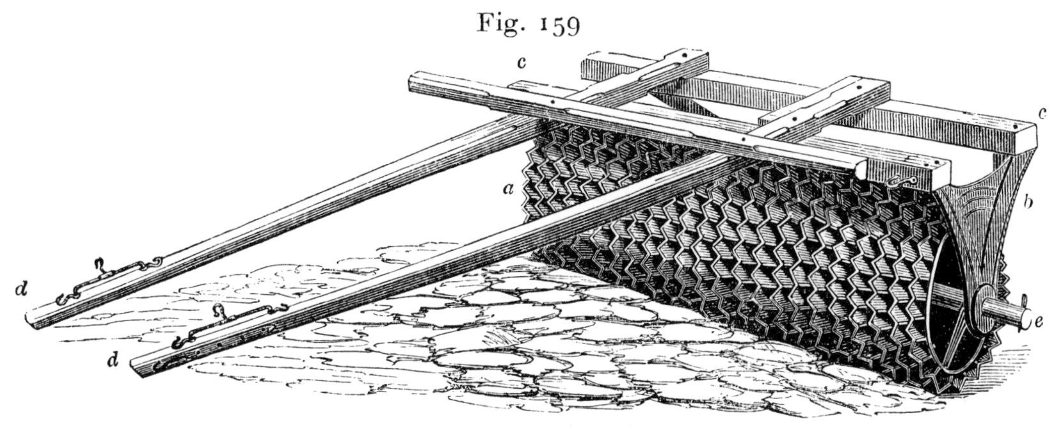

Crosskill's clod-crusher.

a Roller.
b Cast-iron end frame.
c c Wooden top frame.
d d Horse-shafts.
e Axle of roller.

frame, to which are bolted the horse-shafts. The frame-ends are placed upon the axle, the ends of which are prolonged to form arms on which wheels are placed, and kept on by means of cotterels, for the removal of the roller from one field to another. When the wheels are to be placed or removed, a hole is dug in the ground under each wheel, while the roller rests on the ground. The roller consists of a number of toothed wheels, supported on 4-feathered arms, and an eye formed in the centre fitted to move easily on the axle of the roller. Fig. 160 shows a side view of 1 of those wheels, by which its action upon the soil may be easily understood. When such a great number of angles, acting like so many wedges, are brought into contact with the indurated clods, they infallibly split them into numerous fragments, and the repetition of the process produces a well-pulverised surface. The effect is quite different from that of the plain roller, with which, if a clod does not crumble down at once with its pressure, it is forced into the soil in a solid state. This clod-crusher has been but partially used by Scottish farmers, though extensively in use in England—perhaps on account of the greater extent of clay soils there, which are always subject to induration by drought. Where the implement has been used in Scotland, the results have proved equally favourable on strong and light soils—in pulverising the strong and consolidating the light. The weight of the implement is 26 cwt.; it forms a good draught for 2 horses, and frequently for 3. 2122.

Fig. 160

Side view of 1 wheel of the clod-crusher.

Norwegian harrows. The action of this machine is to reduce large clods into very small ones, by the insertion of the points of the rays into them, to split them into pieces by their reiterated action. The larger clods are split into smaller pieces by the first row of rays, the second row splits these into smaller ones, and the third row splits those smallest pieces into still smaller ones; so that, by the time the clods have undergone those various splittings, they are probably sufficiently pulverised; but if not, they may be so by another similar process of splitting. 2123.

Fig. 161

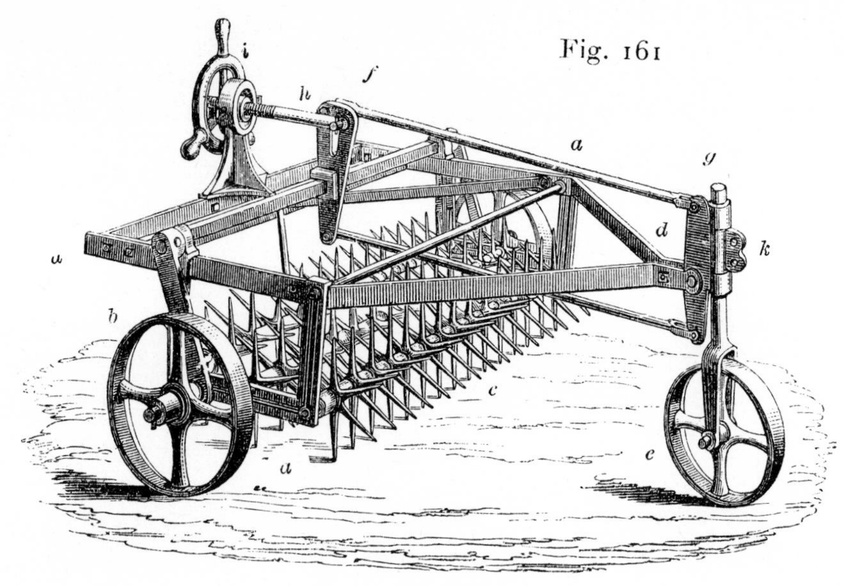

Norwegian harrows.

a a a Frame of iron.
b Two wheels supporting the frame.
b a c a Lower bars of frame supporting 3 axles.
c Discs, each containing 6 long rays.
d Triangular front of frame.
e Pivot-wheel, supporting triangular front of frame.
f g Apparatus for lowering and raising axles of rays.
h Screw of apparatus.
i Handles of winch for turning screw.
k Attachment for horses.

CROSS-PLOUGHING LAND.

Immediately after the sowing of oats is finished, preparations are made for sowing such of the turnip-land with barley as was bared by the direct removal of turnips, or eating off by sheep, after the sowing of spring wheat; and the first preparation for barley seed is ploughing the land across at right angles to the existing ridges. The surface of the ground left by sheep eating the turnips upon it being in a smooth state, trampled firm by the sheep, presenting no clods of earth but numbers of small round stones, when the soil is a dry gravelly loam, the stones should be removed with carts filled by the field-workers before the cross-ploughing is begun to be feered. The small stones are useful for drains, or to repair farm roads, and the large stones for dykes. A plough then feers the ground for cross-ploughing. 1959.

Fig. 162

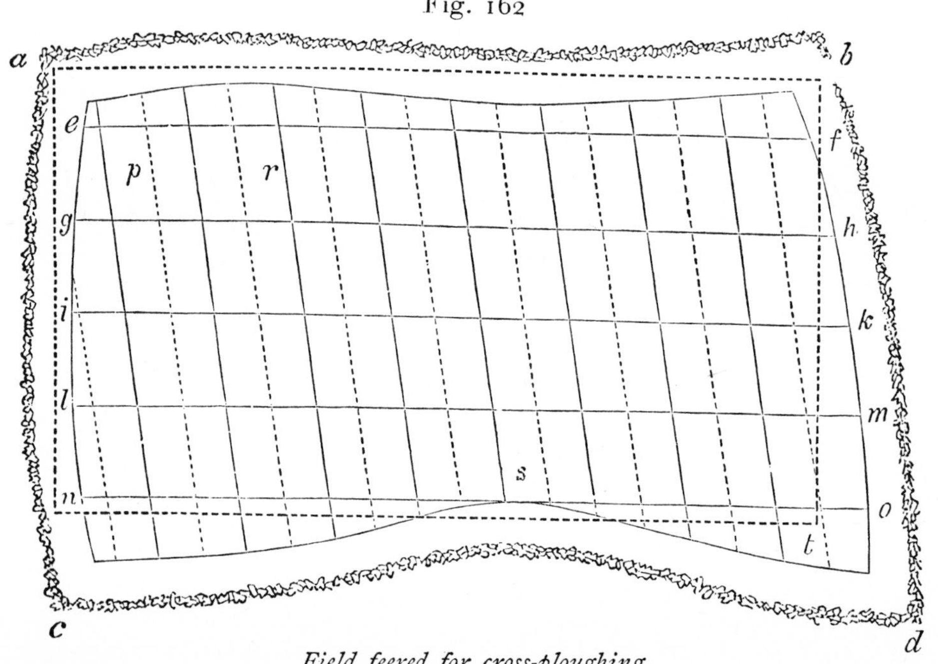

Field feered for cross-ploughing.

RIBBING THE SEED-FURROW.

A species of ploughing with the small plough, in the manner of drilling in the single method, is named *ribbing*. Fig. 163 is a view in perspective of an iron ribbing-plough, which is similar in construction to the common plough, but in smaller dimensions and lightness that a single horse can work with ease. 1962.

Fig. 163

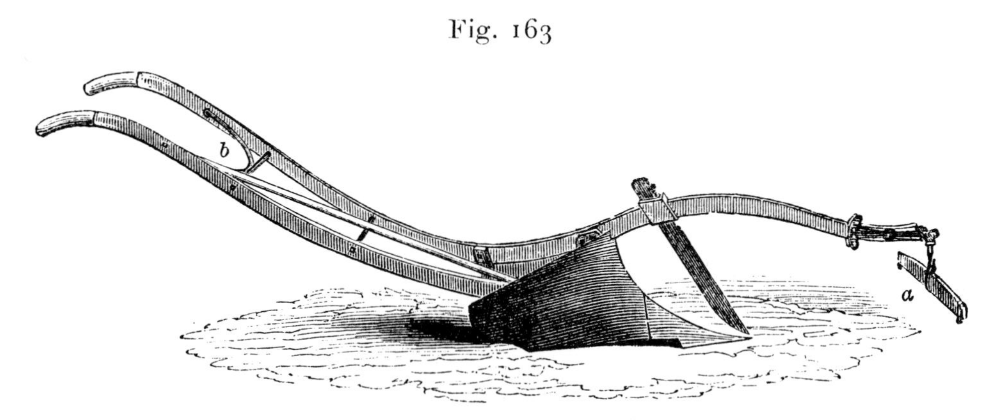

Small or ribbing plough.

a Swing-bar. *b* Diagonal iron rod.

The object of ribbing land is this: When much rain falls on heavy land between ploughing the seed-furrow and sowing barley, the land may become too consolidated for the seed; and were it ploughed again in the ordinary way, a tough heavy clod would be brought up which would be difficult to reduce at that season. Instead of disturbing such waxy ground, it is better to rib the surface with the small plough, which, only stirring it to the depth of 3 inches or so, a sufficient mould is at once afforded to bury the seed—all that is wanted at the time, the land having been sufficiently ploughed before. A couple of these ploughs will soon cover a considerable extent of ground with ribs. 1963.

As the ribbing-plough only makes 1 rib at a landing, and as only 2 such ploughs are found on most farms, and as it may be desirable to rib a considerable extent of ground in a short time, an implement that will do more work, and in a similar manner, should be preferred. Such an implement is the ribbing coulters, fig. 164, which is drawn by 1 horse, making 5 drills at a time. 1964.

Fig. 164

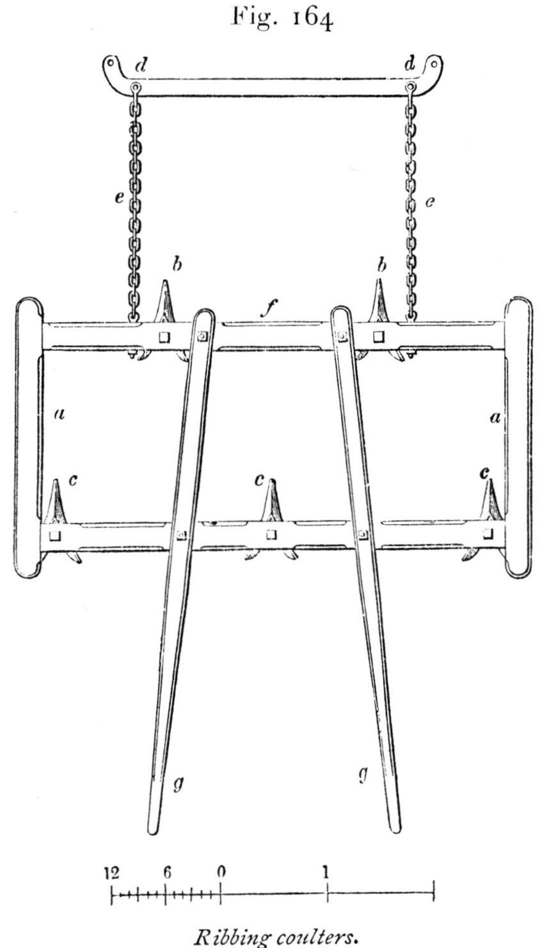

Ribbing coulters.

a a Frame.
b b Front coulters.
c c c Hind coulters.
d d Draught-bar.
e e Draught-chains.
f Point for shackle for 2 horses, if desired.
g g Stilts.

SOWING GRASS SEEDS.

Grass seeds are sown by hand and with machines. The hand-sowing is confined to small farms, while on large farms the machine is universally used. Sowing grass seeds by hand is a simple process, although it requires dexterity to do it well. 1966.

After the grass seeds are sown, the ground is harrowed to cover them in; for which purpose lighter harrows are better than the ordinary, which would bury clover seeds too deep in the ground; and being light, are provided with wings, to cover a whole ridge at a time; so the sowing process is quickly finished. Fig. 165 is grass-seed harrows, with wings, covering a ridge of 15 feet wide at one stretch. 1967.

Fig. 165

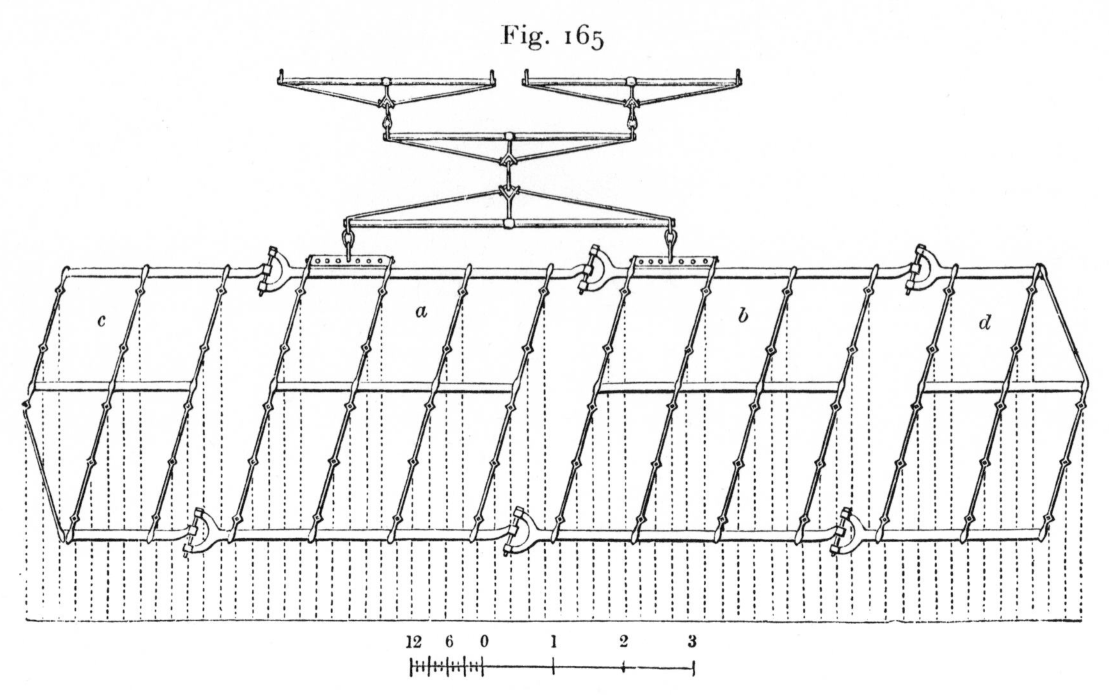

Grass-seed iron harrows, with wings and swing-trees.

a b Main leaves of the harrows. *c d* The 2 wings.

Fig. 166

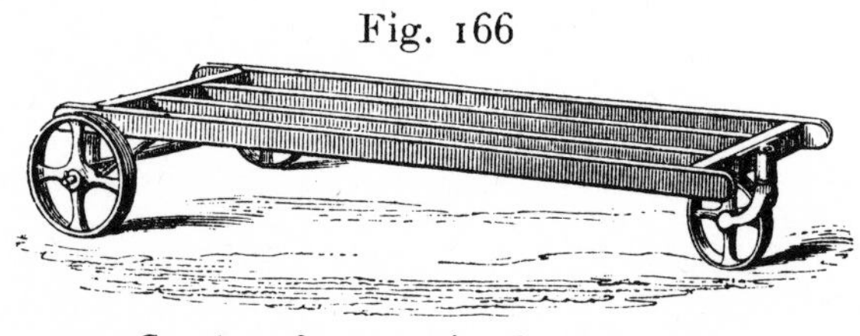

Carriage for conveying harrows, &c.

PLANTING POTATOES.

Having drilled up as much land as will allow the planting to proceed without interruption—having turned the dunghill in time to putrefy the dung into a proper state for the crop—and having prepared the sets ready for planting, let us proceed to the field, and see how operations are conducted and brought to a close. The sets are shovelled either into sacks like corn, or into the body of close carts, and placed on one or both head-ridges or middle of the field, according to the length of the ridges. When the drills are short, the most convenient way to get at the sets is from a cart; but when drills are long, sacks are best placed along the centre of the field. A small round willow basket, with a bow-handle, fig. 167, should be provided for each person who plants the sets; and as a considerable number of hands are required, boys and girls may be employed beyond the ordinary field-workers. The frying-pan shovel, fig. 168, with its sharp point, is a convenient instrument for taking the sets out of the cart into the baskets. Single-horse carts take the dung from the dunghill to the drills. Graips are required to fill the carts with dung; small dung-graips, 3-pronged, are most con-

Fig. 167

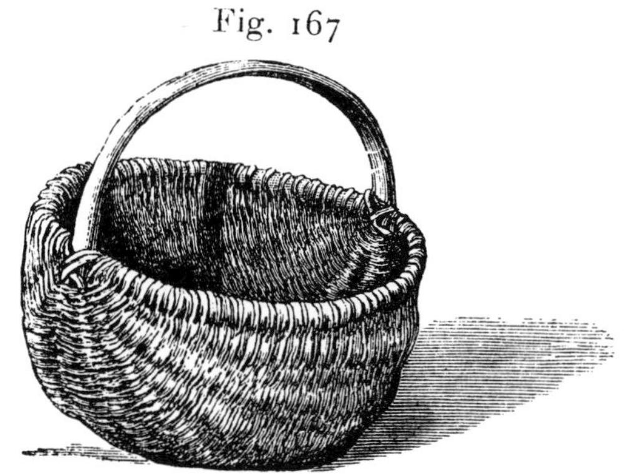

Potato hand-basket.

venient for spreading the dung in the drills, and a small common graip to divide the dung into each of the 3 drills as it falls into the middle drill from the cart. The dung-hawk is used by the steward for pulling the dung out of the carts. If all the drills have not been set up previous to planting, a plough continues drilling in the double method, until as much land has been drilled as desired. When he finishes drilling, he assists the other ploughmen in splitting in. 2000.

Fig. 168 Fig. 169 Fig. 170

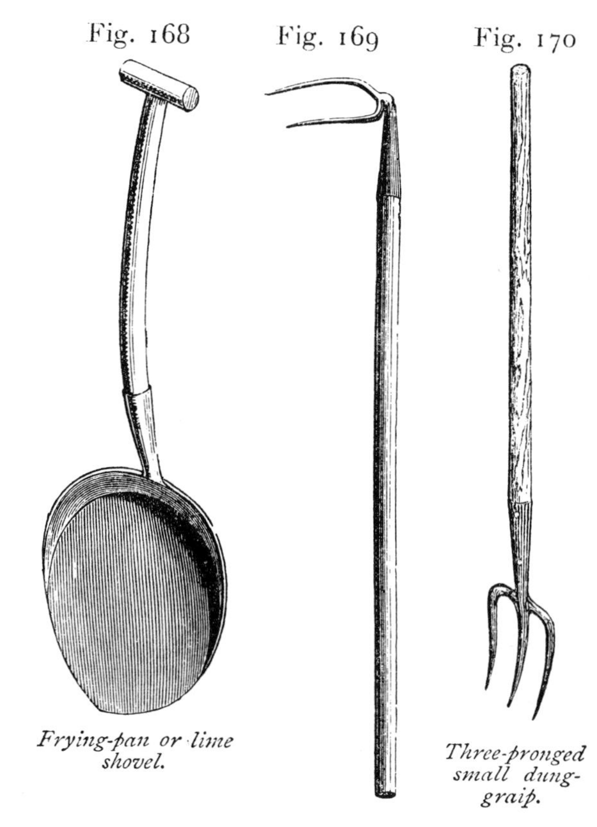

Frying-pan or lime shovel.

Dung-drag.

Three-pronged small dung-graip.

Fig. 171

Potato-planting.

a Ploughman making up single drills in preparation for planting.
b c Single drills on one side of feering.
b c d e Feering for single drills.
d e Single drills on other side of feering.
f Dunghill.
g Cart going with dung.
h Steward hawking out dung for 3 drills.
i Dung-heap in middle drill for 3.
k Worker dividing the dung-heap into the 3 drills.
l m n The 3 drills.
n o p 3 workers, each spreading the dung in 1 drill.
r 3 hindmost planters.
s 3 foremost planters.
t Cart of cut sets of potatoes.
u Ploughman splitting in double drills.

PARING AND BURNING.

Paring is the removal of a thin portion of the surface of the ground, with what may be growing upon it; and *burning* is the reduction by fire to a state of powder, of what has been pared off. The object of the process is to obtain possession of the bared soil for arable purposes sooner than could be by common ploughing and harrowing, and thereby it insures a crop in advance in the season. Common ploughing and harrowing cannot make the soil available at once, because of the rough herbage being of too obdurate a nature to be reduced into friable mould in a short time, they being reduced into that state only through the continued agency of the atmosphere—rain, frost, thaw, and drought. 2024.

Fig. 172

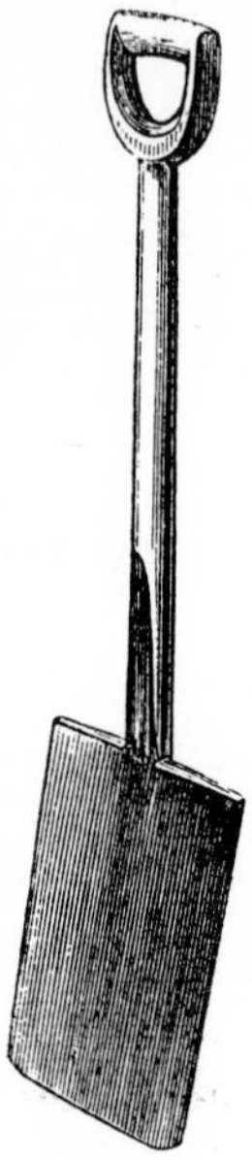

Common spade.

Various implements are employed to execute paring and burning. The common No. 5 garden *spade*, fig. 172, with a sharp edge and its corners a little worn by work, removes rough herbage very well, and it can be set up at the time by the workmen to be dried; but the labour with it entirely is expensive, and is seldom incurred. A more expeditious implement is a spade of a different form, fig. 173; the face of which is angular and sharp, the blade 9 inches broad and 15 inches long; the straight side of which is turned up square 3 inches, with a cutting edge in front; the helve is 5 feet long and flat, provided with a broad cross-handle 2 feet long, fastened at right angles to the helve. The blade is set at an angle to permit the handle to be elevated to a man's haunches,

Fig. 173

Flauchter-spade at work.

while the blade works flat upon the ground. It is called in Scotland the *flauchter-spade*.

[*In England, called a breast-spade. Breast = turf.*]

Fig. 174

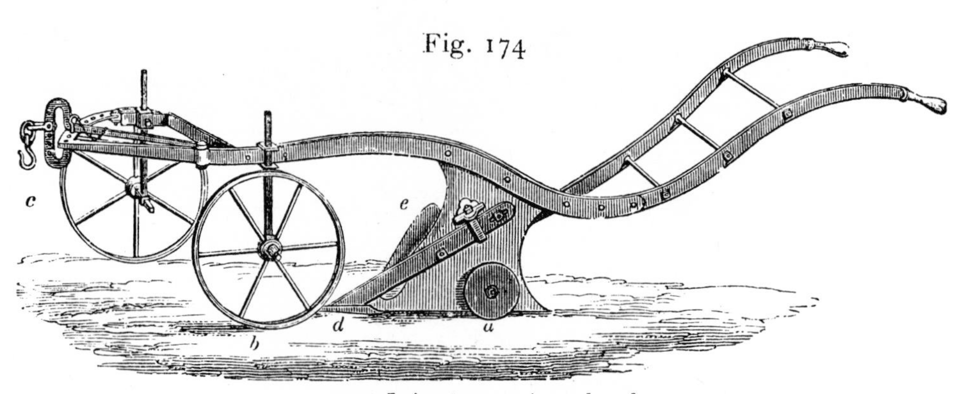

Leicester paring-plough.

a Small wheel near the heel of the plough.
b Large wheel moving on the unpared surface.
c Large wheel moving on the pared surface.
d Coulter.
e Mould-board.

Fig. 175

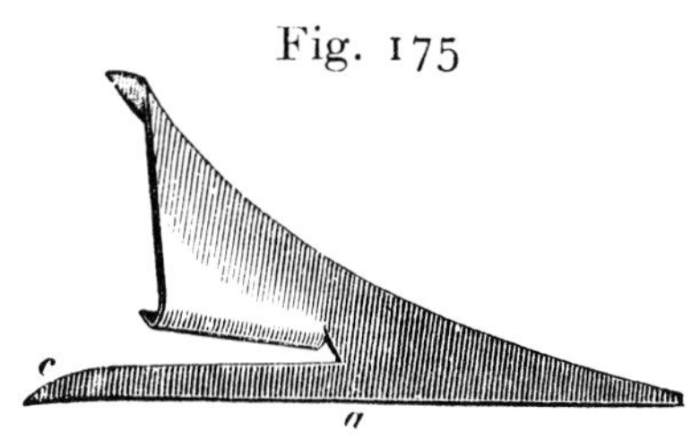

Paring-sock.

a Breadth of sock, 10 inches.
c Ear of feather, 15 inches in breadth from land-side.

The *paring-plough*, used in parts of England in the fens, pares the turf by means of 2 angular shares with the wings facing each other, and just crossing the centre line, one being a little before the other, and they are attached to shanks, placed in front of the mould-board, upon which the turf is raised in a manner similar to the furrow-slice in ordinary ploughing, and is set on its edge upon the pared ground, ready to be dried, as neatly as if done by hand. A better paring-plough, fig. 174, is by Thomas Johnson, engineer, Leicester.

2025

Summer

PLANTING HOPS.

A new hop-ground, after its thorough drainage, should be trenched to the depth of 2½ feet, in this manner: Let the ground be laid off in spaces of 15 feet in breadth to the length of the hop-ground. Let the surface-mould, including its subsoil, to the depth of 15 inches, and 3 feet in breadth across the 15 feet space, be taken away with the common spade and barrow to the other side of the ground, to be ready to finish the trenching when it arrives at that point.

The foot-pick raises a much larger quantity of the subsoil than the hand-pick. Three men work best together when trenching hop-ground, all using the spade when the surface-mould is of the proper depth, and no picking required; but when picking is needed, one man removes the surface with the spade, another picks the subsoil with the foot-pick, and the third, the master workman, shovels up the loose earth. After the surface has thus been removed, the men take each a trenching-fork, fig. 177. This implement consists of 3 connected prongs of iron, 15 inches in length, and 1½ inch in depth at the neck, tapering to a strong point. The prongs are connected with a hose, into which a wooden helve, with a short cross-handle, is fastened. The entire fork is 3 feet 9 inches in length. It is used by thrusting the prongs into the subsoil with the pressure of the foot, like a common spade; and using the helve as a lever, the workman forces the prongs through the subsoil, which is thereby ripped up into pieces, and stones of larger size than the spaces between the prongs are brought up. Should the stones be much larger, the 2-pronged fork, fig. 178, removes them out of the ground more easily. 2140.

Fig. 176

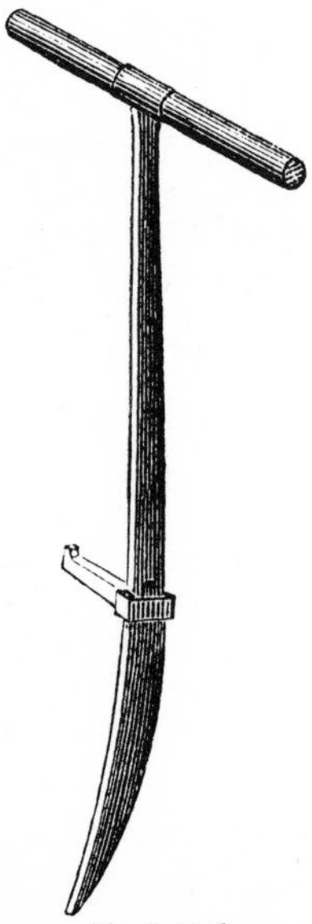

Foot-pick.

Fig. 177

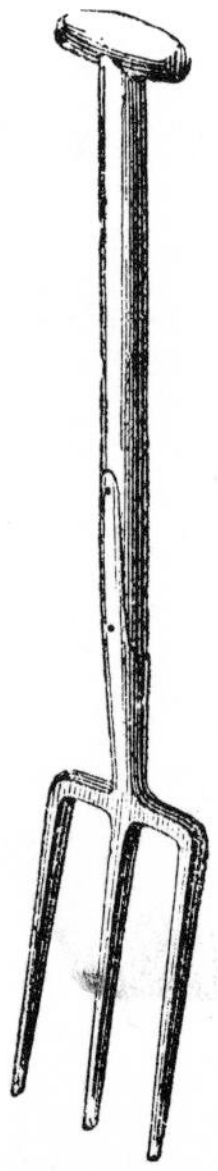

Three-pronged trenching-fork.

Fig. 178

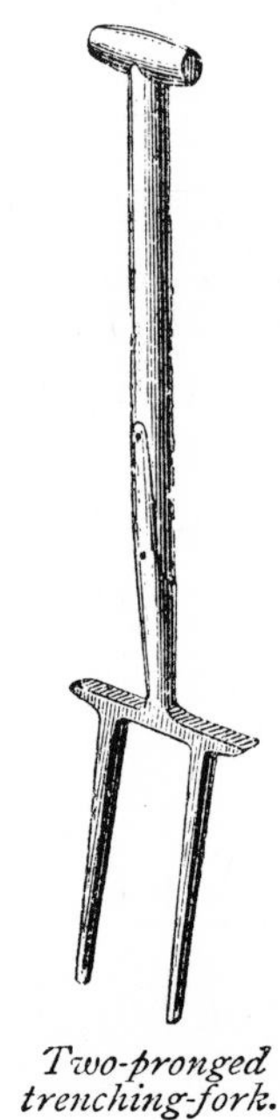

Two-pronged trenching-fork.

Fig. 179

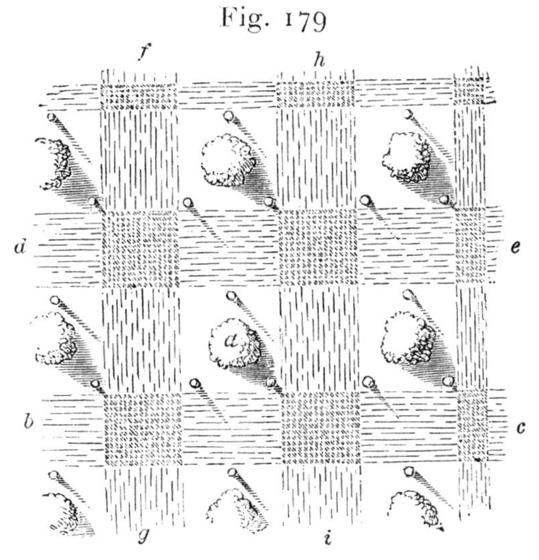

Square mode of planting hops.

a Square hill of hops with 3 poles.

Fig. 180

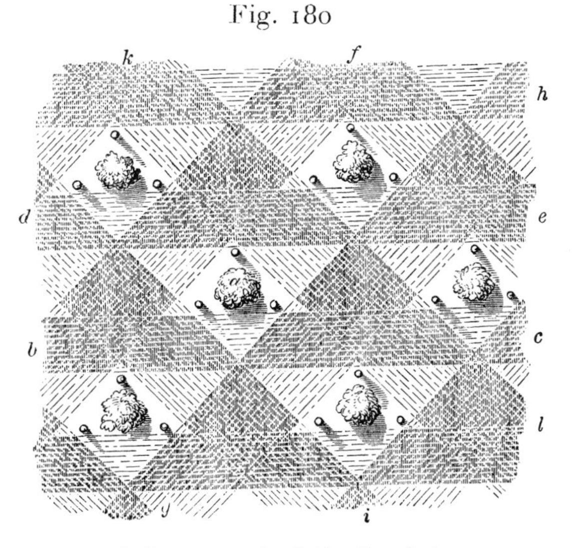

Quincunx mode of planting hops.

Fig. 181

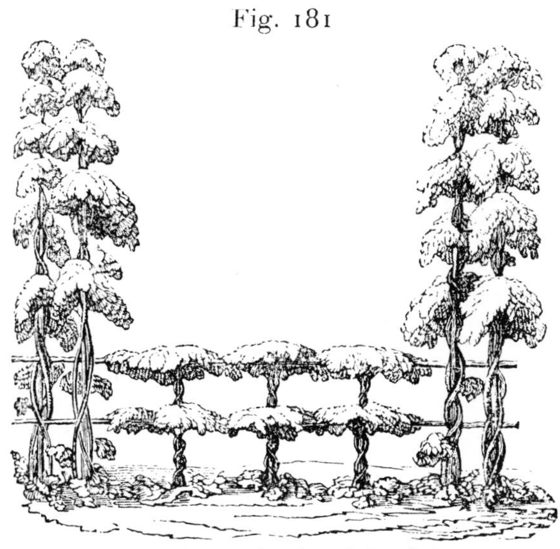

Espalier mode of training hops.

Everything is now prepared for setting off the ground for *planting* the young plants. There are 2 modes of arranging the plants in a hop-ground—one in squares, the other in quincunx; and of these 2 modes the quincunx is the preferable, because the plants, standing independently, are more exposed to sun and air; a greater number of plants are placed on the same extent of ground, in the ratio of 120 to 100; and the ground can be cleaned nearer the plants with the horse-hoe. 2142.

The best hops grown at Lewisham have been trained horizontally in the espalier form, as in fig. 181, on poles 5 feet high, and 3 feet apart, with 1 long pole or 2 at such intervals as may be desired, fixed to the top of the horizontal ones to keep them steady. One plant is set at each stake, and the rows are formed in 1 way across the field. This method may be adopted with success where poles are scarce, and where the ground is exposed to winds. 2146.

SOWING TURNIPS.

Turnip seed is sown with a drill-machine, 2 drills being sown at 1 time, and 1 of the most efficient machines is given in perspective in fig. 182, where its construction shows a depression of the parts forming the framework, which gives the machine an appearance of compactness and strength. The 2 drill-machines are suitable for the larger class of farms, such as those which employ 2 or more pairs of horses; but for farms of a small class, having only 1 pair of horses, a smaller class of machine might answer the purpose; and on this account I give the perspective view of a machine which sows the seed in 1 drill at a time in fig. 183, which consists of a frame of timber formed of the 2 stilts, and a broad transverse bar which carries the seed-box.One man pushes the machine forward along a drill by the stilts, and 1 boy or another man pulls it forward by means of a rope. The pull may be too much for one man's strength, when a pony or horse should be employed. Fig. 185 is a perspective view of the seed-barrel, detached from its seat, in which is seen the axle or spindle in which it revolves, and on the longer end of which the upper spur-wheel is placed.

But turnip seed is not always sown alone, it being deposited along with granulated manure in the drills. Such granulated manure has hitherto been bone-dust. Guano cannot be distributed by means of any drill hitherto known, on account of its clammy consistence, which, if natural, may be rather troublesome to get rid of; but if produced by water being poured into the guano,

Fig. 182

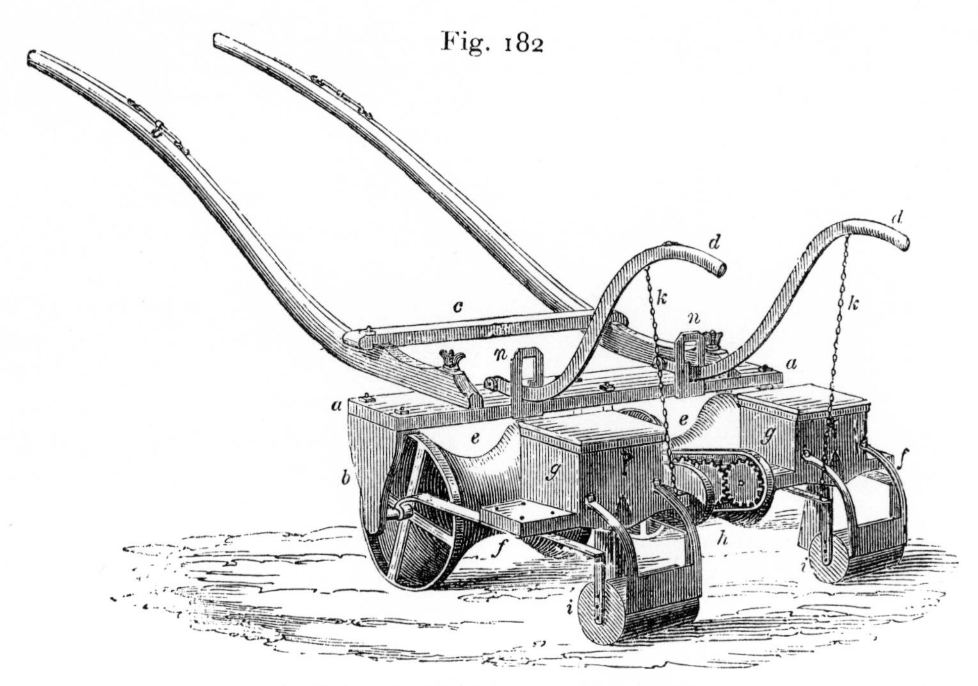

Geddes's two-rowed turnip-sowing drill.

a a Bed-frame plank.
b Pendants upon which the frame is supported.
e e Curved rollers.
c Horse-shafts.
d d Handles.
k k Chains for elevating and depressing the coulters.
g g Seed-box frames.
h Spur-gearing, moving seed axles.
i i Hind covering wheels.
f Scrapers of wheels.

Fig. 183

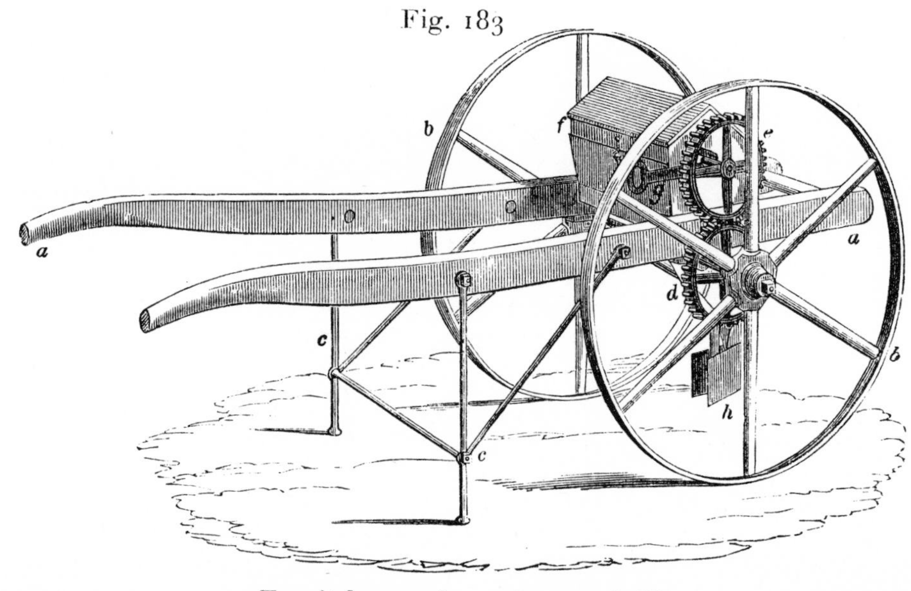

Turnip-barrow for sowing one drill.

a a Stilts.
b b Wheels.
c c Iron legs.
d Lower toothed spur-wheel.
e Upper spur-wheel.
f Lid of seed-box.
g Bottom of seed-box.
h Sheath of coulter.

Fig. 184

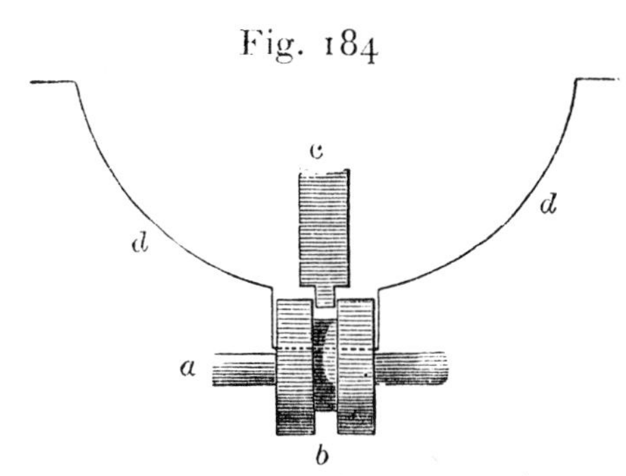

Vertical section of the seed-distributor.

d d Interior surface of the box.
b Brass roller.
a Axle.
c Slider, adjusted by screw.

Fig. 185

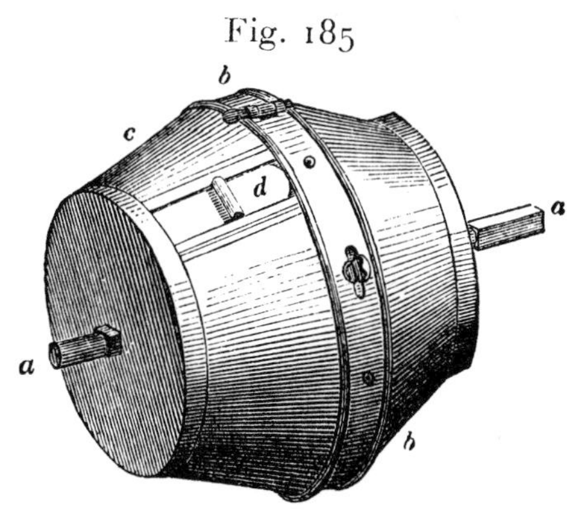

Seed-barrel.

a a Axle.
b Cylindrical band.
c b Conical frustra of seed-barrel.
d Slider covering the hole for seed.

Fig. 186

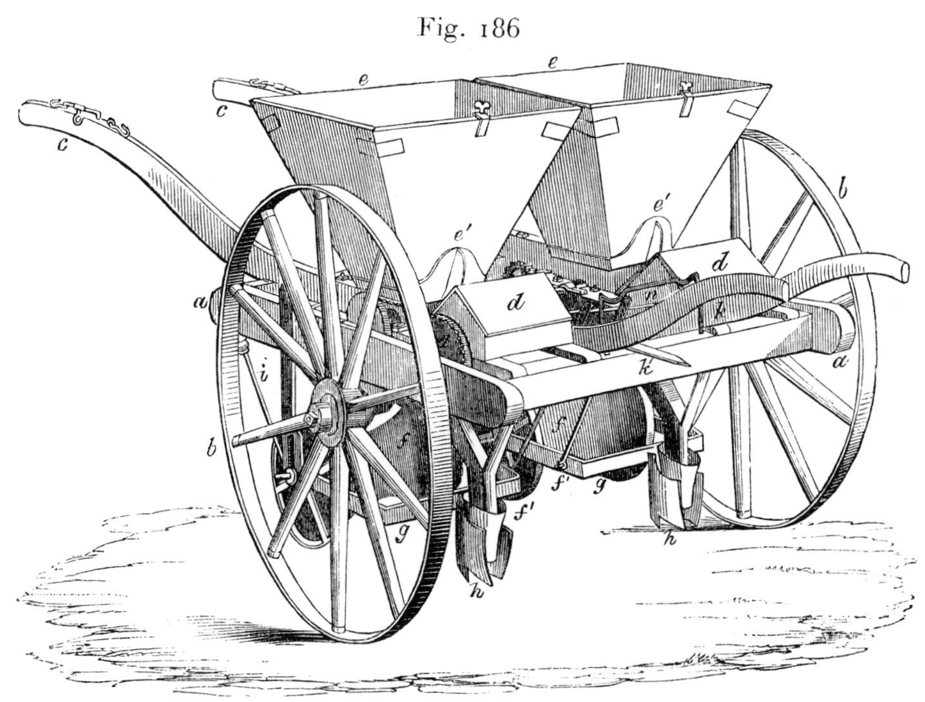

Two-rowed turnip and bone-dust sowing drill.

a a Bed-frame.
b b Wheels on axle.
c c Horse-shafts.
d d Boxes of seed-barrels.
e e Manure hoppers.
f f Pressing rollers.
g g Coulter frames.
h h Coulters.
i Pendants supporting pressing-roller axle.
k Lever handles.
f′ f′ Connecting-rods.
k′ Iron lever.
e′ e Sliding sluices for emission of manure.

Fig. 187

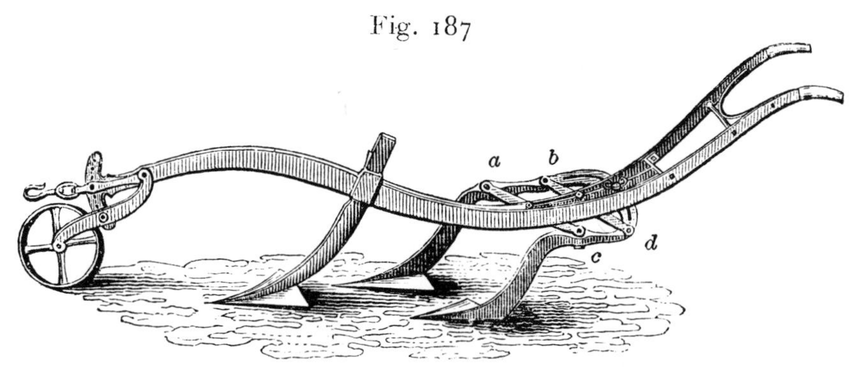

Wilkie's horse-hoe with parallel motion.

a b c d Jointings of the 2 back tines.

to increase its weight, it may be overcome by evaporation, though the process would certainly be attended with trouble and expense. The practical consequence hitherto of this inconvenience has been to distribute the guano by hand. Bone-dust is admirably deposited with the machine, fig. 186, which exhibits a view in perspective of a turnip-seed and bone-dust drill, 2155.

The implement contrived to supersede the plough in paring away both sides of a drill at 1 time, is the *horse-hoe.* Several forms of this implement have been presented to notice; that in fig. 187 is the best I have seen, which is Wilkie's horse-hoe with parallel motion, in which the 2 back tines have their tails jointed to 2 transverse parallel bars, which traverse to a small extent upon pivots placed in the middle of their length, attached to the tail of the beam, by the motion of which a perfect parallelism of the tines is preserved, capable of being secured at any required width by pinching-screws. This is the most perfect mode of adjustment for the tines of a hoe of this construction—3-tined—but it does not apply to those of more than 3. Besides paring, this implement has self-cleaning tines to clear away weeds, which action is named *scuffling.* To reduce the weeds between the drills after the scuffling, the common *drill-grubber*, fig. 188, is a light and convenient implement for the purpose, drawn by 1 horse. The implement used for singling turnips is the *turnip-hoe*, fig. 189. It consists of a thin iron plate faced with steel, 7 inches in length and 4 inches in breadth, with an eye attached to its upper edge to receive the shaft, made of fir, to make the implement light in hand. The shaft should not exceed 3 feet in length, though in some parts of the country it is 4½ feet, whilst in others only 33 inches. The shorter the better, to enable the field-worker to bow closer to the ground and make the best work; but as this position is severe for the back, the shaft is often made as long as to allow the field-worker to stand nearly upright, when the eye and hand are both too far removed from so small an object as a

Fig. 188

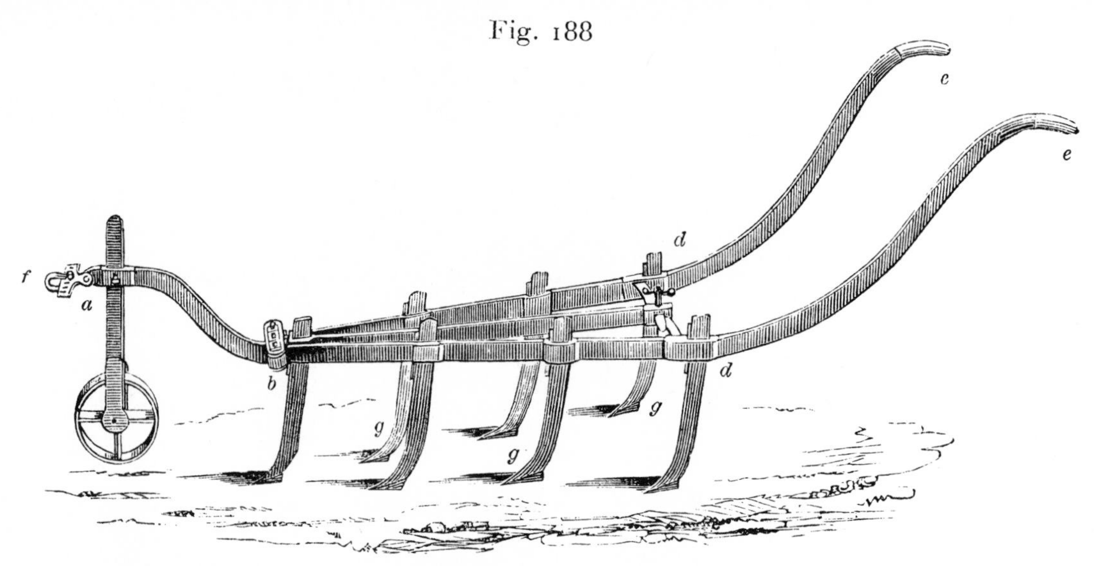

Common drill-grubber.

a b c Central beam. *a* Front wheel. *b d* Wing-bars. *g g g* Tines, duck-footed. *e e* Handles. *f* Bridle with cross-web and shackle.

Fig. 189

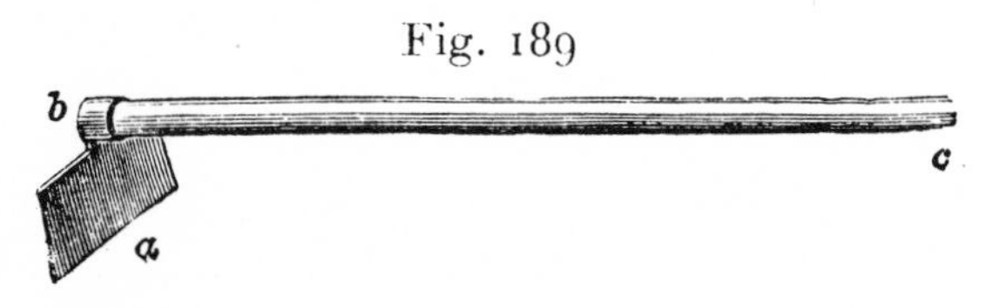

Turnip-hoe.

a Thin iron plate. *b* Eye of plate. *c* Wood shaft.

young turnip plant, to command the implement so effectually in the thinning process, as when the hands are lower down the shaft. The attitude of the workers, the best method of using the hoe, and of arranging the field-workers at singling, is represented in fig. 190. The workers are placed at every 2 rows of the plants, beginning at 1 side of a field, the first worker getting charge of the first 2 drills, the second the second 2 drills, the third the third 2 drills, and so on with the rest of the workers. This particular arrangement gives each sufficient room to work, and the 2 drills cause the workers less seldom to shift their ground. 2162

Fig. 190

Singling turnips.

SOWING, BROADCAST, DRILLED, DIBBLED—THICK AND THIN—AND AT DIFFERENT DEPTHS.

Of all the modes of sowing the seeds of cereals, none requires so much seed as the *broadcast*. The usual quantity sown is 3 bushels of wheat, 4 of barley, and 6 of oats, to 1 acre. 2263.

Fig. 191

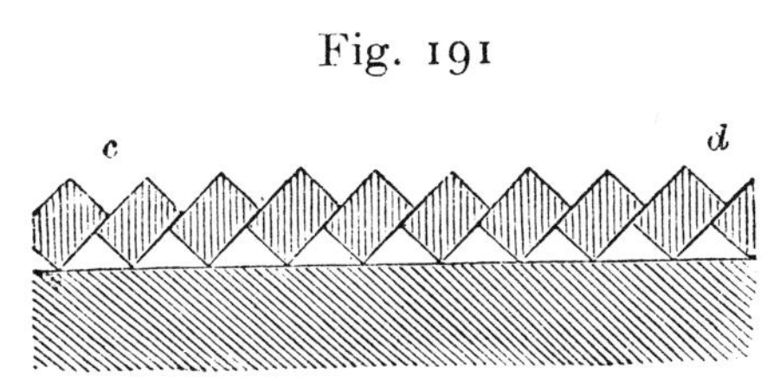

Well-ploughed regular furrow-slices.

c to *d* Regularly ploughed furrow-slices.

Fig. 192

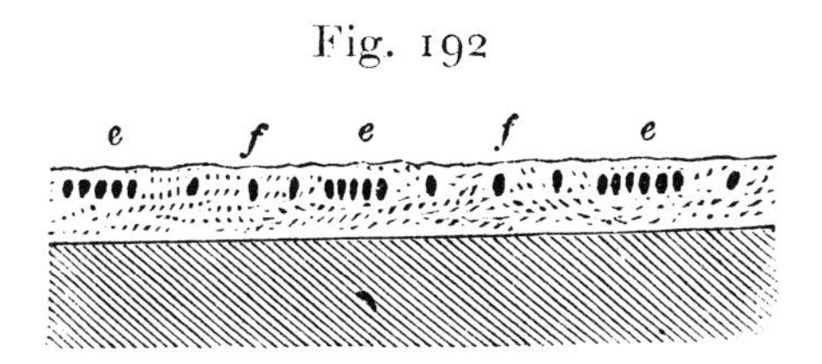

Positions of seeds on regular furrows.

e e e Seeds fallen in the hollows of the furrows.
f f Seeds scattered upon tops and sides of furrows.

Fig. 193

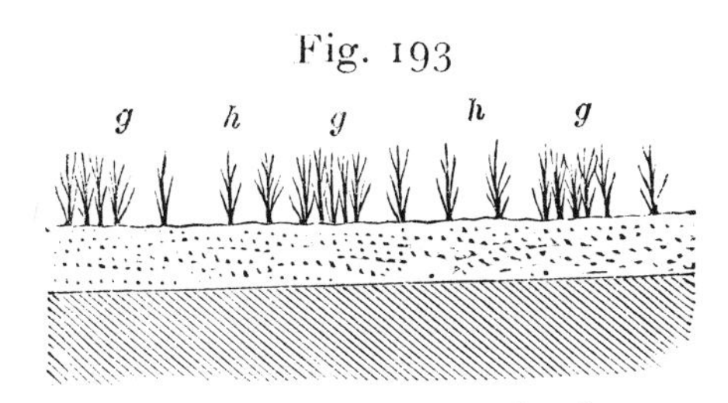

Irregular braird upon regular furrows.

g g g Plants growing in clumps.
h h Plants growing scattered.

Fig. 194

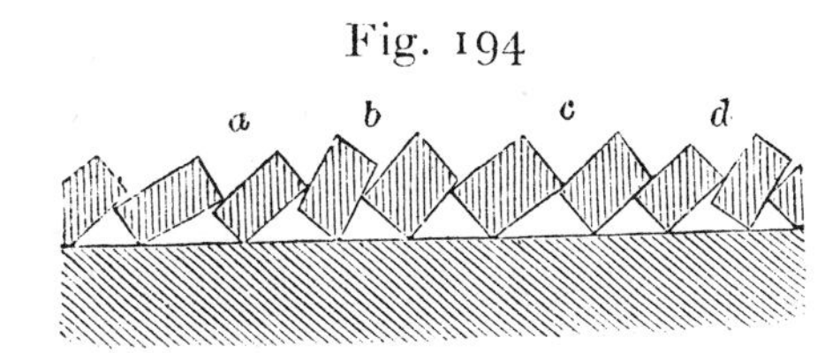

Ill-ploughed irregular furrow-slices.

a Furrow-slice too flat.
b Furrow-slice too high.
c Furrow-slices too wide.
d Furrow too deep.

Fig. 195

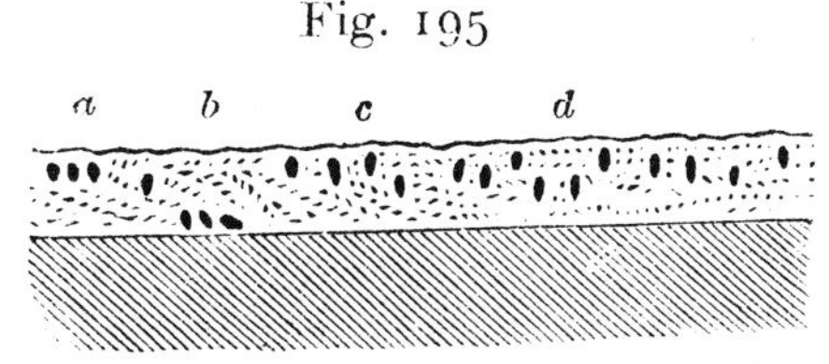

Irregular positions of seed on ill-ploughed furrows.

a Seed clustered and covered shallow.
b Seed clustered and buried deep.
c Seed scattered and covered shallow.
d Seed scattered and covered deep.

Fig. 196

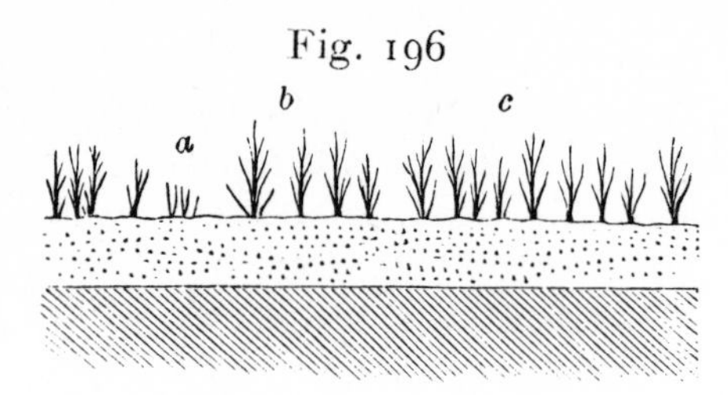

Irregular braird on ill-ploughed furrow.
a Late plants. *b* Early plants.
c Regular growth of plants.

One evident advantage of sowing with a *drill* over a broadcast machine, is the deposition of seed at the same depth,

Fig. 197

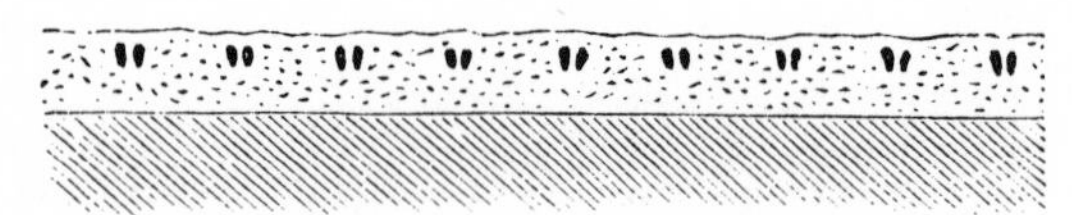

Regular depth of seed by drill-sowing.

whatever depth may be chosen. Fig. 197 shows the seeds deposited at regular

Fig. 198

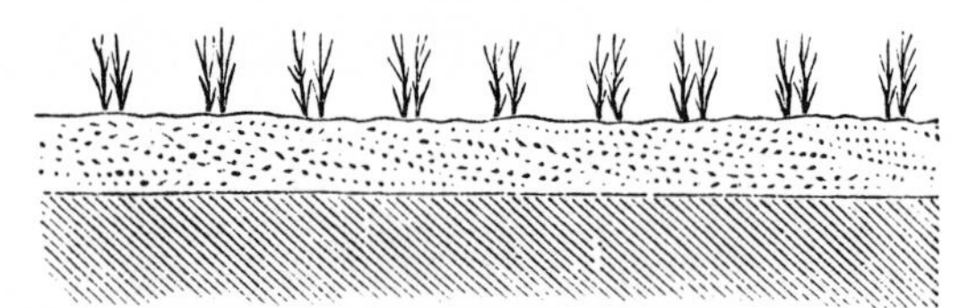

Regular braird from drill-sown seed.

intervals. The braird is shown at the same regular intervals in fig. 198, and its produce will reasonably be of the same quality. What insures drilled seed a uniform depth, is harrowing the land smooth before the seed is sown. 2264. *Dibbling* is distributing seed by means of a dibble at given distances, and at a given depth in the soil, and the distribution may either be in rows or broadcast. The difference betwixt dibbling and drilling is, in drilling placing the seed in lines, while dibbling places it at uniform distances in the line. The object of dibbling is to fill the ground with plants with the least quantity of seed. The seed planted in lines with the dibble appears as in fig. 197, and the plants like those in fig. 198. The depth of the seed and brairding of the plants are as uniform as in drilling, but the plants stand independent of each other in dibbling.

2265.

Fig. 199

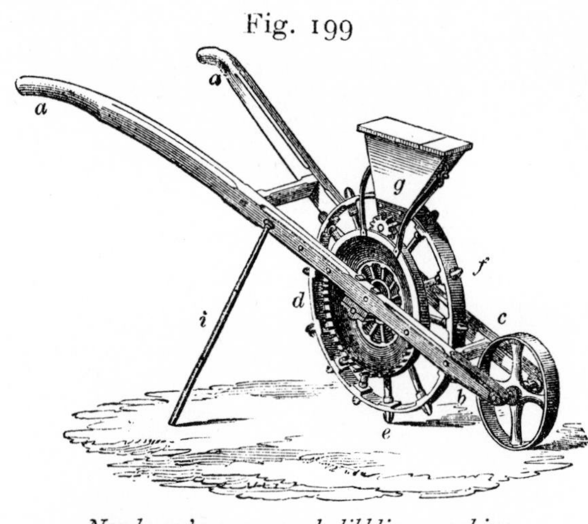

Newberry's one-rowed dibbling-machine.

a a Stilts.
b Fore part of stilts.
c Fore-wheel.
d Hollow flat disc.
e Projecting points or dibbles.
f Large outer ring.
g Hopper.
i Stay to support the machine.

Fig. 200

Newington's 6-rowed dibbling machine.

DISPOSAL OF FAT CATTLE.

Prior to disposing of cattle, their weight and value should be estimated, and, in *judging* them, their form is at once obvious. Hence the *eye* is more used than the hand in judging; and in the case of ripe fed cattle the eye alone is consulted; but the hand, as well as the eye, is brought into use in judging *lean* cattle to be put on grass or turnips. On looking on the *near* side of a *ripe* ox in profile, imagine the body inscribed within a frame of wood of a rectangled parallelogram, placed horizontally, as in fig. 201; and if the ox is filled up in all points, his carcass will occupy the frame as in the figure; but in most cases deficiency or redundancy will exist in some parts.

Fig. 201

Side view of a ripe fat ox.

a Flank. *b* Brisket. *c* Rump. *d* Middle of back. *e* Top of shoulder. *f* Hams. *g* Rib. *h* Shoulder-point. *i* Round. *k* Hook-bone. *l* Belly.

Fig. 202

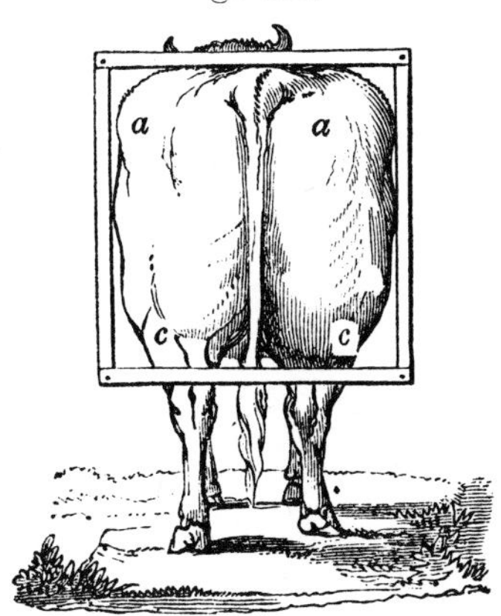

Hind view of a ripe fat ox.

a to *a* Breadth between the 2 hook-bones.
c c Houghs.

Fig. 203

Front view of a ripe fat ox.

a to *a* Breadth between the shoulders.

2315.

Fig. 204

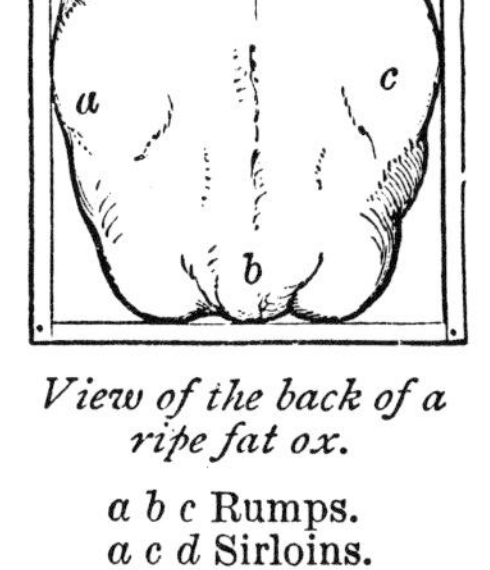

View of the back of a ripe fat ox.

a b c Rumps.
a c d Sirloins.
d to *e* Ribs.

Ascertaining the weight by measuring the body is a more convenient method than by weighing; and when the measurement is correctly taken, and the ox of an ordinary size, the result is pretty accurate. Suppose fig. 205 is an ox whose weight is to be ascertained by measurement. The rule is: Measure with a tape line from the top of the shoulder to the tail-head, which gives the *length;* then measure round the body immediately behind the fore-leg, which gives the *girth;*

Fig. 205

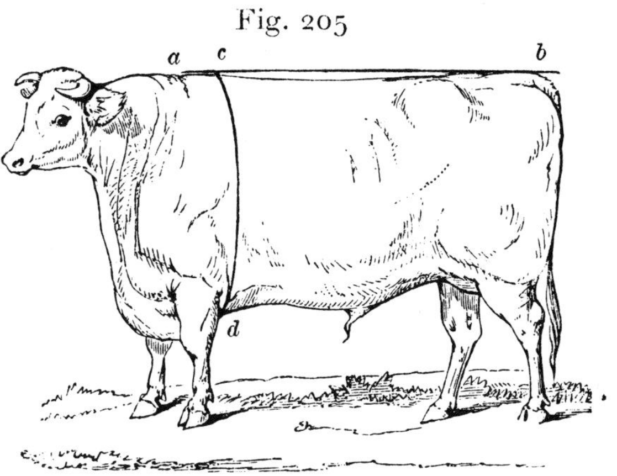

Measuring a ripe fat ox, to find its dead weight, sinking offals.

a Top of shoulder. *b* Tail-head. *c d* Girth behind the fore-leg.

and on consulting a table calculated by the corresponding figures of the length and girth, the product will give the nett weight. Several rules exist. For example, suppose an ox is 5 feet in length and 7 feet in girth. Multiply the square of the girth in inches by the length in inches, and divide the sum by 7238, and the quotient is the weight, in stones imperial of 14 lb. to 1 stone. 2320.

DISPOSAL OF FAT PIGS.

To judge of pigs, we have only to follow the rules for judging oxen. On looking at a well-made pig broadside, fig. 206, we see how near it approaches that

Fig. 206

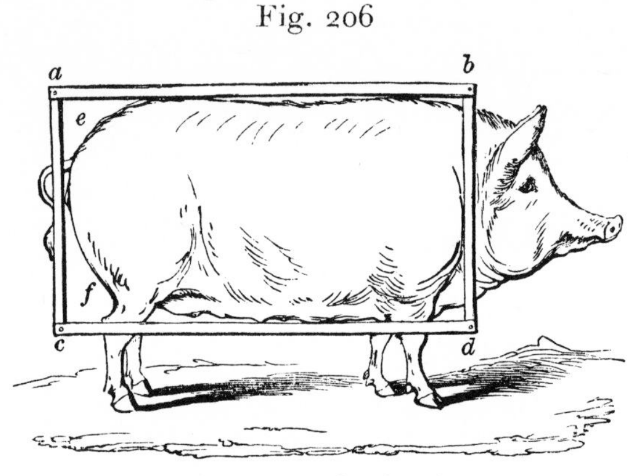

Side view of a fat pig.

a b c d Rectangular frame. *e* Fall to the tail. *f* Fall-in of hough.

of a fat ox. A rectangular wooden frame placed against the body of a fat pig is nearly filled up in the same manner as by a fat ox, the points of difference being in the hind-quarter, where the pig droops suddenly to the tail, and the hams fall in suddenly to the hough. On looking at the pig from before and behind, the carcass has a round form, the square frame showing spaces at the angles. On looking down on the back of a pig, the body carries its breadth fully from the shoulders to the haunch. The hand is of little use in judging of a fat pig—the skin, being thick and tight, does not easily yield to the touch, though an impression may be made upon it by pressing the fingers, and on removing them from the skin it regains its position. The body should be well covered with long hairs lying close to the skin. The shoulder, hooks, back, girth, and flanks are points well filled up in a good pig. 3128.

TREATMENT OF BULLS.

Fig. 207 is a good form of a bull's ring. It consists of 2 round semicircles completing a circle, joined together at 1 side with a rivet passed through the ends of the semicircles reduced ½ in thickness, lapping over each other, and forming a hinge; and the other 2 ends of the semicircles also lap, and are fastened together with 2 countersunk screws. The opened ring is passed through the hole in the bull's nose, and then screwed close as a round ring. Fig. 208 shows the ring screwed together as it hangs in the bull's nose — the joint closed, and the lapped ends also closed, with the countersunk screws flush with the surface of the ring. The ring is of ¼-inch rod-iron, and its diameter over all is 2½ inches. The surface is smoothly filed, and polished with sand-paper. 2402.

Fig. 207

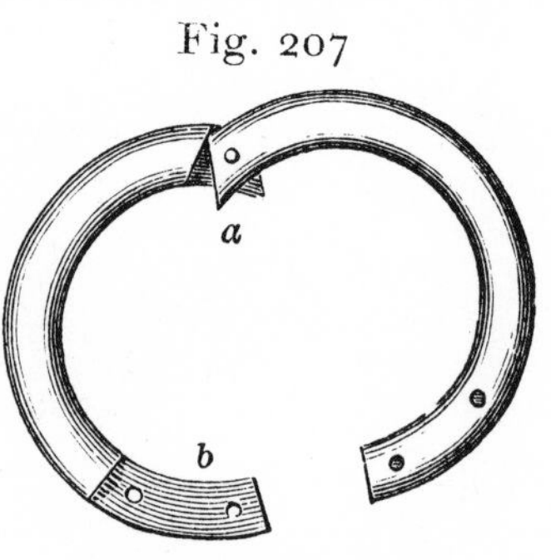

Opened bull's ring.

a Joint with rivet.
b Lapped joint for the screws.

Fig. 208

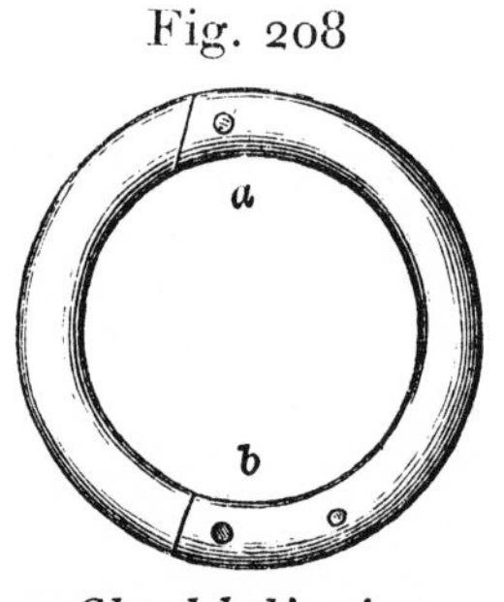

Closed bull's ring.

a Rivet joint.
b Lapped joint with 2 screws.

Besides the rope or chain in the ring, a safe precaution for the keeper is to have a stick, about 6 feet long, with a swivelled spring-hook, like fig. 209, at its end, to slip into the ring, and which gives him a better command over the ring than the rope, and also enables him to keep the bull off to a distance, and to warn his making a rush. 2405

Fig. 209

Swivelled spring-hook.

a Movable part of hook.
d Joint of movable part.
c Swivel-joint of ring of hook.
b Spliced end of rope.

WASHING OF SHEEP.

Sheep are washed prior to being shorn of their fleece, to free the wool from earthy materials and to cleanse their skin from incrusted matter. A pool of about 3 feet deep of water is the best place to wash sheep in, and such a pool can easily be made across a natural rivulet having a slope on each side, and both margins clad with grass, the slope for the egress of the sheep being the easiest, that there be no struggling to get upon the bank, even with assistance, when the wool is loaded with water. 2458.

SHEARING OF SHEEP.

After the wool is dry, the yolk returned into it, and the fleece has indicated a fresh growth next the skin, the sheep should be shorn of their fleeces. It is customary for neighbouring shepherds to assist each other; and though that does not expedite the sheep-shearing of the country, yet the emulation amongst a number of men clipping together not only expedites the shearing of the individual

Fig. 210

Washing-pool and sheep washing.

a a Damming with doors and stobs, the surplus water pouring down in the centre.
b Man catching an unwashed sheep for the first washer.
c First washer, who stands lowest down the pool.
d Second washer, mid-way in the pool.
e Shepherd, farthest up the pool and last washer.
f Washed sheep going out of the water.
g Washed sheep within the enclosure.
h Collie beside the provisions.

flock, but makes the work cheerful, and calls forth the best and quickest specimens of workmanship from each clipper. Other hands are pressed into the service at this time. The steward has not time to clip sheep, but the art is known by the hedger; and if the cattle-man has been a herd, he lends a hand. Clipping being dirty and heating work, the coat is stripped, and the oldest trousers put on, whilst some throw aside the hat, vest, and cravat. Garters or knee-breeches are irksome pieces of dress to clip in. 2463.

Fig. 211

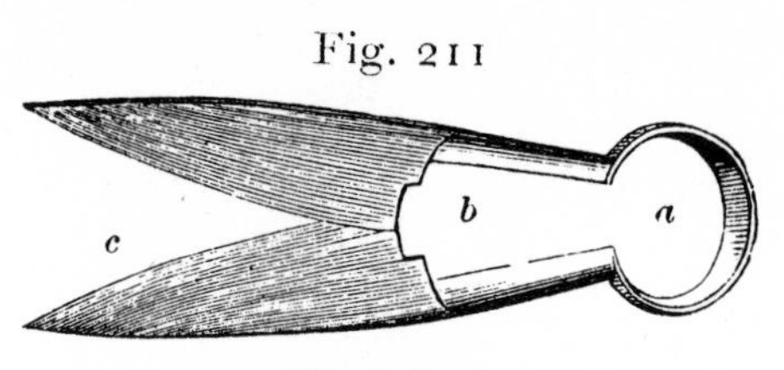

Wool shears.

a Spring-bowl of shears.
b Rounded handles of shears.
c Flat broad blades of shears.

Fig. 212

First stage of clipping a sheep.

a Left leg of the clipper.
b Fore-feet of the sheep under the left arm of the clipper.
c Left arm of the clipper holding down the fore-legs of the sheep.
d Points of the small shears clipping the short wool off the belly.
e Left hand of the clipper keeping the skin of the sheep tight for the action of the shears.
f Scrotum of the sheep.
g g Inside of the thighs of the sheep.
h Tail of the sheep.

The person appointed to roll the fleeces is 1 of the field-workers who has been accustomed to the work, and she, whenever a fleece is separated from the sheep, lifts it carefully and unbroken from the shearing-cloth, and spreads it upon the board upon its clipped side, with the neck end farthest from her. She examines the fleece carefully, that it have no extraneous substances—as straws, thorns, whins, or burs—and removes them; and she also pulls off, not clips, all lumps of dung which may have escaped the notice of the sheep-washers. Fig. 216 shows the

Fig. 213

Second stage of clipping a sheep.

a Bared neck of the sheep.
b Left hand of the clipper keeping the skin of the sheep tight.
c Fore-legs of the sheep.
d Tail of the sheep.
e Right or clipping-hand of the clipper with the large shears.
f Right arm of the clipper.
g Left arm of the clipper.

Fig. 214

Third stage of clipping a sheep.

a Right ankle and foot of the clipper keeping down the head of the sheep.
b Right arm of the clipper clipping.
c Left arm of the clipper keeping the skin of the sheep tight with the left hand
d Freed fleece.

Fig. 215

New-clipped sheep.

a Shoulder-point of sheep.
b Round rib of sheep.
c Hind-quarter of sheep.
e Fore-leg of sheep.
g Neck of sheep.
a to *e* Shoulder to fore-leg.
a to *g* Shoulder-point to top of shoulder.
c to *f* Hind-quarter to hind-leg.

mode of rolling a fleece, where a board is supported upon the tressels, and a field-worker is in the act of winding a fleece.
2479

Sheep-shearing is a joyous season—a sort of harvest—in which a liberal allowance of beef and broth and ale is dispensed to the clippers engaged in the warm laborious work.
2473.

Fig. 216

Rolling a fleece of wool.

a Board.
b c Tressels supporting the board.
d Field-worker rolling a fleece of wool.
e A fleece of wool placed on the board.

Fig. 217

Fleece of wool rolled up.

a Centre of fleece, consisting of the wool from the breech of the sheep.
c Rope of wool from the neck of the sheep twisted round the body of the fleece.
b Body of fleece of wool.

Fig. 218

Weighing and packing wool.

a a Pack-sheet suspended by the corners.
b Man tramping fleeces in the corner of the sheet.
c Man placing a fleece in the corner of the sheet.
d Pack-sheet.
e Worker carrying weighed fleeces to be packed.
f Completed pack-sheet.
g Unweighed fleeces.
h Beam-scale for weighing fleeces.
i Man weighing fleeces.
k Weighed fleeces.

WEANING OF LAMBS.

The ewes which were forsaken by their lambs after clipping should be closely observed by the shepherd, to ascertain whether their milk annoys them, and should be caught and milked until the general weaning takes place. When that has been effected, ewes are milked by the hand a few times till the secretion ceases. 2513.

Ewes are milked in a different manner from cows. A long narrow bught, fig. 219, formed of hurdles on 2 sides when the fence is a hedge, and on 1 side when a stone wall, of the width of a hurdle at the farther end, is erected close to the gate of a field near the steading, and of a size to contain all the ewes in a crowded state. The ewes being driven into it head inwards, women proceed with the milking, which is done by placing a small handy on its edge on the ground, and sitting down *behind* the ewe on a low stool. The milk is stripped clean from the 2 teats alternately with the right hand into the handy, while the left hand presses the udder of the ewe towards the milker. The milker should be on her guard to remove the handy the instant the ewe shows a symptom of voiding water or dung; and a ewe is apt to make water whenever her udder is handled from behind. The milk from every ewe is poured from the handy into a milking-pail. Each ewe is turned out of the bught by the shepherd, who waits for the purpose, as it is milked; and the milkers follow up the ewes in the bught to keep them close together, and prevent them starting forward or aside in the act of milking. 2514.

Fig. 219

Milking ewes.

a a Bught of hurdles. *b* Milking-stool. *c* Small handy. *d* Pail for holding the milk.

MARKING OF SHEEP.

When lambs cease to bleat for their mothers, they should be *marked* and *buisted*, not only to identify them with the flock of the farm on which they are bred, but as a record of the strain of blood from which they are descended. The *markings* are confined to the *ears*, and consist of small pieces punched out of the fore or back margin, a slit in the tip with a sharp knife, holes made with punching-nippers, or a combination of these marks. 2532.

Fig. 220 are the *punching-nippers*, of which an inverted hollow cone, having its small end sharpened to an edge, is employed to cut the hole—of any form, round, square, or triangular—out of

Fig. 220

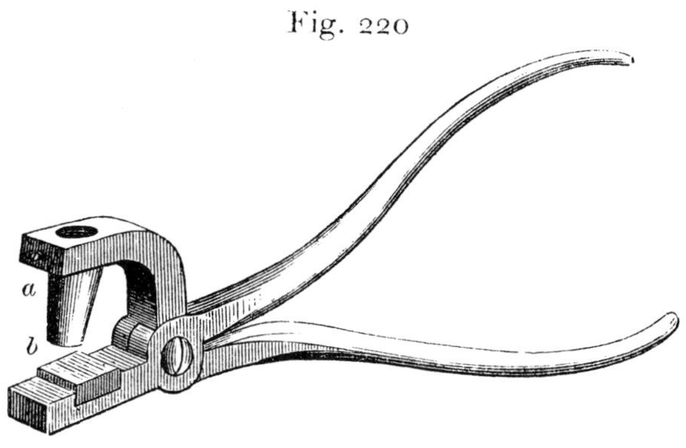

Punching-nippers for sheep.

a Hollow cone. *b* Horn pad.
c Orifice of hollow cone.

the ear; and, to save bruising the ears in punching, a pad of horn is inserted into the straight under-arm, the pieces nipped out rising out of the orifice of the hollow cone. *Buisting* consists simply of stamping a letter or letters, expressive of the initials of the name of the owner or of the farm, or of both, on different parts of the body. The buist is made with a simple instrument, fig. 221, consisting of a wooden handle, an iron shank, and a flat capital letter, as S, cut out of some kind of stiff metal, as copper or iron. The length of the implement is about 2 feet. Its impression is made on the same principle as the marks on the ears, the *near side* indicating the female, and the *far side* the male sheep. Buisting is done upon the skin of clipped sheep, and upon the short wool of lambs. 2533.

Fig. 221

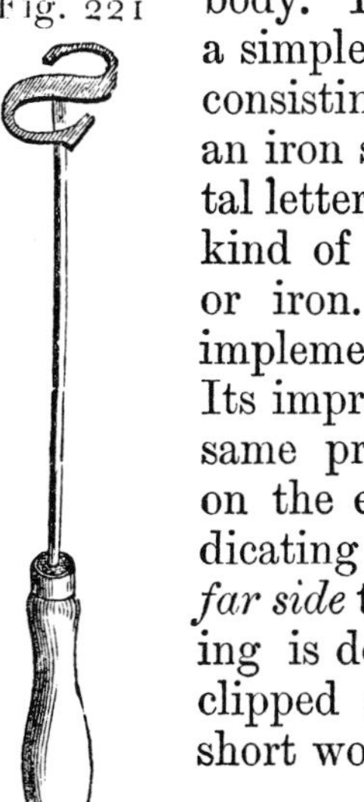

Buisting-iron for sheep.

Fig. 222 is an implement for marking *horned* sheep and cattle. It is made wholly of iron, and on the upper face of the block is cut out as a die the capital letter to be used, as S. The length of the implement is about 18 inches. It is heated in the fire, and the letter burns its form on the hair of the face, on the horns of Black-faced sheep, and on the horns of cattle. 2537

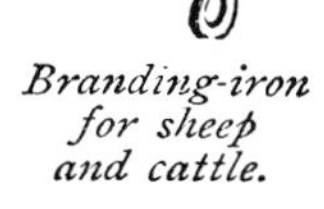

Branding-iron for sheep and cattle.

Fig. 222

HAY-MAKING.

The implement used for cutting grass for hay is the common scythe, with

Fig. 223

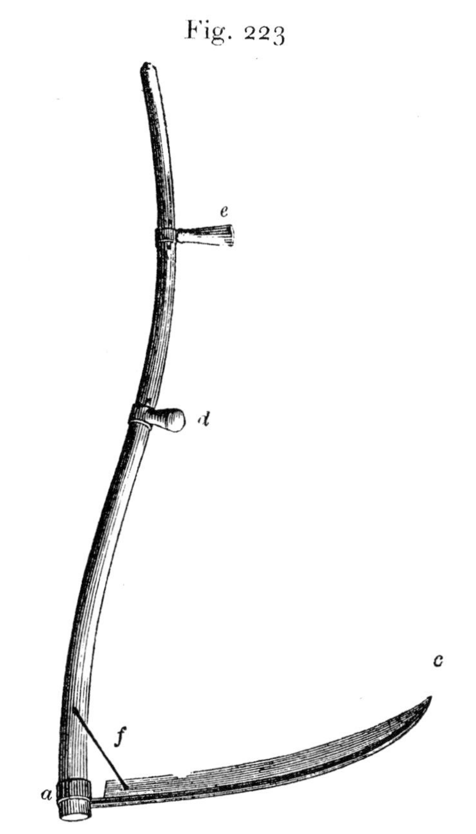

Patent scythe with bent sned.

a Iron ring for blade.
a b Bent sned.
a c Patent scythe-blade.
d Right-hand handle.
e Left-hand handle.
f Grass-nail.

Fig. 224

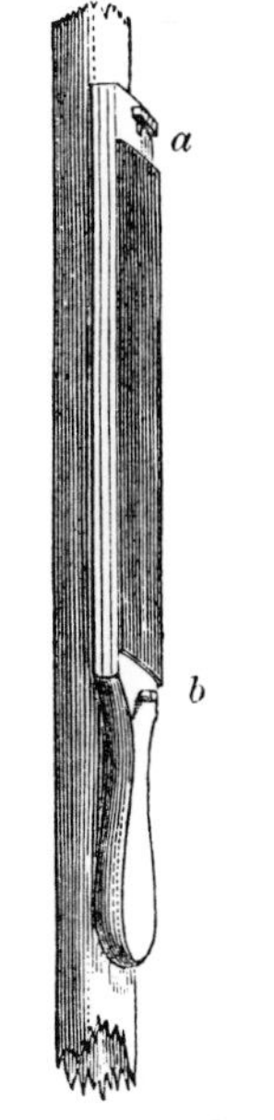

Scythe-strickle.

a b Strickle shipped on the end of the scythe.

Fig. 225

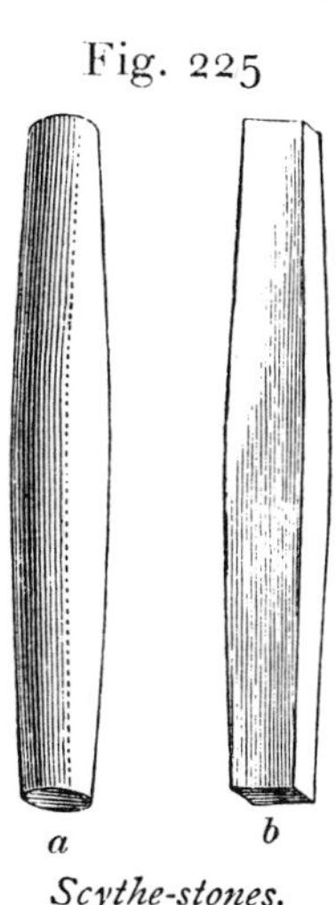

Scythe-stones.

a Round tapering scythe-stone.
b Square tapering scythe-stone.

a bent or straight sned or a cradle. He is the best scythe-man who keeps the keenest edge on his scythe, not only doing more work, but doing it more easily for himself. The edge of the blade is first sharpened by a scythe-stone, round or square, then the sharpness is maintained by the strickle. 2542.

Fig. 226

English hay-tedding machine.

a Transverse bar of carriage.
b b Horse-shafts.
c c c Iron stay-bars.
d d Wheels of carriage.
e Ratchet-wheel.
f Spur-wheel.
g Pinion on hollow shaft.
h Hollow shaft.
i i Rake-wheels.
k k k k 8 rakes.
l l Springs of tumbling-joints.
m n Tumbling-joints.

Fig. 227

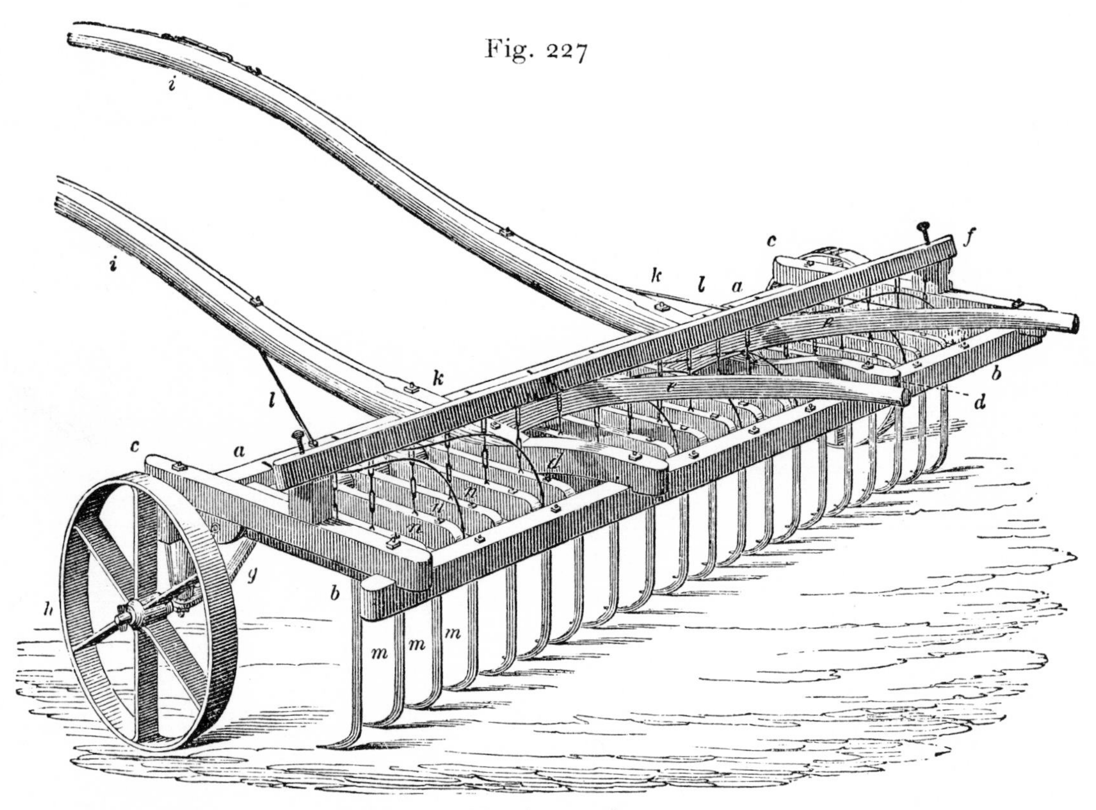

Hay horse-rake.

a a Main beam.
b b Swing-bar.
c c Side bars.
d d Intermediate bars.
e e Handles.
f Lifting-bar.
g Axles.
h Wheels.
i i Horse-shafts.
k k Where shafts are bolted to main beam and intermediate bars.
l l Iron stays to support shafts.
m m m 20 tines.
n n n Rake-heads.

Where is no horse-rake, the grass must be raked together with the hand-rake, and no more raked than can be ricked by the workers. It is evident that where a tedding-machine is at work, there must be a horse-rake to rake the space of ground corresponding to the work. Figs. 228 and 229 are the hand-rakes of the most simple form. They consist of a head of hardwood, which is armed with 12 or 13 wooden teeth of oak or ash, about 3½ inches long. The helve is usually made of ash, but as lightness is an object, its thickness ought not to exceed 1¼ inch, dressed neatly smooth and round, except where the head enters. This part of it is either let into the middle of the head by 1 tenon, as in fig. 229, or split as in fig. 228, and enters it by 2 tenons. It is this difference of construction that makes the variations; but the 1 tenon is defective and weak, hence the necessity of 2 iron stays to support the head. This is attained by the split tenoned shaft with its iron ferrule. Of the 2 sorts of rakes the split-shafted is the lighter and handier. 2548.

The mode of using a hand-rake is, on taking hold of the end of the shaft with the left hand, palm uppermost, the head of the rake is projected as far on the right side of the worker as the length of the shaft and the inclination of the body in that direction, with its weight on the right foot, will admit. This distance is about 7½ feet, or ½ of a 15-feet ridge. The head is then drawn lightly towards the worker, and, as the grass accumulates under it, the right hand assists the raking by its weight upon the shaft with the palm downwards; and as the head approaches with its load, the right hand exerts more strength upon the shaft, while the left hand slips down the shaft as far as to ease the arm, when both hands project the bundle of grass, with a swing of the body towards the left. The rake is used thus by a right or left hand worker. 2549.

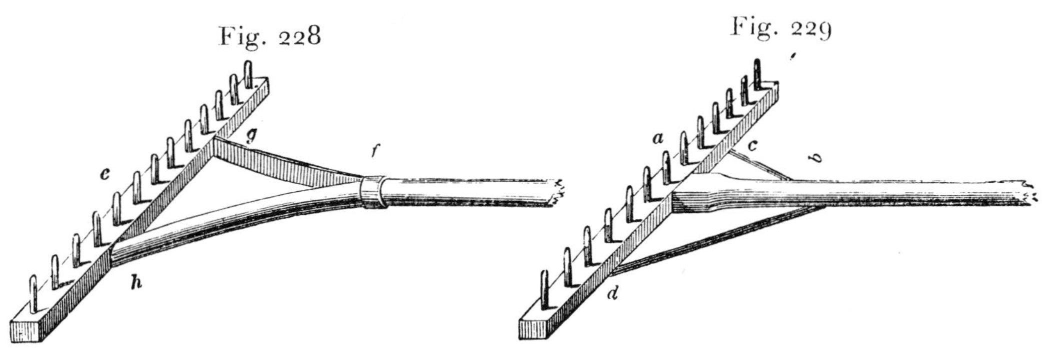

Split-shafted hay hand-rake.

c d, g h Heads.
a, e Wooden teeth.

Iron-stayed hay hand-rake.

b c, b d Iron stays. *f* Iron ferrule.
g h Split shaft.

There is nothing to prevent the English mode being proceeded with from this point; but here the Scotch mode interferes and puts an end to it. The grass is seldom or never tedded in Scotland, which may account in part for the absence there of the tedding-machine. It is windrowed—that is, the swathes of grass are not tedded, but rolled along to a destined ridge, there to be put into small cocks. I should prefer the tedding-machine and hay-rake to prepare the grass being put into small cocks. The cocks are made in this way: The swathes are cleared from 2 ridges on to the third, fig. 231, on both sides of the third ridge, so that the cocks are made on every fifth ridge. On clearing the 2 ridges, 2 forkers and 2 rakers (the forkers may be men and the rakers women, or all 4 may be women) are appointed to each ridge, having the ridge on which the cocks are to be made on the right hand, to suit right-handed workers. A man clears the grass with a fork from the open furrow of the first ridge to its crown, and a raker follows and cleans the ½ ridge he has cleared. The man and raker go on to the next swathe. A second man follows the raker with a fork, and tosses the gathered grass of the first swathe from the crown of the first to the open furrow of the second ridge, and the second raker follows and makes clean the ½ ridge cleared. On the second ridge, a third man forks the accumulating swathe from the open furrow to the crown, and a third raker follows and cleans the ½ of the second ridge thus cleared. And last of all, a fourth man forks the grass from the crown over the open furrow to the third ridge, and a fourth raker follows and cleans this last ½ ridge. Of them all, the last man is the hardest worked, the rakers having the same degree and extent of labour. Thus 8 labourers, consisting of 4 men with forks and 4 women with rakes, clear 2 ridges of their grass, and the space cleared by them is just the breadth of 8 swathes of grass, which is more or less heavy according to the weight of the crop; and as mowers usually cut a breadth of 6 feet at each stroke of the scythe, and each breadth constitutes 1 swathe, the area cleared by the 8 workers is 48 feet by 30 feet, of the breadth of 2 ridges. In this way the band of 8 clears 2 ridges at a time, till they reach their end, the grass on both head-ridges being cleared and mixed with that of the 2 ridges. They then wheel round at the end of the 2 ridges to clear other 2 ridges on the other side of the third ridge, which will contain the grass of 5 ridges, forming 1 windrow. A difference in the arrangement of the workers takes place on entering the second 2 ridges, the forker who took the lead at first, having had the lightest share of the work, now becomes the last forker, and takes the heaviest part, and he who had the heaviest then now takes the lightest. To prevent confusion in changing the ridges, inasmuch as all the rakers do the same work, the same raker follows the same forker; so

Fig. 230

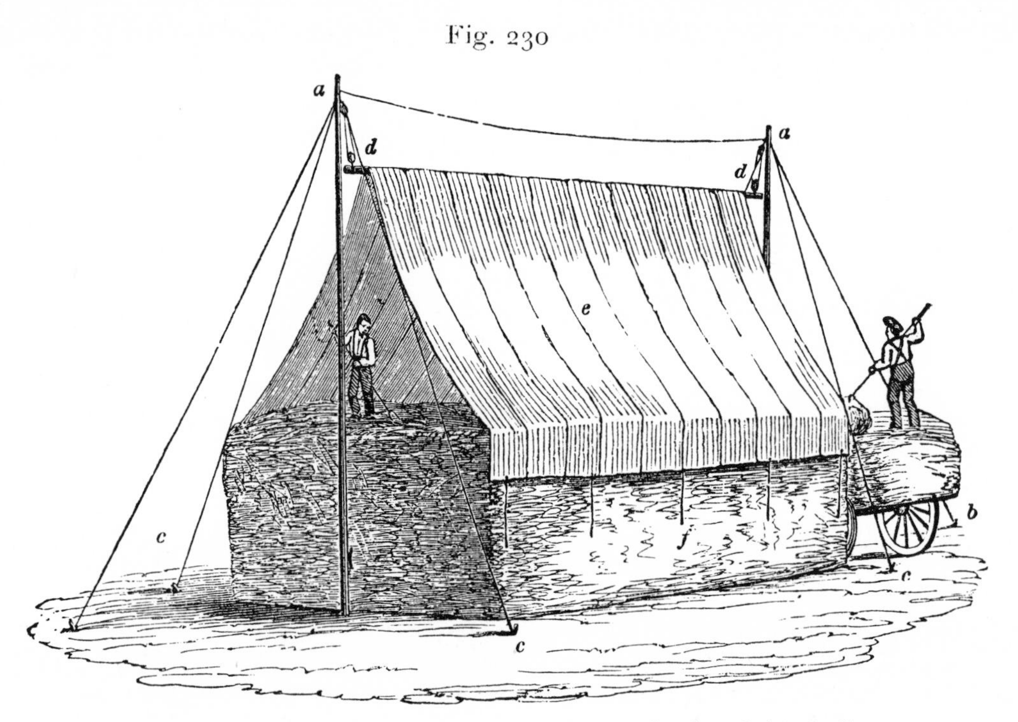

Mode of erecting a rick-cloth over a hay-stack when being built.

a a Wooden spars.
a to *a* Top-rope.
c c c Guy-ropes from side to side of a stack.
b b Guy-ropes from end to end of stack.
d d Blocks and tackle.
e Rick-cloth.
f Reef-points of cord.

that the band consists of 4 pairs, each consisting of 1 forker and 1 raker. Women are as able to fork as to rake; but where they are wanting in number, men take the forks and women the rakes. When only 1 band of 4 workers can be spared to make hay, consisting of 2 forkers and 2 rakers, they must go up 1 ridge and down 1 ridge, to clear the 2 ridges on each side of the third ridge. A smaller band than 4 workers makes hay-making a dilatory process, and expensive in proportion to the number employed. The grass collected on the third ridge is called the *windrow*, and the first cocks, being grassy and small, are called *grass-cocks*. They are

Fig. 231

Putting swathes of sown grasses into windrows.

a First forker.
b First raker.
e Second forker.
f Second raker.
g Third forker.
h Third raker.
i Fourth forker.
k Fourth raker.
c d Cleared first ridge.
d k Second ridge being cleared.
l Third ridge.
p Swathes of grass.
o Ridge on other side of third ridge.
m n Windrow on third ridge.

Fig. 232

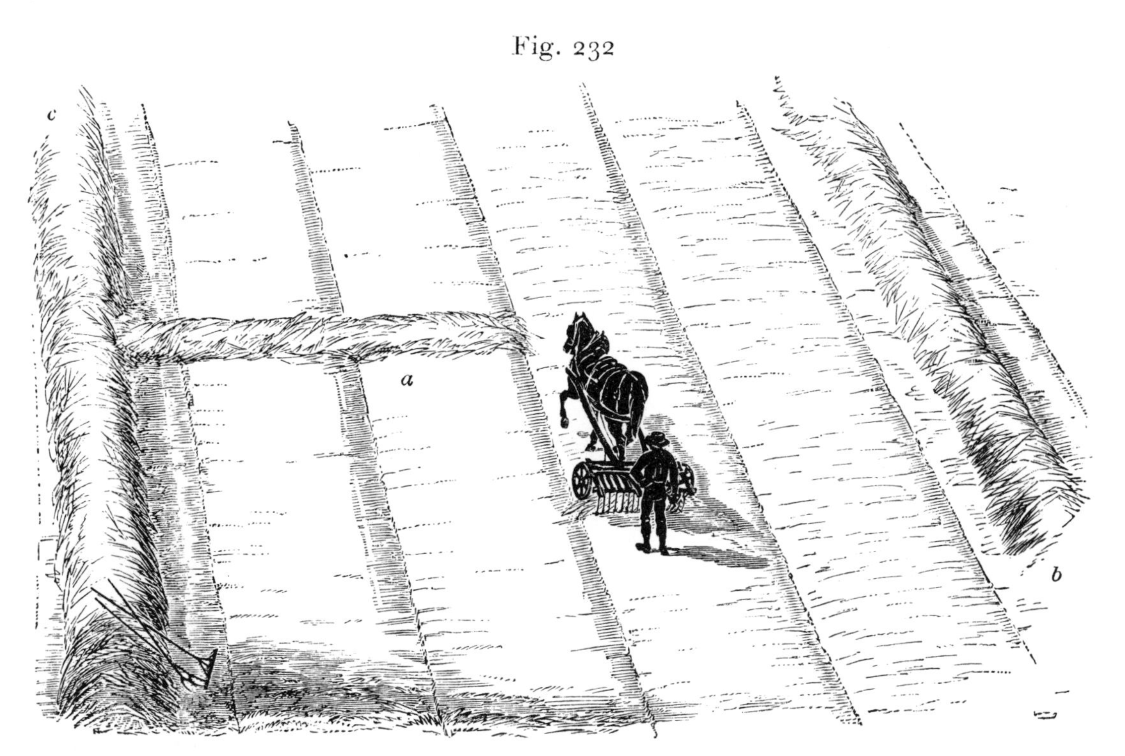

Hay horse-rake cleaning ridges between windrows.

b to *c* 4 ridges cleared by the workers with forks.
b and *c* Windrows on every fifth ridge.
a Row of grass raked in line by the horse-rake.

put together either with the fork or the arms, with narrow bottoms, and high in proportion to their breadth, about 2 feet in height. As there is not room on the ridge to put such small cocks in 1 row, they are put up so as not to crowd each other, and to afford room for the rakes to clean the ground. It is considered slovenly work in a hay-field to neglect cleaning the ground with the rake which had been cleared of its grass by the fork. The raking at the time of cocking will not occupy more than 2 workers, the rest being employed to assist the forkers to put up the cocks. 2559.

THRESHING GRASSES IN THE FIELDS.

When ryegrass seed is wanted, the number of acres of the hay-grass that will produce the quantity, where most ryegrass is growing, should remain unmown until the seed is ripe enough for mowing, rather than that the whole crop of hay should be injured by standing too long for the sake of the seed. Even the ryegrass intended for seed should not stand until the seed is ripe, because ryegrass seed is very easily shaken from its stalk. When mown, it should be tied in sheaves with thumb-made straw-ropes, and set in stooks for a few days to win. After that the sheaves are built in hand-cocks, and when these are won they are either taken to be thrashed by the thrashing-machine, or are thrashed on the ground. In using the thrashing-machine for this purpose, it is troublesome to clean it effectually; so I think the better plan is to thrash the crop in the field. It could be done in the stack-yard, but the business is most quickly done in the field. Fig. 233 represents the particulars of this work in a graphic picture. An outside door answers for the thrashing-floor, and at both ends is set upon a cushion of hay, which gives elasticity to the stroke of the flail. A field-gate is cushioned similarly in continuation of the door, and the large barn-sheet is spread under the gate to receive seed. The hand-cocks containing the sheaves are brought to the thrashing-floor by 1 horse, which is yoked to them by the haims attached to a cart-rope passing round the base of the cock. When the horse pulls, the cock slides upon the ground to its place of destination. A field-worker rakes

Fig. 233

Thrashing ryegrass seed in the field, either in sheaf or in bulk.

a Horse bringing hand-cocks.
b Raker.
c Worker supplying hay to thrashers.
d e Thrashers.
f Worker shaking thrashed hay over the field-gate.
g Worker removing the thrashed hay from the gate.
h Heap of thrashed hay.
i Worker building coll as a man forks the hay.
k Barn-sheet on which a worker is riddling hay-seed.
l Heap of hay-seed.
m Sacked hay-seed.
n o Finished colls of thrashed hay.
p Ladder.
r Spare rake.
s Provisions.

the ground upon which it stood clean, while another loosens the sheaves and pitches them upon the door with a fork, with the seed end towards herself: 2 men, 1 on each side of the door, use the flail. Another field-worker, at the junction of the door and field-gate, pulls the thrashed hay with a long fork upon the field-gate, over which she shakes it, and another field-worker removes the shaken hay with a fork from the gate to the ground. The thrashers occasionally clear the door of seed with their flails upon the gate, through the spars of which it collects on the barn-sheet below. When the spars are filled, the seed is carried to a heap, and riddled by a field-worker upon a sheet preparatory to being put into sacks, to be carried to the corn-barn and winnowed. The thrashed hay is forked by 1 man to 1 field-worker upon a rick, which she builds of the form of a pike. A ladder is used to come down from the rick: a basket and bottles indicate that a drink of beer is acceptable to the workers in warm weather. Thus, if 1 part of this busy band of workers supplies the other with sufficient materials, the work goes on pleasantly and without collision. The seed will more quickly part with its impurities in the winnowing, after it has lain to dry and win on the barn-floor for some days. After it is winnowed, it should be stored in the granary to dry. When sufficiently dry, it should be winnowed in the granary, measured, and laid thicker together; and in spring it should again be winnowed, and freed from the many fresh impurities which will have found their way into it during the winter, such as cats' and vermin's dung, cobwebs from the roof, and dust. Whatever proportion of the seed is not required for the use of the farm may be disposed of to a seed-merchant or farmer. A fair crop of ryegrass, even when not too much ripened, should yield about 26 bushels of seed to 1 imperial acre when thus treated. 2583.

A flail consists of 2 parts, the hand-staff or helve, and the supple or beater, fig. 234 The hand-staff is a light rod of ash about 5 feet in length, slightly increased in breadth at the farther extremity, where it is perforated for the passage of the thongs that bind the beater to it. The beater is a rod of from 30 to 36 inches in length, made of ash, though a more compact wood, as thorn, is less likely to split; and to prevent this disintegration of the wood, the beater should be constructed to fall upon the *edge* of the segmental portions of the *reed* of the wood, which is easily accomplished in its formation. The usual form of the beater is cylindrical, the diameter being from 1¼ to 1½ inch. For the most part it is attached to the hand-staff by a thong of hide untanned; eel-skins make a strong durable thong. A general practice is to have the beater club-shaped, or thickest at the furthest extremity, intended to give better effect to the blows; but when we consider the effects arising from the manner of wielding the instrument, any additional weight at the extremity seems misapplied. The greatest amount of useful effect will be produced by the beater when every point in its length strikes the floor with an equal amount of momentum or force; but there will be a constant tendency to a larger amount of momentum at the extremity than at any other point, and a club-shaped beater will always augment this tendency—for the greater velocity of the extreme end, during the gyration of the implement, multiplied by its greater weight, must give an undue preponderance of effect to that part of the beater, thereby lessening the general effect upon the work under performance. The opposite mode, to make the beater thinner towards the extremity, is more consonant to the laws of dynamics, and there can be no doubt that its practical effects will be equally favourable as compared with those of the club-shaped beater. A long wand would beat out the best ripened and largest of the seed from the bunches of ryegrass as well and more easily, as regards labour, than the flail. The beater of the flail in the United States of America revolves in swivel fashion around the end of the staff. In Holland and Belgium the beaters are short, thick, and heavy. In Switzerland, flails are diminutive in size, and in using them 4 or 5 women range themselves in a circle on the thrashing-floor upon their knees, and beat out the grain from the straw in short sharp strokes following one another in rapid succession around the circle of thrashers. The flail as a thrasher-out of grain is still much in use in England; but the locomotive thrashing-machine will supersede it on large farms. Small farmers who have not means to procure thrashing-machines, or accommodation for them in their steadings, still use the flail in Scotland. 2584.

Fig. 234

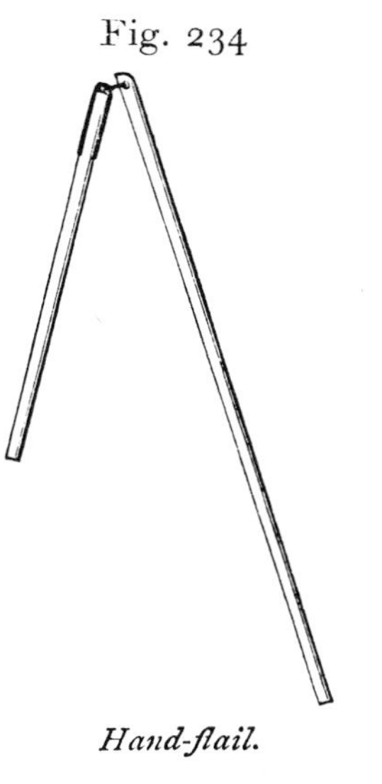

Hand-flail.

CULTURE OF WHEAT.

The weeding of the cereal crops in summer is an indispensable work for their welfare. It may be done solely with manual implements, or with manual and horse combined. Among broadcast grain, weeding must be performed with manual implements, and the most effective is the simple *weed-hook*, fig. 235. It consists of an acute hook of iron, the 2 inner edges of which are flattened and thinned to cut like a knife, and which are as far asunder at one end as to embrace the stem of succulent herbaceous plants which are destined to be cut down.

A sharp spud with a cross-head handle is the best instrument for cutting weeds with strong stems—as docks, thistles—with a push. 2589.

Fig. 235

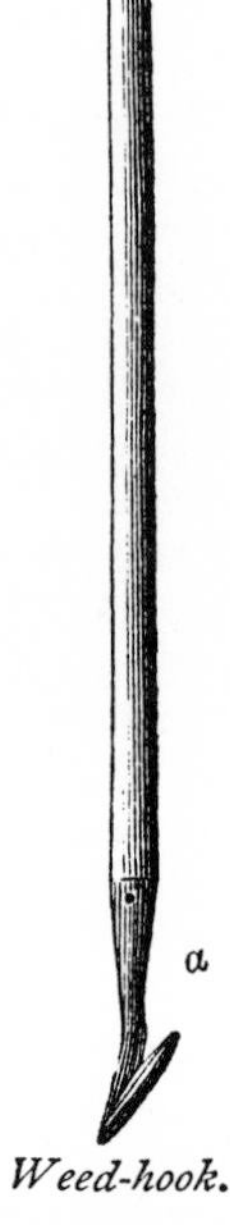

Weed-hook.

a Acute hook with 2 sharp edges.

There are many forms of horse-hoes for cleaning the ground between the rows of corn, but I have seen no one that pleases me so well as the steerage horse-hoe of Smith of Northampton.

In using this hoe the horse is put into the shafts; the driver holds on by the handles, and steers the hoes along the centre of the rows of corn, which he is enabled to do by the movement of the connecting-rods upon the hooks attached to the brackets at the framing. Should the horse swerve from the row he walks in, the driver can sustain the hoes in their places until the horse regains his proper track. A steady horse will not leave the row he walks in from end to end of the landing, and a young horse is unsuited for this work. A steady man to steer the hoes is as requisite as a steady horse; otherwise his carelessness will send the hoes across the rows of corn-plants, and cut them through as well as the weeds. 2593.

Fig. 236

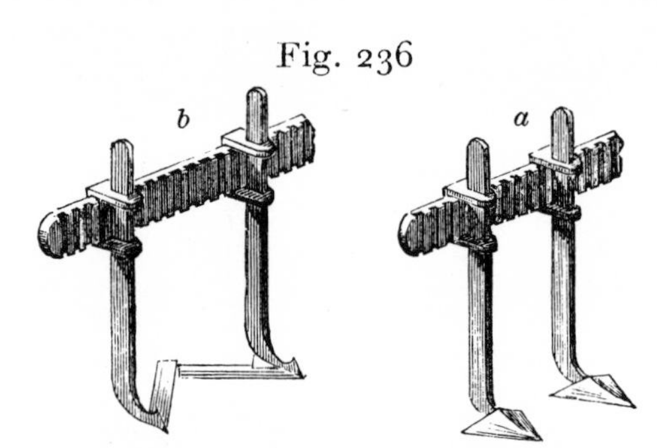

Long and short shares for Smith's horse-hoe.

a Short shares for 7-inch rows.
b Long shares for as much as 18-inch rows.

Fig. 237

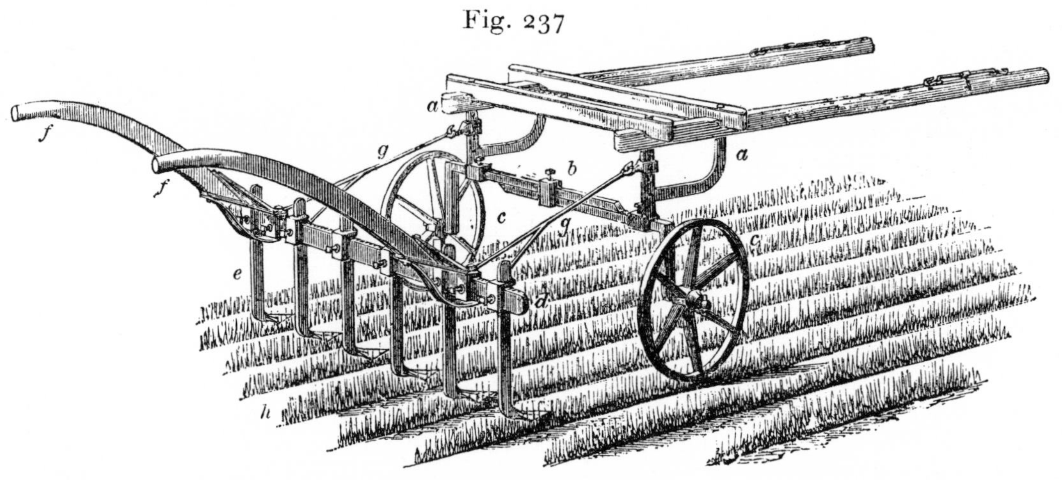

Smith's steerage horse-hoe.

a a Framing and horse-shafts.
b Iron axle, expandible, and fixed by a pinching-screw.
c c Wheels.
d Iron bar bearing the hoes.
e Duck-footed hoes.
f f Handles for guidance.
g g Connecting-rods.
h Rows of growing corn.

MAKING BUTTER AND CHEESE.

The dairy of a farm of mixed husbandry is necessarily limited, both as regards time and produce. Until the calves are all weaned, which can scarcely be before the end of June, there is no milk to make into butter and cheese but what suffices for the farm-house; and as some of the cows will have calved 4 months before others, they cannot yield much milk, even on grass. But though limited, the dairy may produce a considerable quantity both of good butter and cheese, according to the taste and skill of the dairy-maid. Butter may be made from cream, or from the entire milk—fresh for market, or salted in kits for families or dealers. Cheese also may be made from sweet and skimmed milk for the market, and any variety of fancy cheese—as Cream-cheese, Stilton, Cheddar, Gloucester, Dunlop. Milk, in many forms, finds its way to the table of the farmer. The only difference between a mixed husbandry and dairy farm is that the work is conducted on a much smaller scale. 2655.

The *utensils* which a dairy requires, comprise a number of articles of simple construction. The *milk-dishes* are composed of stoneware, glass, wood, metal, or stone. The stoneware is of common ware and Wedgewood; the wooden of cooper-work; the metal of block-tin or zinc; the stone of polished sandstone, pavement, or marble. Besides these simple, a combination of materials is used—as wooden vessels lined with block-tin or zinc, and German cast-iron lined with porcelain. Of all these, the stone and wood lined with metal are stationary, the others movable. The form of all milk-dishes should be broad and shallow, for exposing a large surface of milk of small depth to the air for the disengagement of its component parts. There is a difference in opinion which of those substances has the greatest influence in disengaging the largest proportion of cream from the milk. Common stoneware milk-dishes are brown outside and glazed yellow inside, of round form, shallow, tapering to the bottom, and no mouth to pour the milk by. They are generally 15

Fig. 238

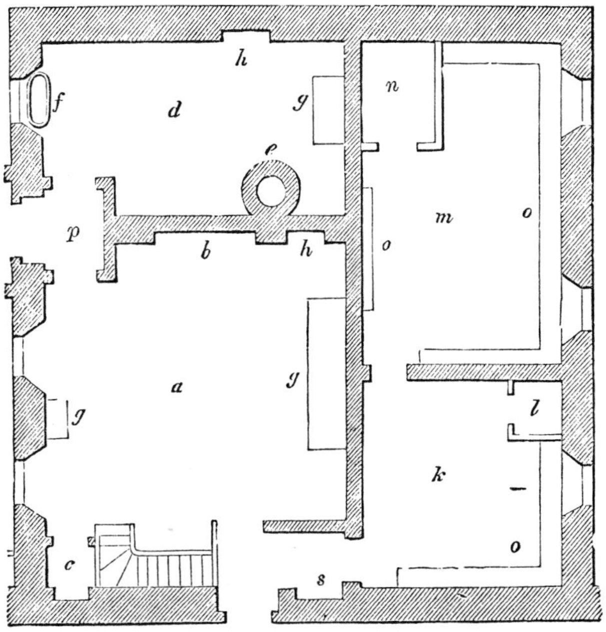

Ground-plan of a milk-house in relation to the kitchen for a farm-house of mixed husbandry.

a Kitchen in back-jamb.
b Fireplace.
c Stair to cheese-room, &c.
g g Dressers.
h Wall-press.
d Scullery.
e Boiler.
f Sink.
g Dresser.
h Fireplace.
p Kitchen-door.
k Kitchen pantry.
l Larder.
o Wooden shelving.
s Wall-press at door of kitchen pantry, and into the farm-house.

Fig. 239

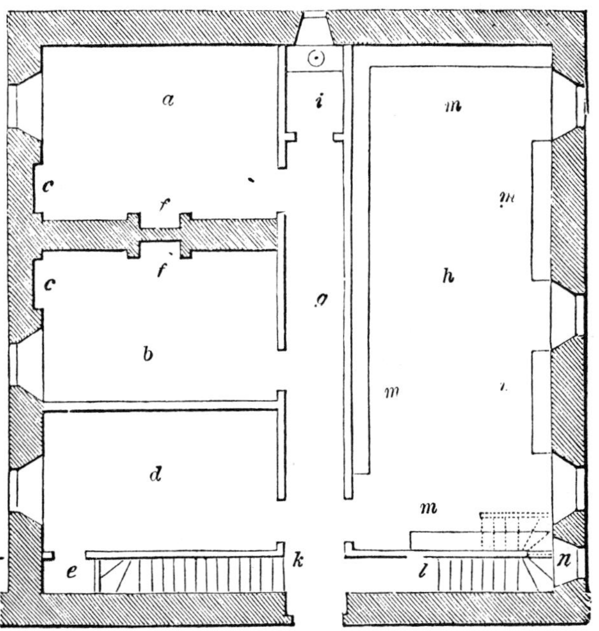

Plan of cheese-room, &c.

h Cheese-room.
m Broad wood shelving.
k Stair from kitchen, and door into farm-house.
g Passage.
a b d 3 bedrooms.
f f Fireplaces.
c c Wall-presses.
e Closet.
l Stair to garret.
n Window.
i Water-closet.

inches in diameter and 4 inches deep, inside measure. They are easily cleaned and broken, and the glazing is not durable. Fig. 240 is a milk-dish of white

Fig. 240

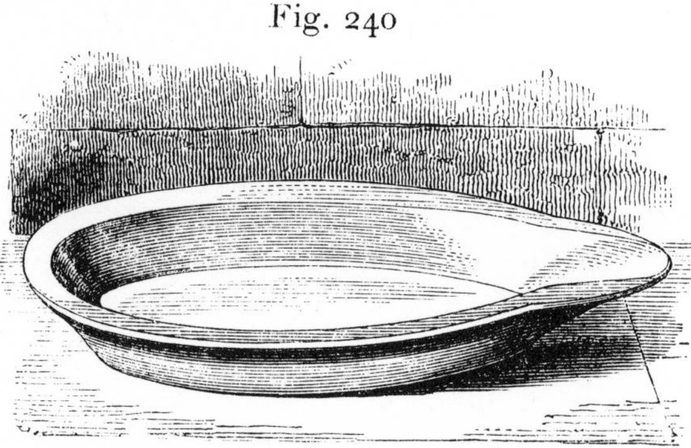

White Wedgewood-ware milk-dish.

Wedgewood ware, oval, 16 inches long and 3 inches deep, inside measure, with a mouth. This ware is hard, not easily broken, the glazing durable and easily cleaned. Wedgewood ware is also made of the form of the wooden dish, fig. 242, with the addition of 2 clutch-handles to lift the vessel by. Fig. 241 is a milk-

Fig. 241

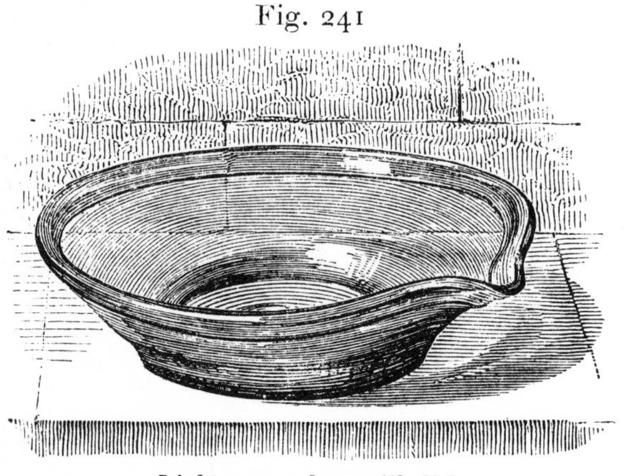

Light-green glass milk-dish.

dish of light green-coloured glass, circular form, 16 inches in diameter, 4 inches deep, and with a mouth. It is easily cleaned, and easily broken if carelessly handled. Glass milk-dishes were first introduced by the celebrated glass manufacturer, Mr Pellat of London. Fig. 242 is the common wooden milk-dish, of cooper-work, composed of staves of oak and flat hoops of iron, and without a mouth. It is 16 inches in diameter, and 4 inches deep, inside measure. This is the most durable of milk-dishes, though it requires much scrubbing to keep it clean and the iron hoops bright. Fig. 243 is a milk-dish of zinc, of a circu-

Fig. 242

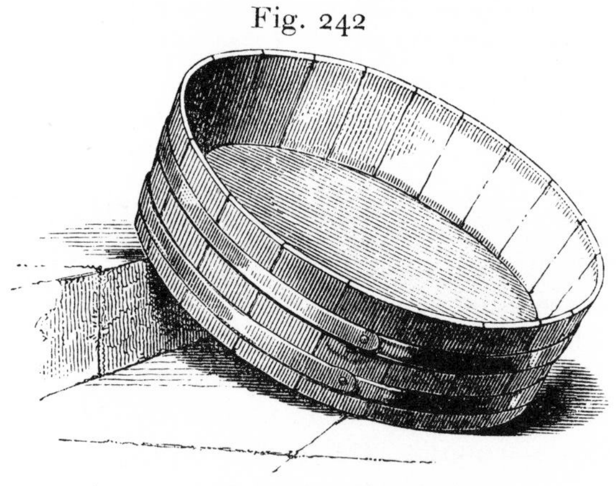

Wooden milk-dish.

lar form, 18 inches in diameter and 3 inches deep, with a mouth. It requires

Fig. 243

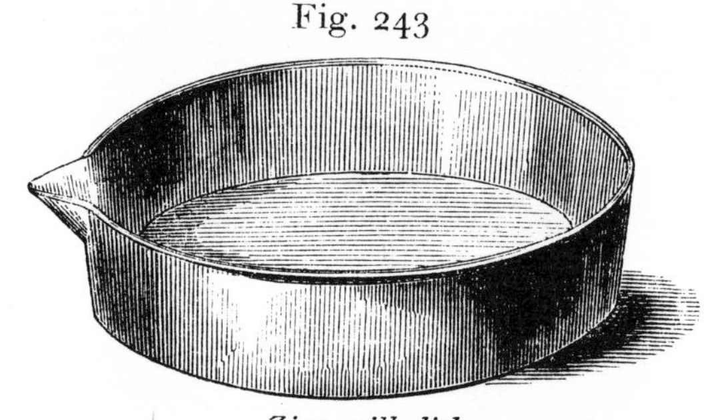

Zinc milk-dish.

much cleansing, and is apt to be bruised, though not easily broken. These are

Fig. 244

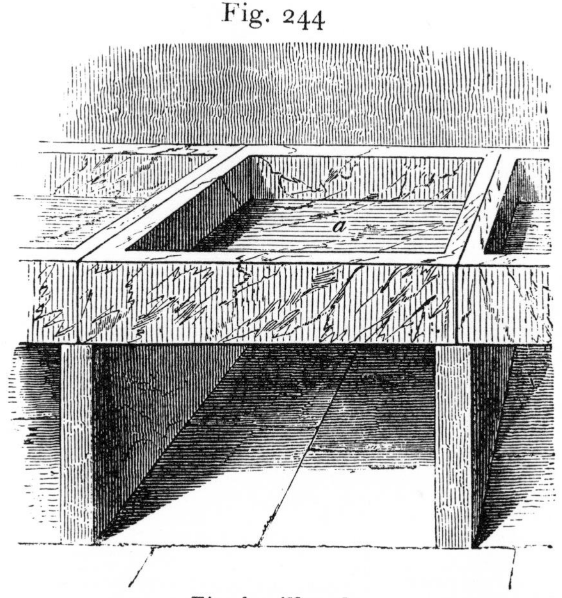

Fixed milk-cooler.

a Marble milk-cooler, polished.

movable dishes: a fixed one is seen at fig. 244, of stone—sandstone, slate, or marble —the marble is the best, being cool, cleanly, and handsome. An orifice is made in the bottom, at the near side, through which the milk runs out of the dish, as also the water which has been used to wash it. The dimensions are at pleasure, 3 feet long and 2 feet broad being a good size; but the depth should not exceed 4 inches, to contain from 2 to 3 inches of milk. When made of wood lined with zinc, block-tin, tin, or lead, the form is the same as this. The sandstone and marble coolers are each hewn out of single blocks and polished, and placed upon upright slabs of stone; and the wooden with metallic lining are framed along the walls of the milk-house, and subdivided into separate coolers. It is only in large dairies that these fixed coolers are used. 2657.

Another utensil required in a dairy is a milk-sieve, fig. 245, which con-

Fig. 245

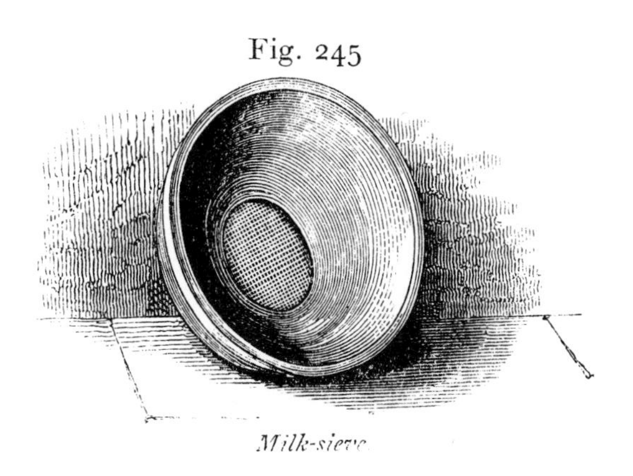

Milk-sieve.

sists of a bowl of the wood of the plane-tree, 9 inches in diameter, having an orifice covered with wire gauze in the bottom for the milk to pass through, and to detain the hairs that may have fallen into the milking-pails from the cows in the act of milking. The gauze is of brass wire, and, when kept bright, is safe enough; but silver wire is less likely to become corroded.—The creaming-dish, fig. 246, of stoneware, skims the cream off the milk. It is thin, circular, broad, and shallow, having on the near side a sharp edge to pass easily between the

Fig. 246

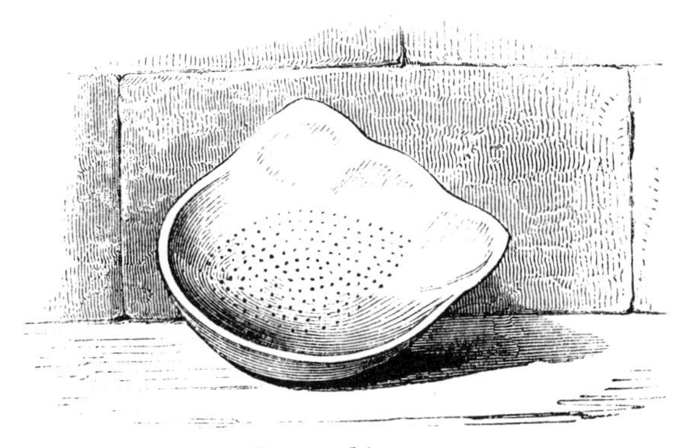

Cream-skimmer.

cream and milk, and both ends of the edge are formed into a mouth for pouring the cream into any vessel. At the bottom are a number of small holes for milk to pass through.—The cream, until churned, is kept in a jar of stoneware, fig. 247, about 18 inches in height and 10 inches in diameter, with a movable top, having an opening in its centre, covered with muslin to keep out dust and let in air. 2659.

Fig. 247

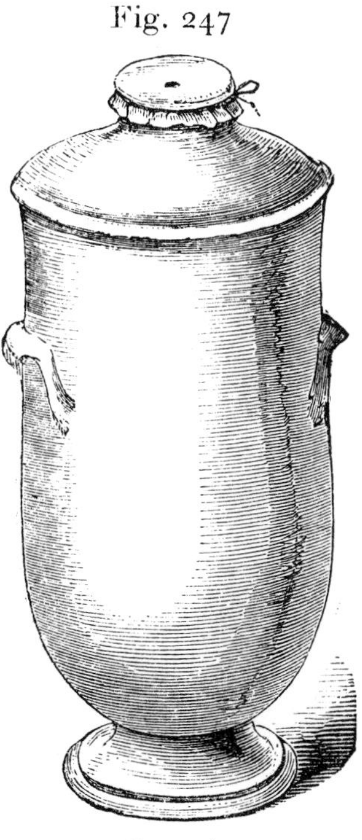

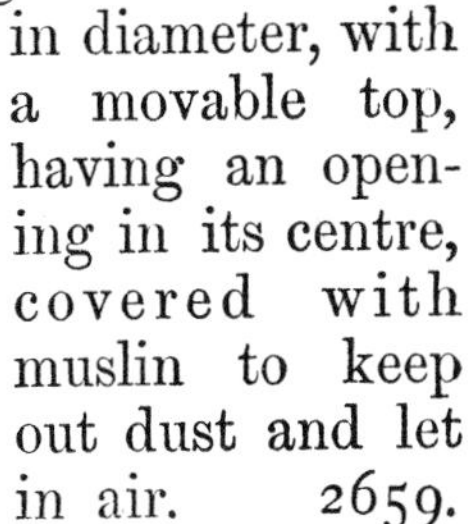

Cream-jar.

Churns may be classed under 4 kinds: (1), Those in which both the fluid and the containing vessel, with its agitators, are in rotative motion; (2), those in which the containing vessel is at rest, and the agitators in rotative motion horizontally; (3), those in which the containing vessel is at rest, and the agitators in rotative motion vertically; and (4), those in which the containing vessel is at rest, and the agitator in a reciprocating vertical motion. Of these sorts of churns there is an immense number of varieties; I shall only mention those of simple construction. The old-fashioned upright plunge-churn, belonging to the 4th kind, when worked by the hand, is chiefly used by small farmers and cottars; but when moved by inanimate power, it is used in extensive dairies. The barrel-churn, which belongs to the 1st kind, and was once in vogue, is now rarely used. It has been superseded by the box-churn, whose agitators move vertically, and which belongs to the 3d sort. The box-churn with horizontal agitators, which belongs to the 2d sort, is small, and suited to small quantities of cream. 2664.

Fig. 249

Box hand-churn.

Fig. 248

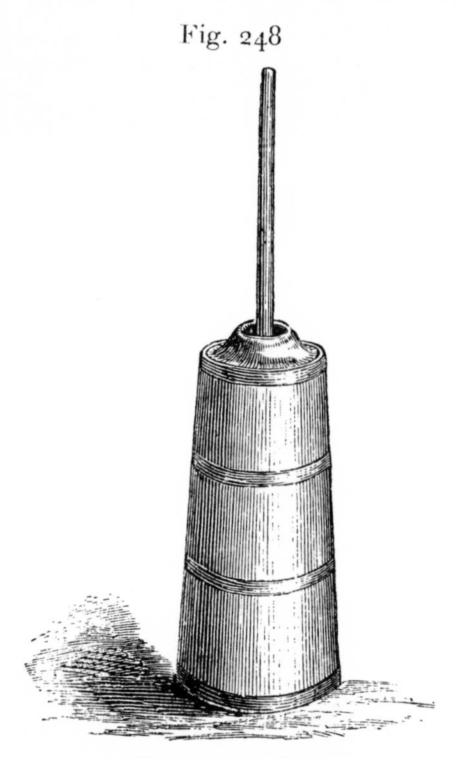

Hand plunge-churn.

Fig. 250

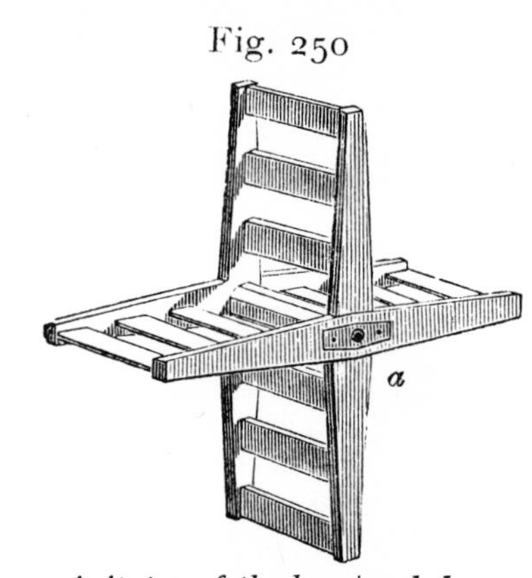

Agitator of the box hand-churn.

a Socket-plate of iron let into the agitator on both sides.

Fig. 251 gives a butter stamp 1½ inch diameter for small prints for the table, as also a couple of hands, with longitudinal and transversal parallel ridged lines on their respective faces for forming small jagged balls and rolls of butter, also for the table. The hands are 4 inches square in the face, and 4 inches long in the handles. 2670.

Fig. 251

Butter-stamp and hands.

Objections have been raised against using the bare hand in making up butter, and small wooden spades are recommended as substitutes. A woman having hot clammy hands should never be a dairy-maid, for butter is very susceptible of taint, and its flavour will doubtless be spoiled by the heavy smell of sweaty hands; but naturally cool hands—made clean by washing in warm water and oatmeal, *not soap*, and rinsed and steeped in cold water—make up butter freer of butter-milk, and more solid in texture, than any implement of whatever material. Less handling will be given to butter with the spade in the first process of dividing, rubbing, and rolling it on the bottom of the flat kit; but no implement can possibly expel butter-milk from butter as effectually as beating by hand. Fig. 252 is a butter-spade of shape long used in a dairy, the face being 4 inches square and the handle 4 inches long. 2671.

Fig. 252

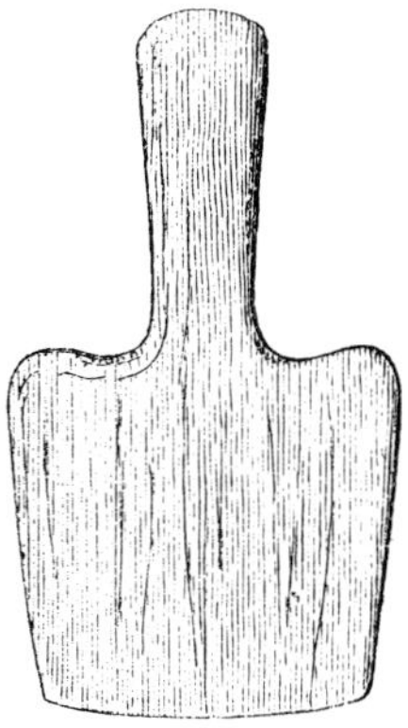

Butter-spade.

The utensils required in *cheese-making* are—tubs in which to earn the milk; a curd-cutter; a curd-breaker; a drainer to lay across a tub while the whey is straining from the curd; vats for forming the cheese; a cheese press; a furnace and pot for heating water and milk. 2681.

When the milk is sufficiently coagulated, which it will be in ½ an hour, the curd is cut in the tub with a knife. On being cut, the curd lets out its whey, which is drained off by means of a soup-plate being pressed against the curd-cloth (linen of open fabric) spread upon the curd. As much of the whey is removed in this way as practicable, when the curd is comparatively dry; and it then receives a more

Fig. 253

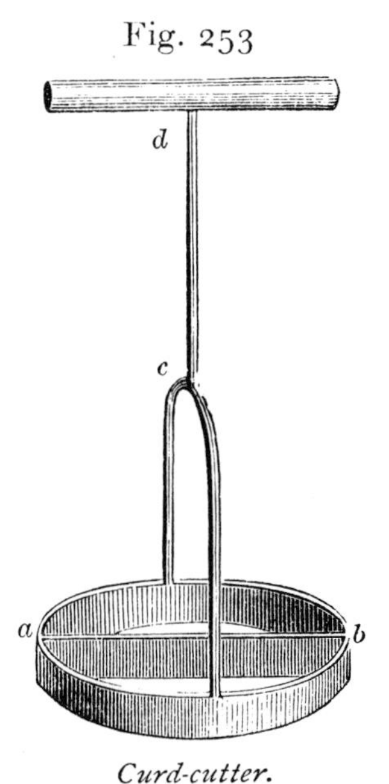

Curd-cutter.

a b Longitudinal axis of curd-cutter.
c Point of junction of fork and rod of iron.
d Wooden handle.

minute cutting with the curd-cutter, and the whey again expressed from it. The curd is then lifted out of the tub, wrapped in the curd-cloth in the form of a bundle, placed upon the drainer, fig. 255, lying across the mouth of a tub, where the whey is pressed out of it by main force. This is the laborious manual part of cheese-making; and, to save time and labour in large cheese-dairies, the bundle of curd is put into a large cheese-vat, and pressed in the cheese-press, or under large weights, to get quit of the whey. The curd becomes very firm after this pressing; and

Fig. 254

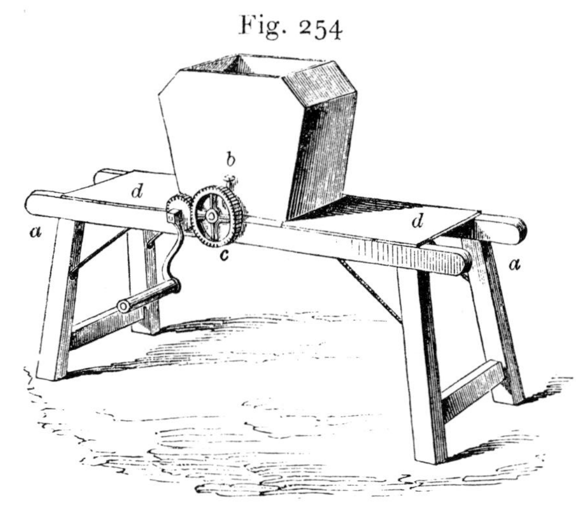

Curd-breaker.

a a Frame of 2 bars.
d d 2 boards connecting the 2 bars.
b Hopper and screw-pin.
c Large pinion.

to reduce it small with comparative ease, it is first cut into thin slices with a knife, and the slices are ground down in a curd-breaker before the curd is put into the vat. 2685.

Fig. 255

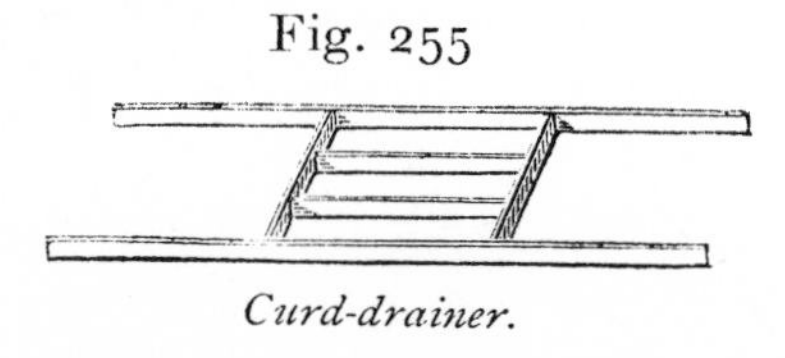

Curd-drainer.

Fig. 256

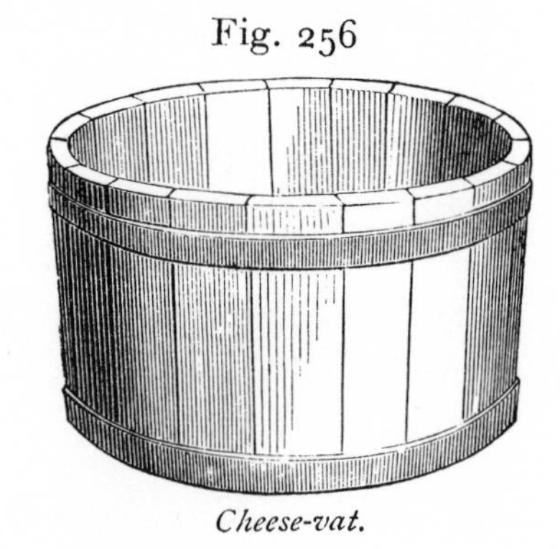

Cheese-vat.

Of the *cheese-press* the varieties are numerous, though those most in use may be classed under 2 kinds—namely, the old stone-press, and the combined iron lever-press. Of the lever-press the varieties are most numerous, passing from the single lever, through the various combinations of simple levers, to the more elaborate one of the rack and levers. An essential characteristic of the rack-and-lever press is that the load, when left to itself, has the power to descend after the cheese which is pressed, and which sinks as the whey from the curd is expelled. None but these lever-presses should be used in any dairy. 2689.

The large churn, moved by power in extensive dairies, may be like the box-churn or the common-plunge churn. Fig. 257 with a double plunge churn, moved by power, as fitted up and used in Renfrewshire, is a view in perspective of the horse-course and churning-room, which is more clearly shown by removing a portion of the wall that separates them. The power in this case is 1 horse. Where are a thrashing-machine, straw-cutters, and bruising - machine along with the churn, a steam-engine would be an economical power. 2696.

Fig. 257

Plunge-churns with power.

a Swing-tree for horse.
a b Lever.
c Pit for bevelled-wheel.
d Lying shaft.
f Reciprocating lever.
g Connecting-rod.
h Oblique groove.
k Fly-wheel.
l Light shears.
i 2 plunge-churns.

Fig. 258

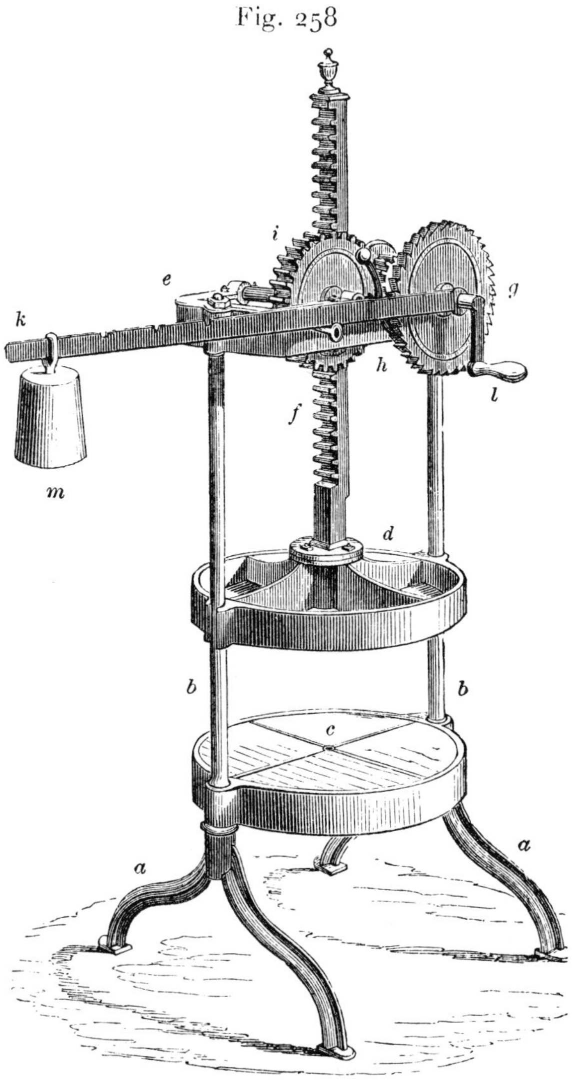

Combined lever cheese-press.

a a Pair of cast-iron feet.
b b Malleable-iron pillars.
c Lower fixed sill-plate.
d Upper movable sill.
f Rack-bar fixed to movable sill.
e Top frame.
g Ratchet-wheel.
i Wheel on the top frame.
k Lever.
l Winch-handle.
h Pin supporting lever.
m Weight on lever.

Fig. 259

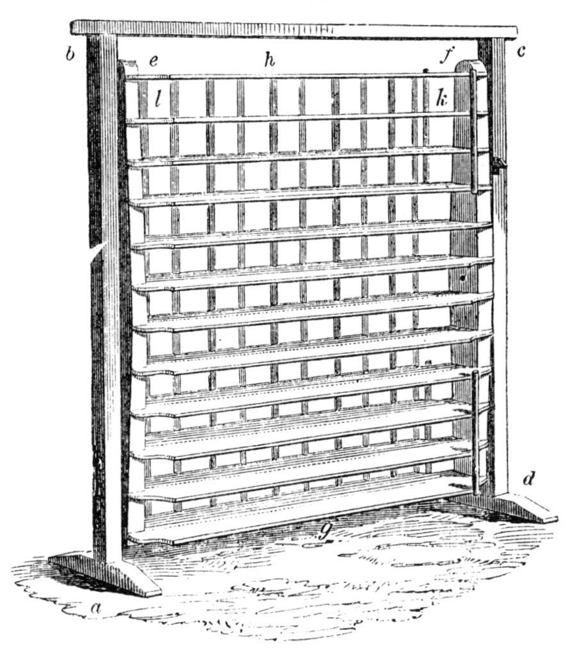

Cheese-turner.

a b c d External frame.
a b, c d Outer posts of frame.
a, d Cross - foot of outer post.
b c Top-rail.
e f 2 interior posts.
h to *g* 12 shelves.
k Vertical laths.
l Knife-edged laths.

The *tumbling cheese-rack*, or *cheese-turner*, is a machine invented by William Blurton of Fieldhall, Uttoxeter, and its merits are sufficient to warrant its adoption on dairy farms. The object of the rack is to save much of the labour required in the daily turning of a large number of cheeses in the drying-room; and this it does very effectually, for with a rack containing 50 cheeses they are turned over in very little more time than would be required to turn a single cheese. 2697.

Autumn

Some curious anomalies in farm labour occur in autumn. One is sowing a new crop of wheat, while the matured one of the same grain is being reaped; another, that while spring is the natural season for the reproduction of animals, autumn is that for the reproduction of sheep, the most valuable animal of the farm. 2756.

REAPING WHEAT, BARLEY, OATS AND RYE.

All kinds of corn are cut down either by 2 very simple implements, the sickle and scythe, or by reaping-machines. Reapers provide their own sickles, but scythes are furnished to the mowers by the farmer. The arrangement of the reapers in the field is different when using these implements and machines. The oldest implement is the sickle, the next oldest the scythe, and the newest the reaping-machine. I shall describe them in this order. 2823.

The *sickle* is a very efficient implement. Its varieties are confined to 2 very distinct forms, the *toothed* and the *smooth-edged* sickle. Fig. 260 is the *toothed* sickle, an implement having a blade of iron, with an edging of steel; the teeth are formed by striking with a chisel and hammer, in the manner of file-cutting, the cutting being only on the lower side; but when the blade has been bent to the proper form, tempered, and ground on the smooth side, the serratures are brought prominently out on the edge of the blade; and as the striking of the teeth is performed in a position oblique to the edge of the blade, at an angle of about 70°, the serratures on the edge acquire what is called a *hook* towards the helve, thus causing the instrument to cut keenly in that direction when drawn through the standing corn. When the blade has been thus finished, a wooden helve of the simplest form is fitted upon the pointed tine at its root. The toothed sickle is made

Fig. 260

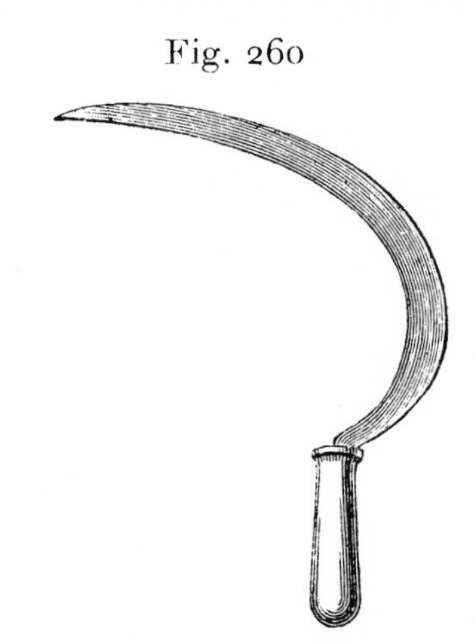

Toothed sickle.

with various degrees of curvature and weight, but chiefly as represented in the figure; and it has been the subject of several patents, chiefly depending on the formation of the blade. One of these is now of some years' standing, and is an important one. Sorby & Son of Sheffield are the patentees, and the principle upon which their patent is based is a blade of rolled cast-steel swedged into a form that gives a sufficient degree of stiffness to the blade, without the increase of weight that accompanies the thick-backed or the other patent ribbed-back sickles.

In the new patent, the advantage of a small quantity of the very best material—cast-steel—is combined with extreme lightness and a due degree of strength and stiffness, the latter arising from the swedge or moulded back. The toothed sickle cannot cut straw until the straw is held firm, either directly by the hand, or against a handful of cut corn. Its proper use, therefore, is to cut the corn in small portions at a time. It requires no sharping, and occasions no cessation of work. In the formation of the sickle, the curvature of the blade is a point of more importance than to a careless observer may appear; and though the ordinary reaper is seldom qualified to judge in this matter, he may feel pleased to be informed that there is a certain curvature that will give to the muscles of his right arm the least possible cause for exertion, while there are other curves that, if given to the blade of the sickle, would cause him to expend a great amount of unnecessary exertion in the arm, and a consequent unnecessary fatigue would follow. Fig. 261 is the large, *smooth-edged* sickle, hav-

Fig. 261

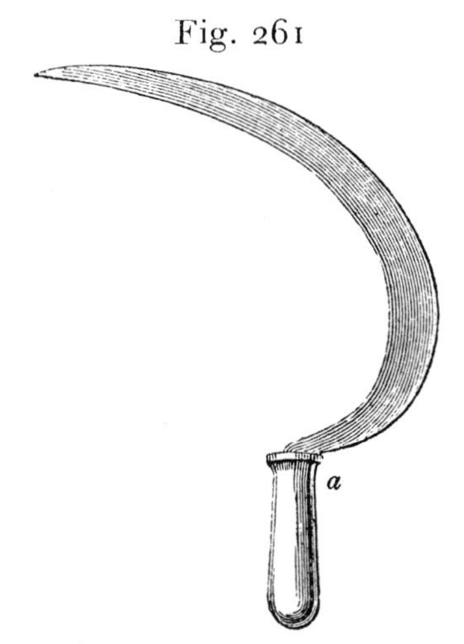

Large smooth-edged sickle.
a Centre of the handle of the sickle.

ing a curvature approaching very near to that which, in this implement, may be termed the *curve of least exertion;* and throughout that portion of the sickle which performs the cutting process, it possesses this peculiar property from the following circumstance, that lines diverging from the centre of the handle of the sickle, and intersecting the curve of the cutting edge, all the diverging lines will form equal angles with the tangents to the curve at the points of intersection. This property gives to the cutting edge a uniform tendency to cut at every point in its length without any other exertion than a direct *pull* upon the helve. Were the curvature less at any point, a pressure of the hand would be required to keep the edge to the work; and were the curvature greater at any point, or on the whole, the exertion to make the cut would be greater, as it would then become more direct, instead of the oblique drawing or *sawing* cut, which in all cases is the most effective, and productive of least resistance. This sickle is broader in the blade than the toothed kind, though in curvature it resembles it; and the chief difference lies in being ground on both sides, to form a fine and thin sharp edge. This edge is kept keen by means of a fine-grained sandstone, like a scythe-stone, 6 inches long and 1 inch square, and it is only used on the under or rounded side of the sickle. Some reapers fasten a narrow strap of leather along the handle of the sickle, in order that it may pass in an oblique direction across the back of the hand, with the view to assist the *draw* of the implement through the straws of the grain; but if the sickle be kept sharp, which every reaper ought to be able to do, such a strap is rather an encumbrance than assistance to the reaper. The sharp edge of this sickle will cut through straw with a stroke, although the straw be not held by the hand. From this circumstance it may be supposed that this is a much easier implement to cut with than the toothed sickle; and so it really is, but the dexterous use of either implement depends altogether on habit and practice. 2824.

There are various arrangements of harvest-work in which the sickle is used, 1 of which is the *bandwin* method. A bandwin of reapers consists of 7 persons divided into 3 reapers on each of 2 ridges, and 1 bandster for both ridges. The bandster must be a man, a woman not being able for the work of binding sheaves. The reapers may all be men, or all women, women being able to cut as much corn as men; but the best distribution of men and women in a bandwin is 1 man and 2 women on each ridge. The man in the centre makes the band for the sheaves, and cuts as much corn as he can, the women constantly cutting and laying the corn into the bands. The reason for this bandwin arrangement is, that 1 man can bind the corn cut by 6 reapers, and 6 reapers can reap 2 acres in 1 day. 2827.

Fig. 262

Reapers in a bandwin.

f a e First ridge in bandwin.
d c g Second ridge in bandwin.
a Man making a band.
b Band laid down.
c Man reaping.
d Leading reaper on second ridge.
e Reaper clearing the furrow of corn, leaning on the right leg.
f Leading reaper on first ridge, leaning on the left leg.
g Reaper going to lay sheaf on band.
h Sheaf ready for binding.
i First 2 sheaves of stook.
k Bandster and stooker carrying sheaves to stook.
l Provisions.

As every 2 sheaves are bound, they are set up as an isosceles triangle, and 8 or more sheaves are set up to make a stook, fig. 263. All kinds of corn are stooked in this form, for quickly winning the corn for the stack. When the weather is likely to continue good, this mode of stooking is preferred, especially now, when few weeds are allowed to grow amongst the corn, and the stooks stand in the field for only a short time. Nevertheless in wet, and even damp weather, and in high situations, corn would be too much exposed in such stooks, so that others which afford greater security against the weather should be used. One such other is in fig. 264, where 2 first sheaves are set opposite to each other in the centre of the stook, then the 2d pair of sheaves are set opposite each other, then the 3d pair, then the 4th pair, then the 5th pair, and last of all the hood-sheaves are set. Each pair of sheaves stands independently of the others, the entire pairs constituting the body of a

Fig. 263

Ordinary stook of wheat.

Fig. 264

Barley or oat stook hooded.

a First 2 sheaves set. *d d* Fourth 2 sheaves set.
b Second 2 sheaves set. *e* Fifth 2 sheaves set.
c Third 2 sheaves set. *f* Hood sheaves set.

stook containing 10 sheaves standing upright. 2831.

The proper size of sheaf is ascertained by a *sheaf-gauge*, fig. 265. This implement is carried in the hand by the steward, who does not gauge every sheaf as it is bound, and before it is stooked, but only those which seem to him too small, and which his eye easily detects after a little experience—and there is little fear of any being too large. 2833.

Fig. 265

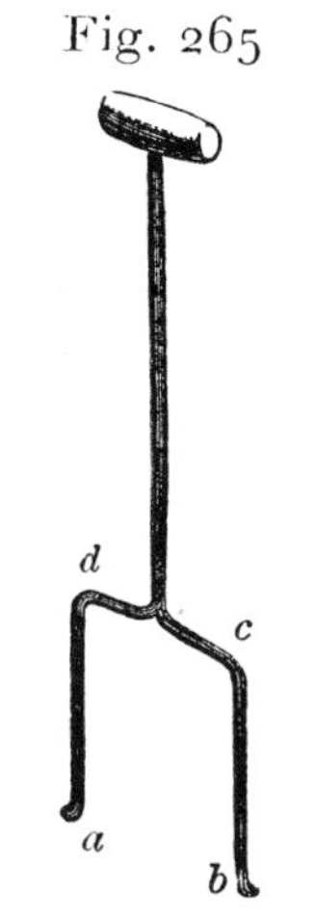

Sheaf-gauge.

a b c d Prong of gauge.
a b Points of prong.
c d Upper part of prong.

A mode of setting up corn to dry quickly is in *gaitins*—that is, the band of the sheaf is tied loosely round the straw, just under the corn, fig. 266, and the lower part of the sheaf is made to stand by spreading out the straw's end in a circular form. Gaitins are set by the bandster upon every ridge; the wind whistles and the rain passes through them. Gaiting is only practised in wet weather, and even then only when a ripe crop is endangered in standing by a shaking wind. It is confined to oats, 2848.

Fig. 266

Gaitin of oats.

a Band loosely tied. *b* to *c* Base of sheaf spread out.

The Hainault or Flemish scythe may be regarded as an intermediate implement between the sickle and the cradle-scythe. It is held in the right hand by a handle 14 inches long, supported by the forefinger, in a leather loop. The blade, 2 feet 3 inches in length, is kept steady in a horizontal position by a flat and projecting part of the handle, 4½ inches long,

Fig. 267

Reaping with the Hainault scythe.

acting as a shield against the lower part of the wrist. The point of the blade is a little raised, and the entire edge bevelled upwards to avoid striking the surface of the ground. On this account the sharping-stone is seldom used; the handle of the hook, being of hard wood, is used as a strickle. 2839.

Another mode of cutting corn is with the *scythe*. Scythes are mounted in various ways for reaping, and for a considerable time have been mounted in Banffshire or Aberdeenshire in the form of the *cradle-scythe*. Of this form of mounting there are many varieties; but they all agree in 1 point, that of having 2 short helves, the one branching out of the other, instead of 1 common long helve or sned. Fig. 268 is a view of the cradle-scythe in its most approved form, wherein the scythe-blade is 3 feet 4 inches to 3 feet 6 inches long; the principal helve is 4 feet in length, to which the blade is attached in the usual way, the hook of the tine being sunk into the wood, and

Fig. 268

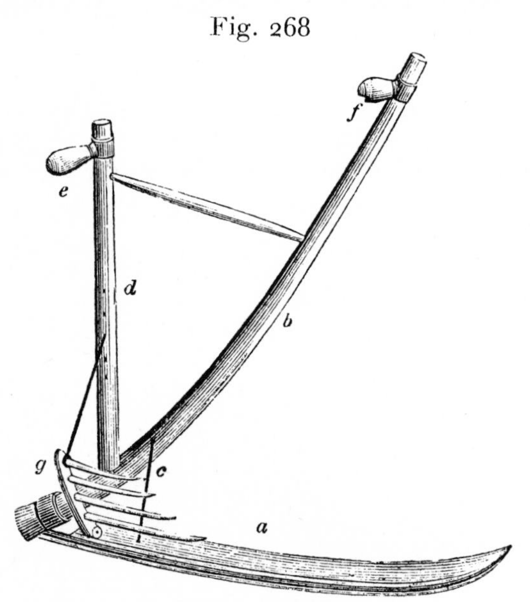

Cradle-scythe for reaping.

a Scythe-blade.
b Principal or left helve.
d Minor or right helve.
c Grass-nail.
e Right-hand handle.
f Left-hand handle.
g Cradle or rake with its stay.

an iron ferule brought down over the tine, binding it firmly to the wood; but the blade is further supported by the addition of the light stay, the *grass-nail*.

The *cradle* or rake consists of a little wooden standard, about 8 inches high, jointed to the heel of the blade, so as to fold a little up or down across the blade. Into this is inserted 3 or 4 slender teeth, following the direction of the blade, and may be from 6 to 15 inches long: the head of the standard is supported by a slender rod of iron, which stretches about 18 inches up the handle, where it is secured by a small screw-nut capable of being shifted up or down to alter the position of the standard and its teeth to suit the lay of the corn. 2840.

Fig. 269

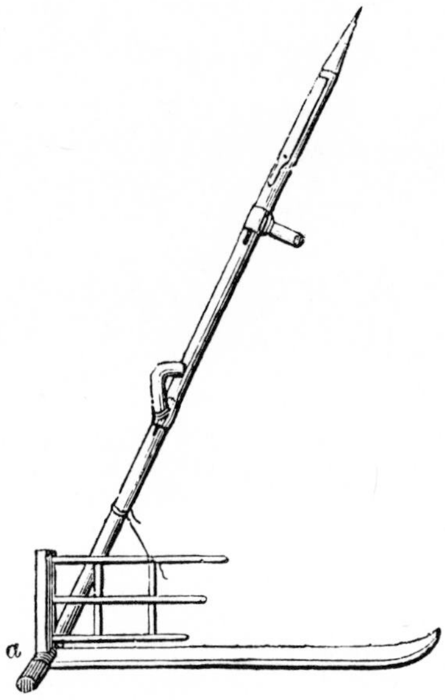

Common reaping-scythe.
a Cradle.

Fig. 270

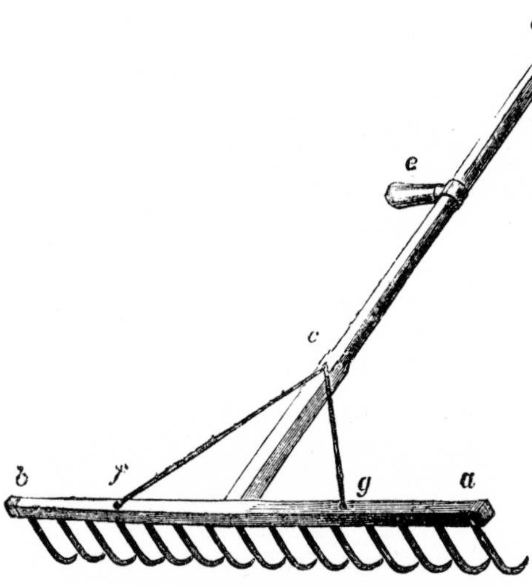

Hand stubble-rake.

a b Head of rake.
c d Helve.
e Handle.
f c g Iron braces.

Reaping with the scythe is best executed by the mowers being placed in *heads*—namely, 1 head of 3 scythemen, 3 gatherers, 3 bandsters, and 1 man-raker; or, what may be regarded as good an arrangement, 1 head of 2 scythemen, 2 gatherers, 2 bandsters, and 1 woman-raker. A number of heads on the second arrangement may be employed on a large farm, while a small farm may employ 1 head on the first arrangement. The best beginning of scythe-reaping a field is to mow the ridges parallel with the fences from the top to the bottom, or from the bottom to the top, as the corn happens to be laid; and if not laid, with the inclination of the corn by the wind. After this, both the head-ridges should be mown in the direction of the wind. Both acts can be done at once with 2 heads of mowers. Thus the 4 sides of the field are opened up, leaving angles of the standing corn to commence future operations across the ridges. Every head should be conducted by an experienced and steady mower. The mowing is conducted across the ridges, as the scythes go most easily across the open furrows, laying the corn in swathes at right angles to the line of motion, over 6 ridges or 30 yards, which is as far as scythes will cut at 1 sharping. 2842.

Fig. 271

Mowing corn with the scythe.

a a a Swathes of corn.
b b b 3 mowers.
c c c 3 gatherers.
d d Open sheaves.
e Bandster binding a sheaf.
f f Bandsters setting a stook.
g Stook.
h Man raker.
i Hand stubble-rake.
k Bound sheaf.

A third mode of reaping is with a *machine*. Reaping-machines are worked by the power of horses. Those which have received the assent of farmers are constructed on 2 principles. One when the machine is pushed forward by the horse propelling from behind, which is done in Bell's machine, a Scotch invention. It has the advantage of clearing its way into any field of corn, but it is heavy, and the horses are not easily guided by the driver, who is obliged to be on foot. In the other principle, horses draw the machine. This principle is exemplified with 2 modifications—one is M'Cormick's, whose machine lays the swathe of corn aside as the work goes on; the other is Hussey's, which leaves the swathe immediately behind it. Both these machines are American inventions, and were first made known to this country at the International Exhibition of London in 1851. Neither of these machines can open a way for itself in a corn-field as Bell's, but must have an opening made for it. M'Cormick's, made in this country by Burgess & Key, can cut the corn continuously round the field without stopping, as it lays the swathe out of its way; while Hussey's, made in this country by Dray, lays the swathe in the way behind it, which must be removed before the

Fig. 272

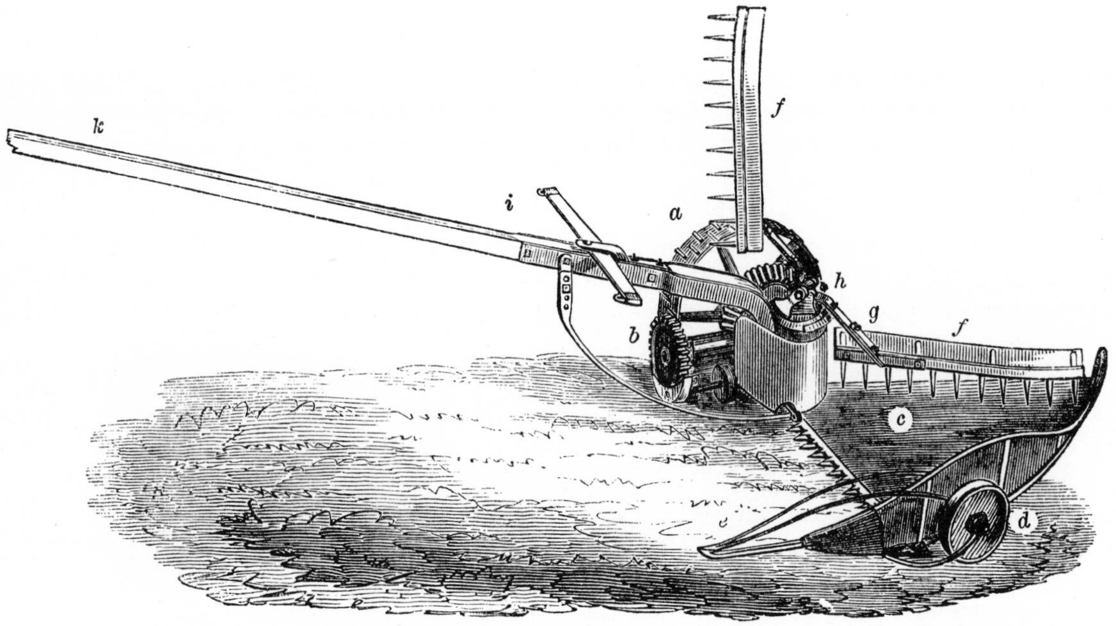

Brigham & Bickerton's sheaf-delivery reaper.

a Driving-wheel.
b Gearing, fenced from the corn by a curved iron rod.
c Platform.
d Supporting wheel.
e Iron guide-rods.
f f Rakes.
g Bar and axle of rake-arms.
h Revolving vertical spindle.
i Swing - bar for yoking horses.
k Pole between the 2 horses.

Fig. 273

Brigham & Bickerton's sheaf-delivery reaper at work.

a a Standing corn.
b Reaper at work.
c Sheaf of corn as delivered by the reaper being taken up by a field-worker.
d Band for receiving the cut sheaf.
e Bandster making a stook.

machine can go on with its next swathe. On this account I would not use Hussey's machine in preference to M'Cormick's, but as it is simple in construction and low-priced, it is employed by many farmers. The principle of M'Cormick's machine is what might be recommended, although it is rather complex and high-priced. All 3 machines cut the crop well, lay the swathes regularly, clip the straw with shears, are propelled by 2 horses, and, except Bell's, afford a seat to their driver. Of M'Cormick's principle, the best modification I have seen is made by Brigham & Bickerton at Berwick-upon-Tweed. It not only cuts clean and lays the swathe aside, but lays it divided into portions fit for making into sheaves, and is thereby called sheaf-delivery reaper. Fig. 272 is a perspective of this small compact reaping-machine, which as yet attains the object of its work nearer than any I have seen. 2847.

STACKING WHEAT, BARLEY, OATS, BEANS, AND PEAS.

While the first reaped-corn is winning in the field, the stackyard should be put in order to receive the new crop by removing everything that ought not to be in it.

The tops or frames should be put on the tilt-carts: the corn-carts should be put on their wheels and the axles greased; and the ropes should be attached to the carts. 2889.

The tops or frames for placing upon tilt-carts are a light rectangular piece of framework, fig. 274, where are 2 main bearers, fitted to lie across the shelvements of the cart; the foremost is slightly notched, and the hindmost rests against the backboard of the cart, the top sides of which being first taken off; 1 pair of slight side-rails is applied on each side, crossing the bearers, and notched upon and bolted to them with screw-bolts, these being crossed by 2 rails behind, and by 3 more in front; and as these last project over the back of the horse, they are made in arch form, fig. 274, to give freedom to his motions. The extreme length, from outside to outside of the front and back-rails, is usually about 10½ feet, and the breadth in the same manner is about 7¼ feet, affording a superficial area for the support of the sheaves of corn of 76 square feet. A simple and effective method of securing the frame to the cart

Fig. 274

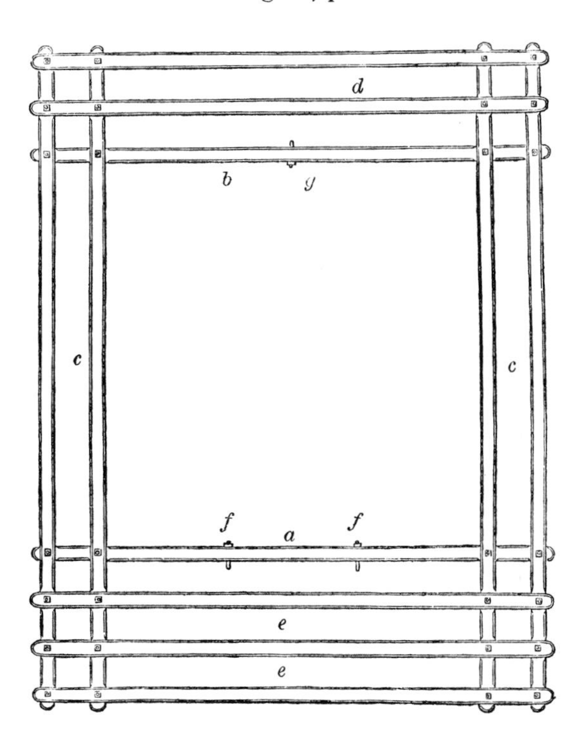

Corn and hay cart tops or frame.

a Foremost main bearer.
b Hindmost main bearer.
c c Pairs of slight side-rails.
d 2 hind cross-rails.
e e 3 arched fore cross-rails.
f f Bolts through rail in front of cart.
g Bolt through rail on backboard of cart.

is by means of the bolts in the bearers, the front ones passing through the head-rail of the front of the cart, and the hind one through the top-rail of the tail-board.

Fig. 275

Common corn and hay cart.

a a Shafts of Baltic fir. *b b* Cross-heads. *c c* Oak standards. *d d, d d* Inner top-rails. *e* Broad load-tree. *f f, f f* Outer rails, front and rear.

But the common corn or hay cart is a more convenient and efficient vehicle for carrying the corn crops into the stack-yard than the tilt-cart with the frame, inasmuch as the load is more on a level with the horse-draught, and, the body being dormant, the load is not liable to shake with the motion of the horse. Fig. 275 is a perspective view of such a cart. Lightness being an object in its construction, the shafts are usually made of Baltic fir, and are about 17 feet in length, of which 6½ feet go for the horse-yoke and 10½ feet for the body, measuring over the cross-heads. These are secured to the shafts by iron standards passing through them and the shafts. Their sides are supported by oak standards; and these in their turn, along with the iron standards, support the inner top-rails, 12 feet in length, and the broad load-tree. The outer rails, also 12 feet long, are supported by iron standards resting on the extremities of the cross-heads, and also by those of the broad load-tree. The extreme breadth of the outer rails is 7 feet, and as the outer rails support the sheaves of corn over the wheels, and are 12 feet in length, the superficial area of the cart for the load is 84 square feet, which is greater than that of the top-frame of the tilt-cart. The 2 front cross-rails over the horse's rump are arched, to give him freedom of motion. The body is usually close-floored, besides having a low ledge-board running inside the standards to keep in the corn that may have shaken out of the sheaves. Corn-carts are not furnished with wheels of their own, the body being set upon those belonging to the tilt-carts. The broad load-tree, 9 inches broad, is convenient to sit upon in driving, and to stand upon when forking the sheaves in unloading. The cart weighs 8 cwt. It is easily converted into a *dray-cart* by simply removing the framework, which should then have the standards based upon 2 longitudinal rails, instead of being mortised into the shafts. In such a form it is eminently useful in carrying large timber.

2891

A corn and hay cart, simple in construction, but possessing complete efficiency, and greater safety from upsetting than the former—a useful property in a petty farm—was contrived by a farm-servant, Robert Robertson, and was introduced in 1832 in the W. of Fifeshire, and of which fig. 276 is a view in perspective, with its wheels and axle in full working order. 2892.

Fig. 276

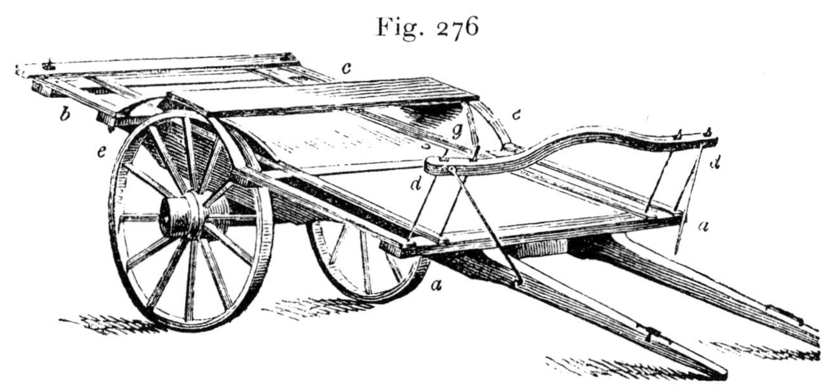

Robertson's corn and hay cart.

a a Fore cross-heads.
b Back cross-heads.
c Broad load-tree.
d d Light frame.
e e Arched iron bars.
g Side-boards.

The loads of corn and hay on the carts are fastened with *ropes*, which should be made of the best hemp, soft and pliable. Ropes are either single or double, and both are required on the farm. Double cart-ropes are from 30 to 24 yards long, and single ones ½ those lengths. 2894.

Fig. 277

Coiled-up cart-rope.

Fig. 278

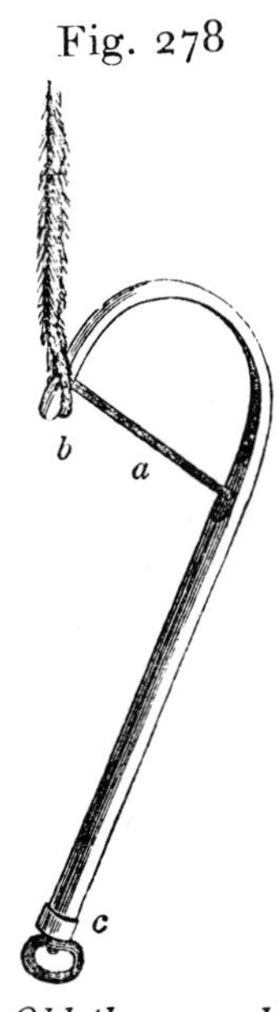

Old throw-crook.

a Iron stay.
b Projection for end of rope.
c Ferule and swivel ring.
c b Line of direction of rope.

Fig 279

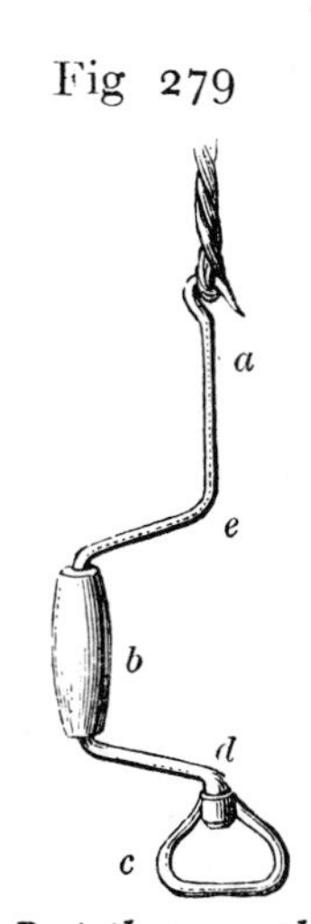

Best throw-crook.

a Hook, and
a e d Curved spindle of iron.
b Perforated cylindrical handle of wood.
c Swivel-ring.
e b d Curved part of iron spindle.

[*Throw crooks, in England straw twisters, used to make ropes for corn stacks.*]

Fig. 280

Straw-rope spinner.

a a Sole-frame.
b Post tenoned into the sole.
c d Cross head-case.
e e e 3 hooks.
f Winch-handle.

Straw is twisted into *ropes* by a throw-crook, fig. 281, in this manner: The left hand of the twister, a field-work-

Fig. 281

Making a straw-rope with a throw-crook.

er, holds by the swivel-ring, fig. 279. Her right hand grasps the hollow cylinder of wood. On the spinner, a man, sitting on a stool or a bundle of straw, placing a little drawn straw in the hook, the twister causes the hook to revolve round an axis, while walking backwards along a path swept clean, in a shed or the stable. The spinner, nearly closing the left hand, lets out the straw gradually between the thumb and the fingers, retaining it till sufficiently twisted, while the right hand is engaged supplying small portions of straw in equal and sufficient quantities to make the rope uniform in thickness throughout and strong enough, the twister drawing away the rope as fast as the spinner lets it out. 2896.

Fig. 282

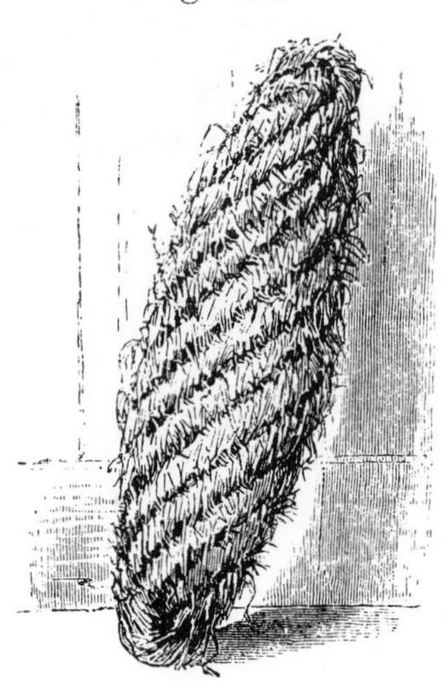

Coil of straw-rope.

When stacks are built upon the ground, stools of loose straw are made to prevent the sheaves at the bottom receiving injury from the dampness of the ground.

Fig. 283

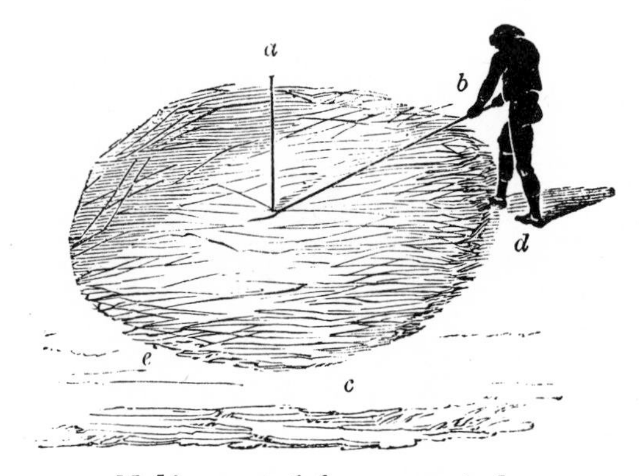

Making a stool for a corn-stack.

a Fork stuck into the ground.
b Fork 7½ feet long.
d Man making the circle of stool with his feet.
e c d Circle of stool 15 feet in diameter.

In setting a loaded cart to a stack, the carter should take advantage of the wind in forking the sheaves from the cart. The *stack* should be *built* in this way: Set up a couple of sheaves leaning on each other in the centre of the stathel, and another couple against their sides. Place other sheaves against these in rows round the centre, with a slope towards the circumference of the stathel, each row being placed half the length of the sheaf beyond the inner one, till the circumference is completed, when it should be examined; and where any sheaf presses too hard upon another, it should be relieved, and where a slackness is found, a sheaf should be introduced. Keeping the circumference of the stack on the left hand, the stacker lays the sheaves upon the outside row round the stack, placing each sheaf with his hands upon the hollow or intermediate space between 2 of the sheaves laid in the preceding row, close to the last one, and pressing it with both his knees, fig. 284. When the outside row is thus laid, an inside row is made with sheaves whose butt-ends rest on the bands of the outside row, thereby securing the outside sheaves in their places, and at the same time filling up the body of the stack firmly with sheaves. A few more sheaves may be required as an inmost row, to raise the heart of the stack at its highest part. 2905.

Fig. 285

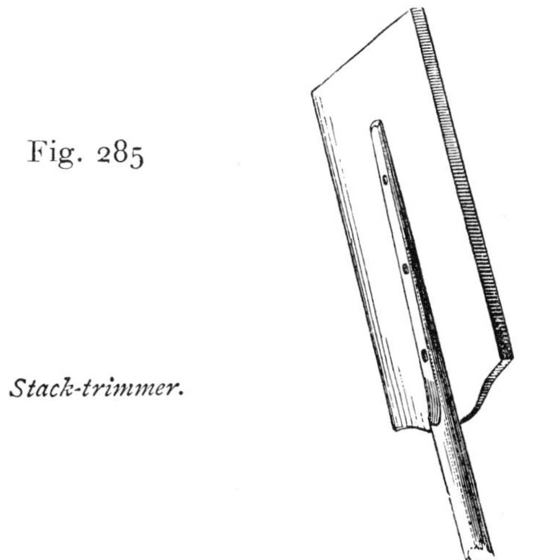

Stack-trimmer.

Fig. 284

Building a stack of corn.

e Loaded cart of corn alongside a stack.
f g Sheaves of corn with their butt-ends outwards.
m Carter forking up a sheaf.
k Field-worker receiving the sheaf with a fork.
h Stacker kneeling on the outside row of sheaves.
i Sheaves of the inside row.
l Sheaf placed most conveniently by the field-worker for the stacker.

Seldom is leisure found to *thatch* stacks as long as there is corn to carry

Fig. 286

Lozenge mode of roping the covering of a corn-stack.

a Apex or ornamental top.
e f First rope for securing the apex in its position.
f g Second rope for farther securing the apex in its position.
h Last rope on that side of the stack.
i Last rope on the opposite side of the stack.
l Eave of thatch.
l k Eave-rope.
c d Diameter of the stack, 15 feet.

in, and finer the weather less the leisure. A damp day, however, which prevents carrying, answers well for thatching, as thatch straw is not the worse of being a little damp; but in heavy rain it is improper to thatch and cover up the wet ends of sheaves. The materials for thatching should all be at hand before commencing —drawn bunches of straw, coils of straw-ropes, ladders, forks, hand-rakes, and graips. To get on with the business quickly, 1 man and 2 assistants are required for each stack—the most thrifty assistants being field-workers, to supply the thatcher with straw and ropes, and tie the ends of the ropes. 2906.

Fig. 287

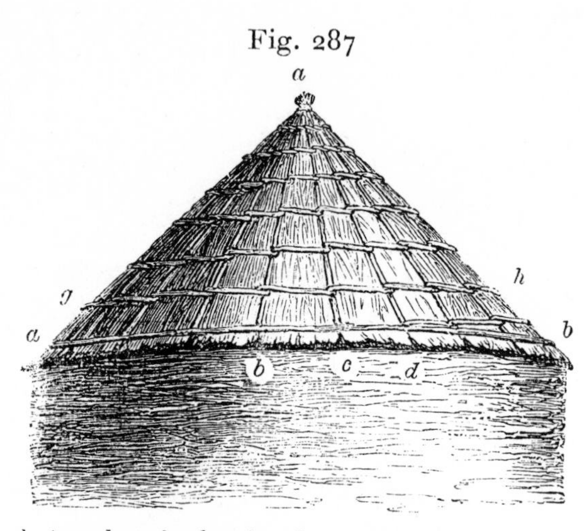

Net-mesh mode of roping the covering of a corn-stack.

a Top or rosette.
a b, a c, a d Form of triangles on the thatch.
a to *d* is the spiral rope round the top, from the top to the eave.
g h are ropes round the top parallel to the eave.

Fig. 288

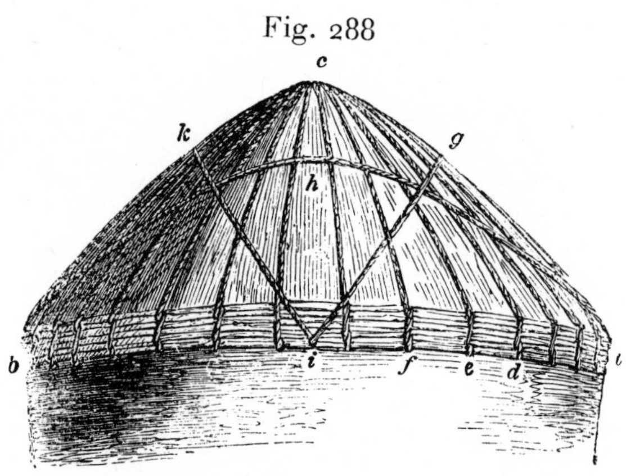

Border mode of roping the covering of a corn-stack.

c Crown of stack, upon which the thatcher stands.
c b to *c a* Ropes passing over the crown of the stack.
f e d Ends of ropes fastened to the eave-rope.
a b Band of rope-ends round the stack.
h, i k, i g Strap-ropes quartering the top of the stack.

BATHING AND SMEARING SHEEP.

Immediately after the tups are put to the ewes, part of the sheep stock is prepared for fattening on turnips, and the preparation is bathing them with, or in, a particular liquid. Sheep are affected by a troublesome insect—the ked, or sheep-tick—which increases in numbers as the wool grows, and becomes troublesome to sheep in autumn; and were means not taken to remove it, the sheep would rub themselves on every object they could find, and tear their fleece, and deteriorate its value. Another reason for bathing sheep is, cutaneous eruptions are apt to appear on the skin on a change of food from grass to turnips, which deteriorate the fleece even more than the rubbing occasioned by the ked. In severe cases of scab, bathing is too mild an application. 2958.

Fig. 289

Bath-jug.

Fig. 290

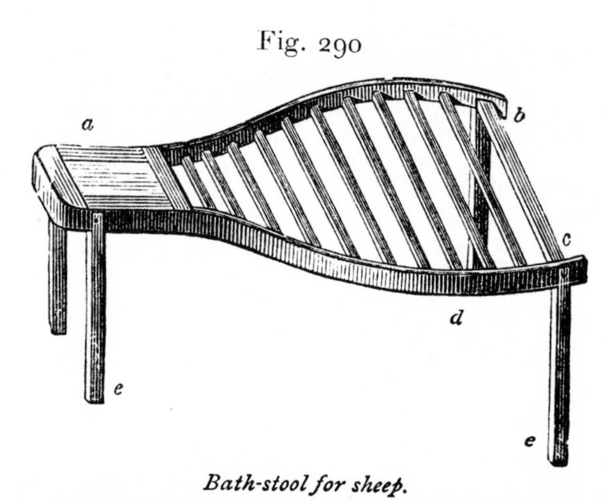

Bath-stool for sheep.

a Seat for shepherd.
a b, a c Sparred frame.
d Widest part of frame.
e e Feet.

The materials used for the *bath* are tobacco, spirit of tar, soft soap, and sulphur. The tobacco is best in the state of leaf, but I understand it is illegal for tobacconists to sell it in that state. 2959.

The shepherd and his assistant will bath 40 large sheep in 1 day. The bathed sheep are put on the right into a different pen from the unbathed. Fig. 291 shows the tub of tobacco liquor, the quart measure, the greybeard containing the spirit of tar, and the wine-glass, all at hand, the faithful collies waiting for employment. 2960.

Fig. 291

Bathing sheep.

Instead of bathing sheep in this manner, it has been recommended to dip them bodily in tubs containing a bath-liquor. It is evident that any liquid, to be applied with certainty to the entire body of the sheep through its wool, must be as limpid as water; and hence all dipping compositions are dissolved in large quantities of water. A solution of corrosive sublimate will easily kill keds and harden the skin, and it is as limpid as water. Bigg's well-known sheep-dipping composition is sold at 9d. per lb., or in casks of 100 lb., sufficient to dip 500 sheep, for £3, 10s., which is rather more than 1½ per sheep, and is thus a cheap application. W. Reed's, Granton, sheep-dip does not discolour the wool, which is always an advantage. Many other sheep-dipping mixtures are advertised, of which I have no particular knowledge, but I would employ none that had arsenic in it. It has been proved in evidence that the dripping from bathed sheep had so poisoned the grass it had fallen upon as to kill the sheep which had grazed upon it. 2963.

Fig. 292

Wilson's sheep-dipping apparatus.

LIFTING AND STORING POTATOES.

Two modes are followed in lifting potatoes — one with the plough, and the other with the hand by means of the potato-graip. The plough is the most expeditious means, though the ground is most thoroughly cleared and pulverised by the graip. 2970.

A modification of the plough for taking up potatoes was made by J. Lawson of Elgin. It consists of 6 malleable-iron bars, fig. 293, the outer ones ⅝ of an inch square, the inner ones ½ inch in diameter, joined together in the form of a brander, 26 inches long, 5 inches in breadth at the fore part, where is a plate of iron. The openings between the rods will thus be rather more than 3 inches at the widest end of the brander. This brander is attached to the right side of

Fig. 293

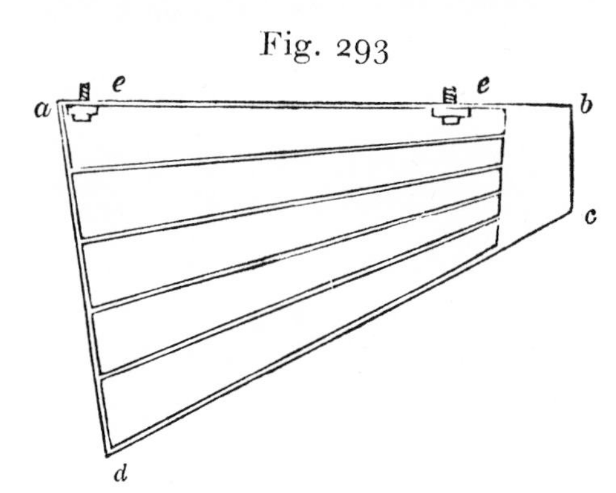

Potato raiser or brander.

a to *b* Brander, 26 inches long.
b to *c* 5 inches broad, with a plate of iron.
c to *d* 27 inches long.
a to *d* 18 inches broad.
e e Screws.

Fig. 294

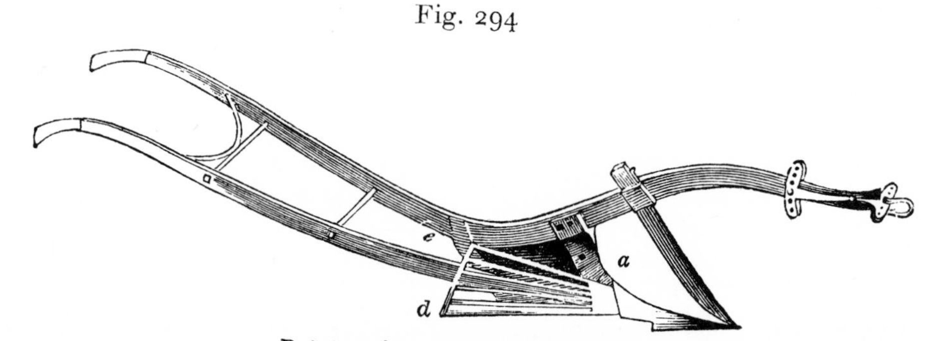

Potato-raiser attached to a plough.

a Narrow end of brander. *e* Upper angle of brander. *d* Lower angle of brander.

the head and stilt of a plough, in lieu of the mould-board, by screws, the fore end being placed close behind the sock, fig. 294, which shows the plough mounted with the brander, having its upper angle 8 inches, and the plane of its face so bent down as to have the lower angle only 4 inches above the sole of the plough. The mode of operation of the brander is, that while the earth partly passes through it, and is partly pushed aside by it, the potatoes are left exposed upon the surface of the ground on the right hand of the ploughman. 2971.

When potatoes are taken up by manual labour, it is done by means of the *potato-graip*, fig. 295, the prongs of which are flattened. To use this graip effectually being rather severe work, men are employed to lift the potatoes with it, 1 man taking 1 drill close beside that of his fellow-workmen, while 2 gatherers, women, boys, or girls, to every man, pick up the potatoes as he turns them out of the ground, and put them into the baskets. 2972.

The object of *storing* potatoes is to place them beyond the reach of frost. No difficulty is found in doing so in the early part of winter, when the temperature is only low, and not frosty, and vegetation dormant. Potatoes may therefore be kept in almost any situation in the early part of winter; but if damp is allowed to reach them for a length of time, they will rot; and if the air finds access to them in winter, the frost will injure them, and if in early spring, vegetation will be awakened in them. To place them beyond the influence of the elements, they should be stored in a dry place, and closely covered up; and no mode affords both requisites as completely as ordinary dry soil. Fig. 296 gives the 2 ordinary forms of pits—1 conical, the other prismatic. The conical form is employed for pitting small quantities of potatoes, and is well adapted for small farms and cottars; the prismatic is used for storing large quantities. 2985.

Fig. 295

Fig. 296

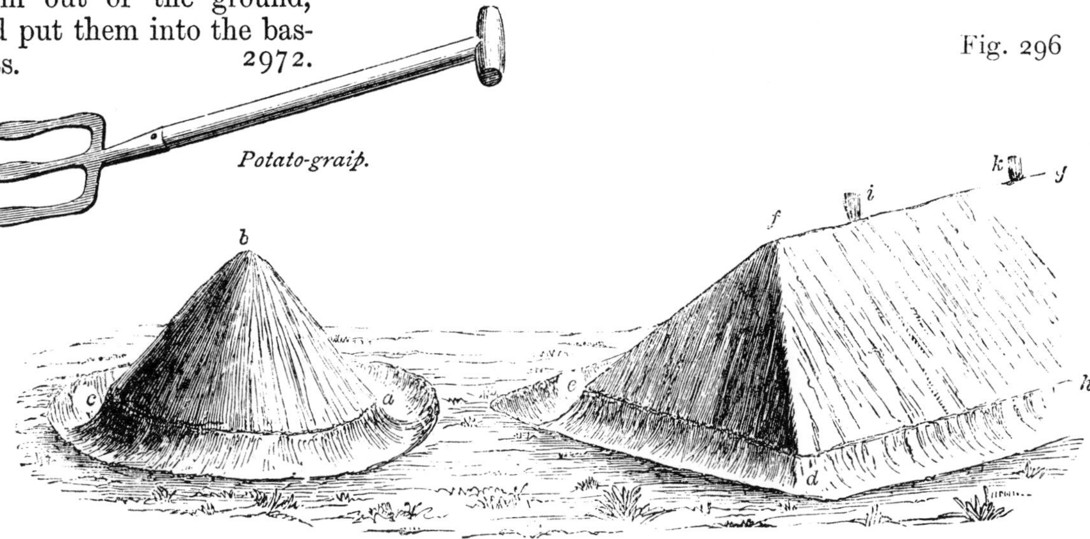

Potato-graip.

Conical and prismatic potato-pits.

a b c Conical pit of potatoes.
b Apex of cone.
c a Diameter of cone and inner edge of trench round the cone.

e d h g Prismatic potato-pit.
d h Side of pit.
d e End of pit.
f g Crest of pit.
i k Straw chimneys.

Realisation

Now that the pupil-farmer has acquired a competent knowledge of farming to conduct a farm on his own account, by having become acquainted with the entire routine of operations throughout the 4 seasons upon a mixed-husbandry farm under an intelligent farmer, and by having studied the instructions contained in the preceding pages, as a guide to anticipate the several operations as they succeed each other, the time has come to look out for a farm for himself. Before doing that, he will have to acquire a knowledge of subjects somewhat different from merely conducting a farm, and which are essential for him to know. These subjects are—to judge of land—to bargain for a lease—to provide stocking for the farm. On possessing the farm, he may have more to do than these. He may have to enclose and drain the farm, and to erect buildings upon it. He should know the correct principles upon which the breeding and rearing of the domesticated animals are founded. These particulars are as yet unknown to the pupil-farmer, but he must become acquainted with them; and he will now proceed to acquire them. 3178.

HEDGES.

Permanent fences of fields are constructed with 2 materials, hedges and low dry-stone walls. Hedges are made of thorns and whins in Scotland, and of various plants in England—thorns, beech, hornbeam, holly, privet, myrtle. Turf walls form the chief field-fences in Ireland. Of late years wire fences have been introduced as permanent, but from the nature of their materials they cannot be regarded as permanent in the sense of hedges and walls. Temporary fences are wooden palings, hurdles of iron and wood, nets, dead hedges. 3317.

Pruning well-grown young hedges consists of only 1 operation—*switching.* The first switching is cutting in prominent branches from the majority which constitute the body of the hedge, and of lopping off the leading shoots to a level line of top. This operation is performed with the switching-bill, fig. 297, which has a curved blade 9 inches long, and 1½ inch broad; a helve 2 feet 3 inches in length; and its weight altogether is about 2½ lb. It feels light in the hand, and is used with an upward stroke, slanting backwards nearly overhead. Hedgers have a strong predilection for the use of the switching-bill. They will, without compunction, switch a young hedge at the end of its first year's existence. 3336.

Fig. 297

Switching-bill.

Allowing a young hedge to grow at liberty for 4 years, and after its first switching, which is merely a trimming, the hedge should be switched so as to assume its ultimate form. The form that is best suited for field-fences is an isosceles triangle, with a sharp apex and 2 equally inclining faces. 3337.

Fig. 298

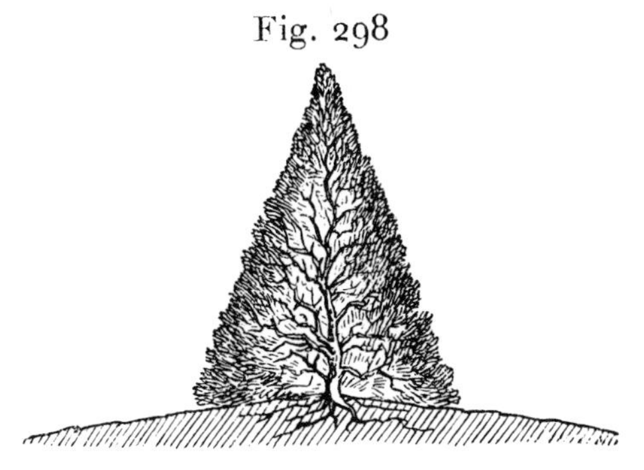

Triangular form of thorn hedge.

Fig. 300

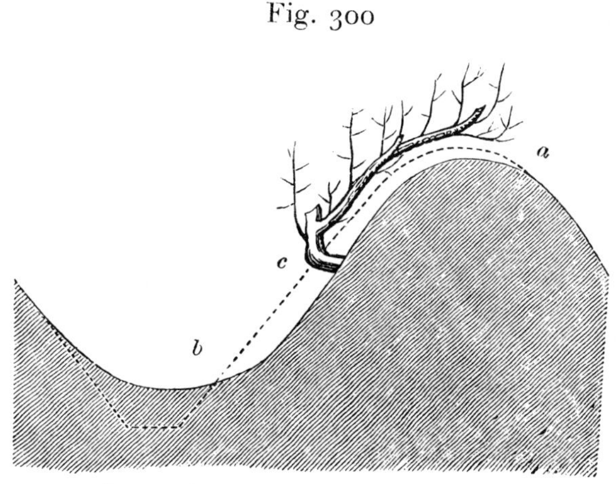

Breasted thorn hedge on bank and ditch.
a Top of hedge bank. *b* Bottom of ditch.
c Main stem cut through.

Fig. 299

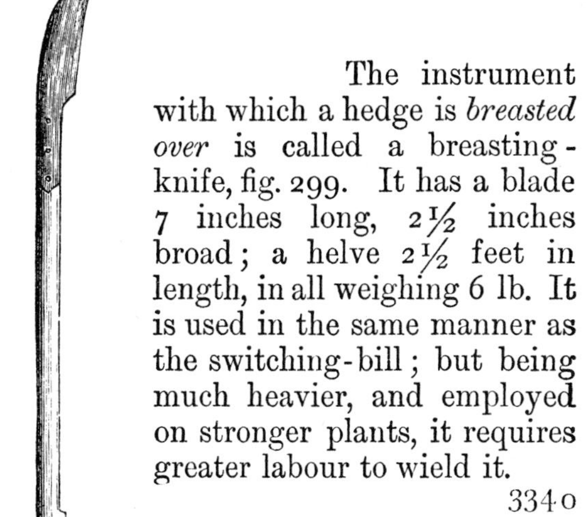

The instrument with which a hedge is *breasted over* is called a breasting-knife, fig. 299. It has a blade 7 inches long, 2½ inches broad; a helve 2½ feet in length, in all weighing 6 lb. It is used in the same manner as the switching-bill; but being much heavier, and employed on stronger plants, it requires greater labour to wield it.
3340

Breasting-knife.

[*Breasting is cutting an overgrown hedge to about 2 feet to encourage near growth. By* cutting down *Stephens means removing the stem* to *within a few inches of the ground and for this purpose the hedger's axe of 3lbs weight, and with a 3 foot helve is used.*]

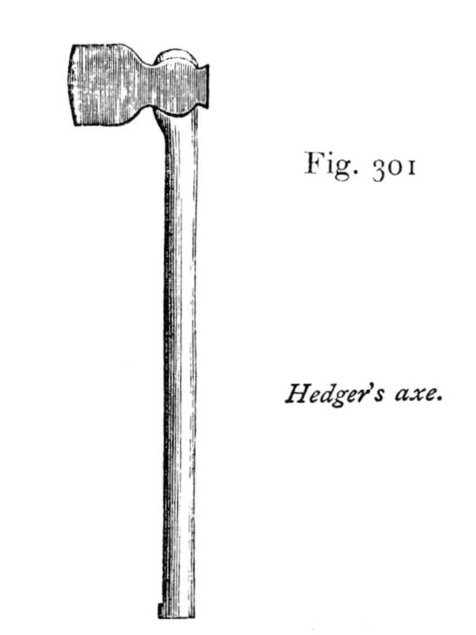

Fig. 301

Hedger's axe.

Hitherto the pruning and cutting have proceeded on the supposition that the hedge cut down will make a sufficient fence when it grows again; but this will not be the case if many of the stems are as far asunder as to leave gaps

Fig. 302

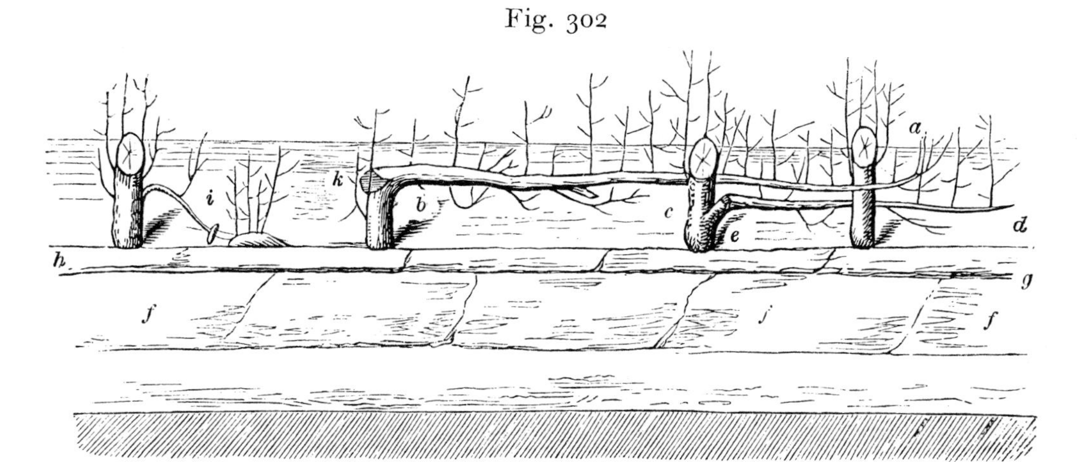

Plashing and laying an old hedge on bank, and water-tabling a ditch.

between them, even after the young twigs shall have grown up. In such a state the pruned hedge will never constitute an efficient fence without *plashing*, which consists of laying down a strong and healthy stem from one or both sides across a gap. 3344.

It is possible in the oldest hedges that gaps of such width as cannot be repaired by plashing are found, and other expedients must be adopted to fill them up, such as laying young shoots from the old stems into the gaps, or filling up the gaps with young thorn-plants. The laying cannot be done until the young shoots are pretty long; but young quicks may be planted immediately after water-tabling is finished. 3346.

The dead-hedge should be set along the direction of the prevailing winds of the locality, otherwise they will tear and upset it. The first thing the hedger does is to lay 1 or 2 spadefuls of earth upon the spot from which the dead-hedge is to run, and the trench he makes should be as large as easily to contain the lower end of a bundle of thorns, as *a*, fig. 303. The

Fig. 303

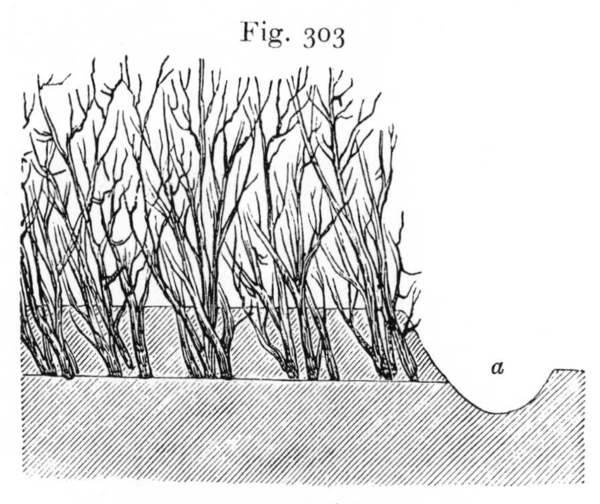

Dead-hedge of thorns.

mound thus laid up forms a lean for the first bundle. When the hedger is ready with the trench, his assistant hands him a bundle with a fork. The hedger receives the bundle with his gloved hands, and places its butt-end in the trench, pushing it with his clogged foot, and making its head slope from him. A tramp of earth is then raised with the spade, and placed against the butt-end of the bundle, to hold it firm. Thus bundle after bundle is set up firmly by the hedger; and after a few yards have been set up, he cuts in any straggling sprays with the breasting-knife, and chops the top and outside of the bundles into a neat form, having perpendicular sides and a flattish top. All the thorns of a strong hedge will not be consumed in a dead-hedge of the same length. A dead-hedge will last as long as until a cut-down hedge again becomes a fence, after which it is removed for fuel. 3348.

A *stake-and-rice* fence is formed of the branches of forest-trees; and where these are plentiful and thorns scarce, it is easily constructed.

Fig. 304

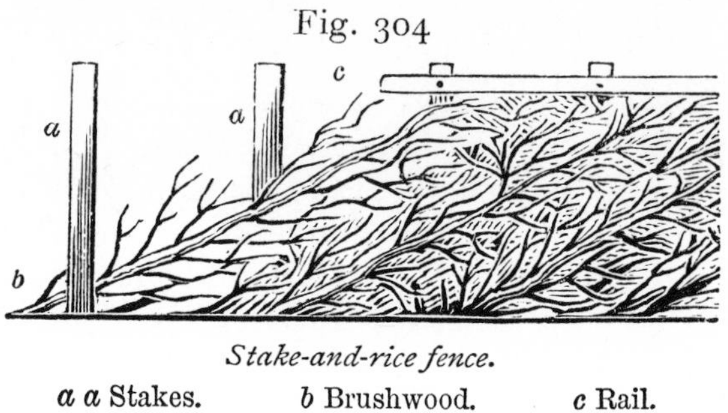

Stake-and-rice fence.

a a Stakes. *b* Brushwood. *c* Rail.

Fig. 305

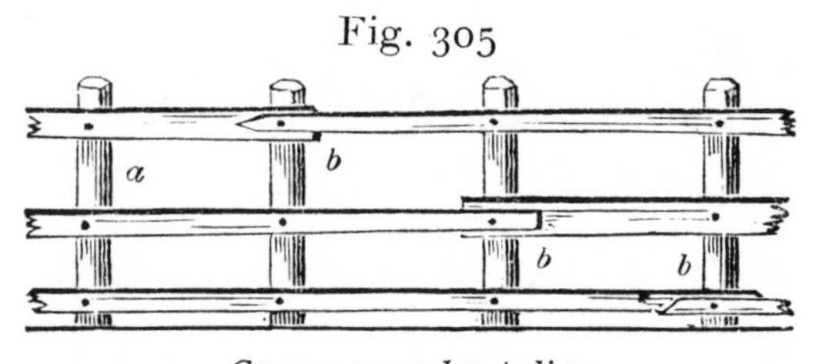

Common wooden paling.

a Stake. *b* Rail.
b b Broad and narrow ends of rail nailed together.

Stake-and-rice forms a better fence and shelter for sheep than a paling, and should be placed on the N. and W. sides of fields, whence the strongest and coldest winds prevail. Its close structure renders it liable to lodge snow that would sink down through the rails of a paling, but not more so than a dead-hedge of thorns. 3349

The implements are few that are required for weeding hedges. They con-

Fig. 306

Hedge-spade.

sist of a hedge-spade, fig. 306, having a thin cutting-face of rectangular form, attached to an iron shank terminating in a socket, into which is inserted a helve 2 feet long with a cross-head. This spade is held horizontally in both hands, and cuts away any grassy tufts along the line of hedge. Another implement is the common

Fig. 307

Fig. 308

Hedge weed-hook.

Dutch hoe, fig. 307, with a helve 5 feet long having a cross-head. It removes the weeds on both sides of the thorns. A small useful implement is the hedge weed-hook, fig. 308, cut from any bush or tree, or made of iron, and which pulls out the weeds between the hedge-roots much better than the hand. 3353.

Dutch hoe.

DRY-STONE WALLS.

The low dry-stone wall is a common field-fence in Scotland, and is there named a *dyke*, to contradistinguish it from wall, which implies a structure of stone and lime. A dyke in Ireland means a ditch, and a ditch a turf-wall. 3365.

The *tools* of a dry-stone dyker are few and inexpensive, consisting only of a mason's hammer, a frame as a gauge for the size, and cords as guides for the straightness of the dyke. A ditcher's shovel is useful in adjusting the ground for the foundation-stones, and in putting the shivers of the stones together into heaps, to be easily removed by carts. 3368.

A dyker cannot work in wet or very cold weather, as handling rough wet stones is hurtful to bare hands; on which account, dry-stone dykes are built in summer. 3369.

When dykes run at right angles to 1 another, and are erected simultaneously, they should be built in connection; but where 1 new dyke comes against another, the old 1 should not be touched, and the new built firmly beside it. Where 2 dykes cross, and the place is naturally swampy, or water be easily brought to it,

Fig. 309

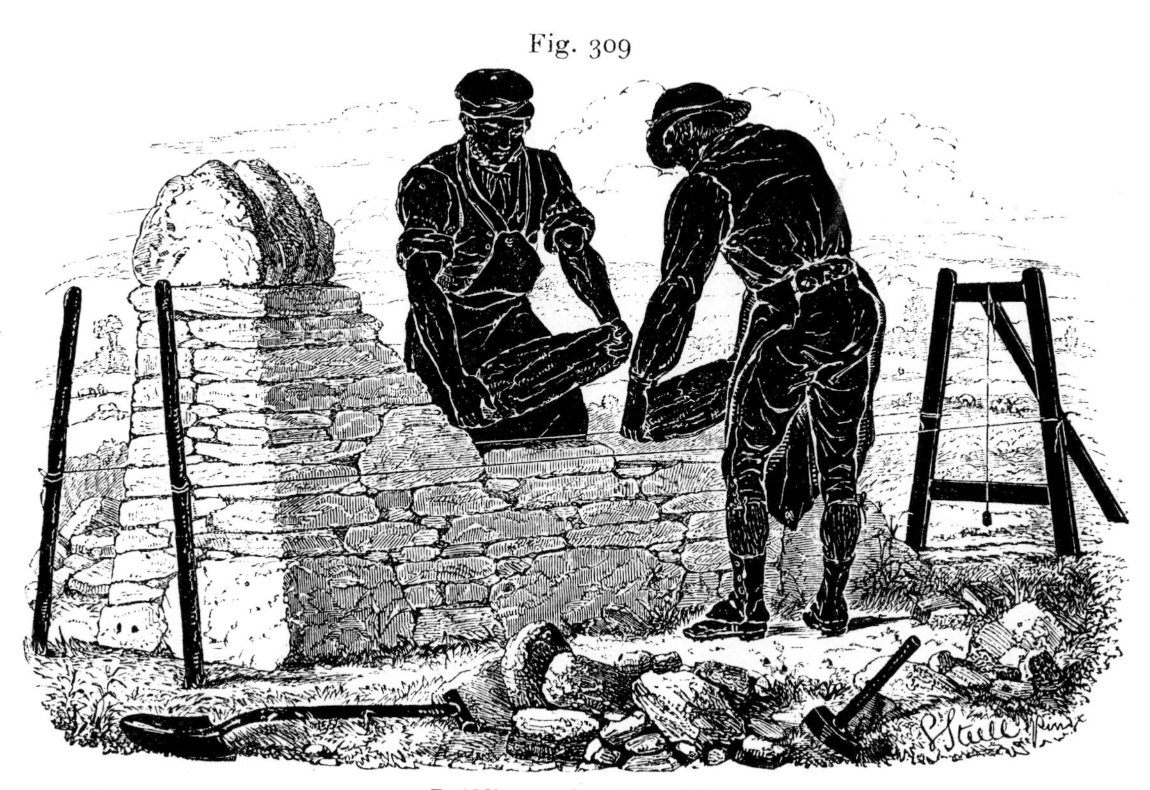

Building a dry-stone dyke.

a watering-pool would serve 4 fields, and the foundation of the pool should be formed before the dykes are built, fig. 310. Where a pond already exists, and its water is too deep for dykes to traverse, the dykes must terminate at its edge, and convert the pond into a watering-pool common to 4 fields. 3376.

Fig. 310

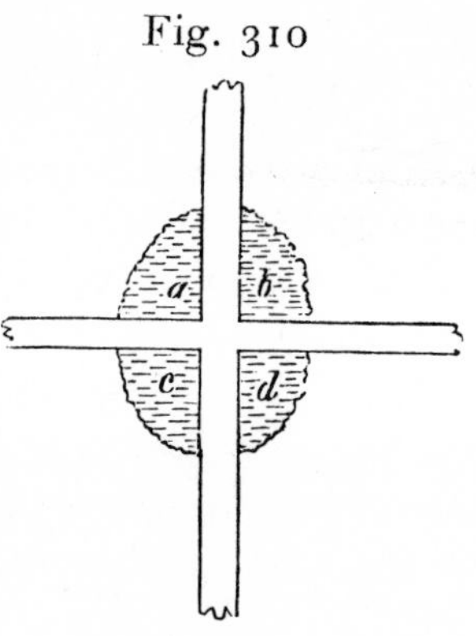

4 watering-pools formed by 2 dykes crossing.

a b c d 4 watering-pools.

Fig. 311

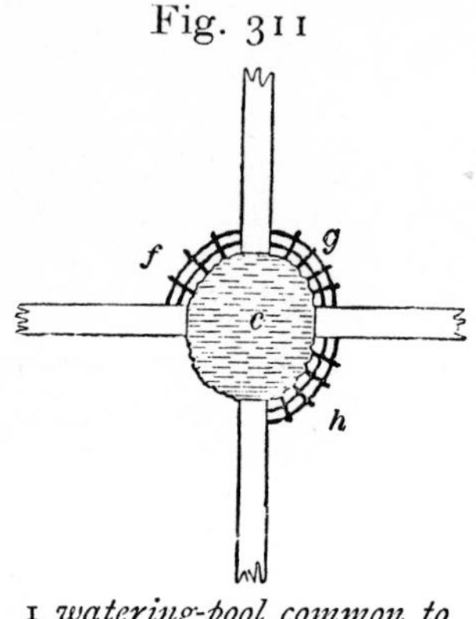

1 watering-pool common to 4 fields.

c Watering-pool.
f g h Hurdle fences in the fields not occupied by stock.

Fig. 312

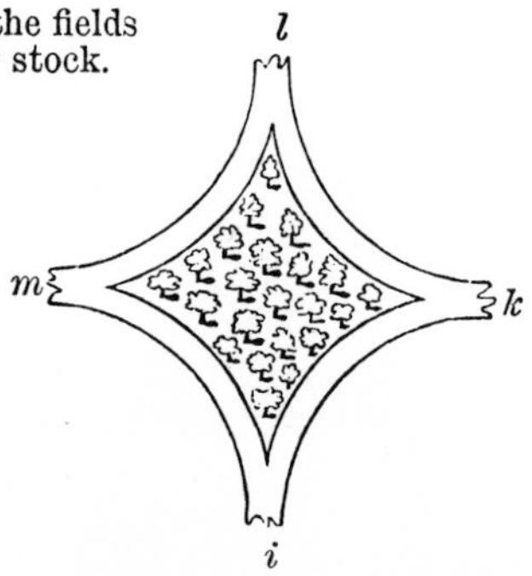

Clump of trees within the meeting of 4 dykes.

i k l m 4 curved dykes.

Fig. 313

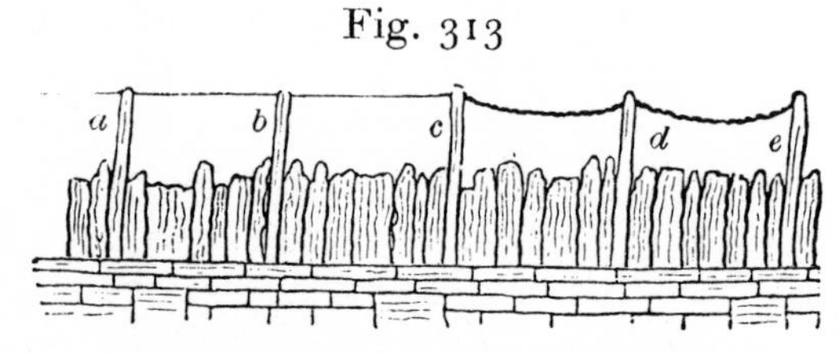

Increasing the height of a dry-stone dyke.

a b c d e Tall cope-stones.
a b c Fillets of wood on the copes.
c d e Straw-ropes on the copes.

WIRE FIELD-FENCES.

Wire fences consist of 3 parts—the straining-posts, the standards or intermediate posts, and the wires. The *straining-posts* are made of wood or of iron; and where wood is cheap it will be chosen, although it can bear no comparison with iron in durability. 3379.

Fig. 314

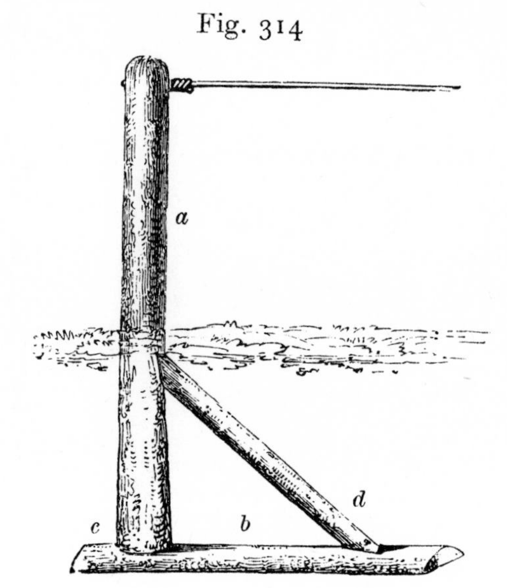

Straining-post, with sole and stay underground.

a Straining-post.
b Sole.
c Junction of post and sole.
d Strut.

Fig. 315

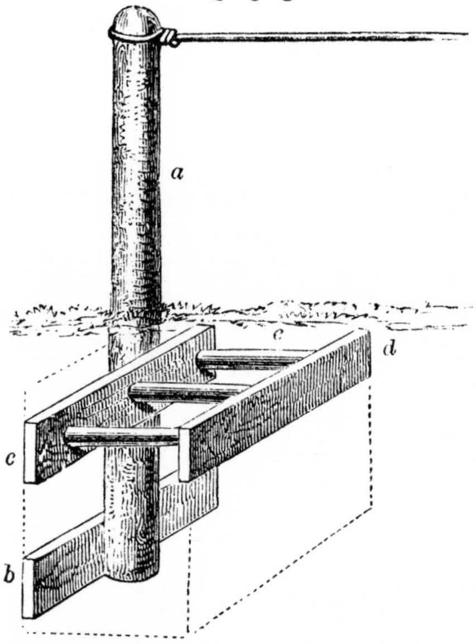

Straining-post, with planks underground.

a Straining-post.
b Lowest plank behind the post.
c Upper plank in front of the post.
d Plank opposite the upper plank.
e 3 pieces of wood wedged in between the 2 planks.

Fig. 316

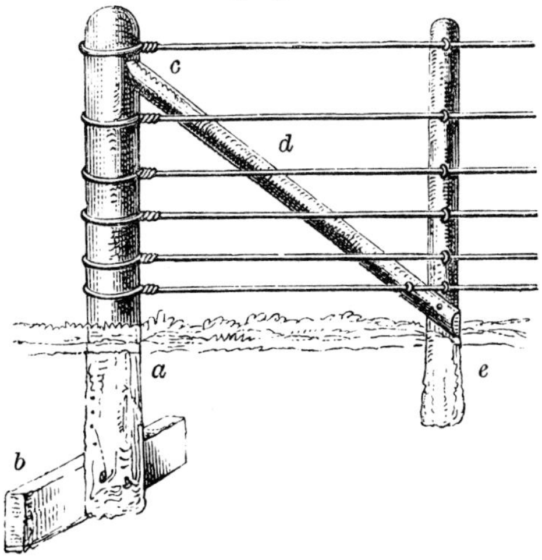

Straining-post, with standard and stay above ground.

a Straining-post.
b Piece of wood nailed behind its bottom.
e Standard-post.
d Strut.
c Points of connection with straining-post and standard.

Fig. 317

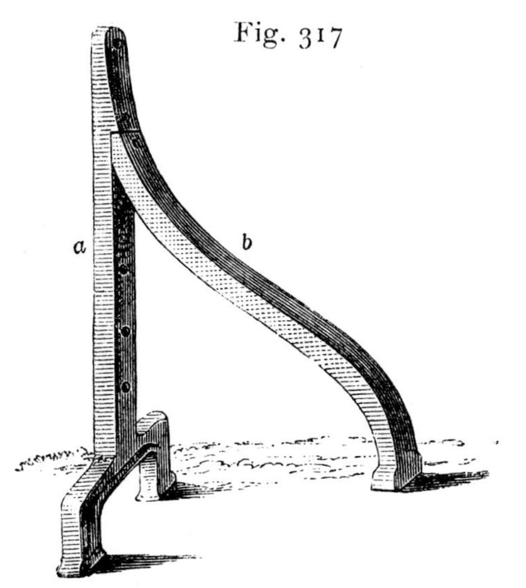

Wrought-iron straining-post.

a Straining-post. *b* Stay.

FIELD-GATES.

A field-gate may be described as a rectangular frame, and a simple rectangular frame is the most liable to change of any connected structure of framework, although it is the most serviceable form. On the other hand, the triangle is the most immutable of any form, and as long as the materials remain, it will never change. To have the most immutable field-gate it ought to have the triangular form; but in practice a gate in the form of a triangle would be most unserviceable, though a combination of triangles produces the requisite figure for a serviceable gate. If we take the most serviceable form for a gate, the rectangular, and apply a bar to it, in the position of a diagonal of the parallelogram, we immediately convert the original rectangle into 2 triangles, applied to each other by their hypotheneuse. Such a combination gives us the true elements of a properly-constructed field-gate, every other part being subordinate, and only adapted to the practical purposes of the gate as a defence or an ornament. Thus, then, the essentials of a field-gate, whether of wood or of iron, are a rectangular frame, consisting of the heel and head posts, and a top and bottom rail; which 4 parts, properly connected at the angles, are rendered of an unchangeable figure by the application of 1 or more diagonal bars, which in no case ought to be applied short of the whole length, between any 2 of the opposite angles, and which convert the rectangle into 2 triangles. Fig. 319 represents such a combination. In

Fig. 318

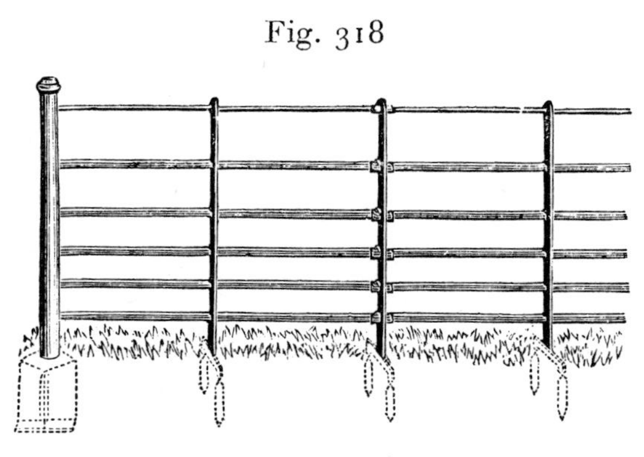

Malleable-iron fence.

Fig. 319

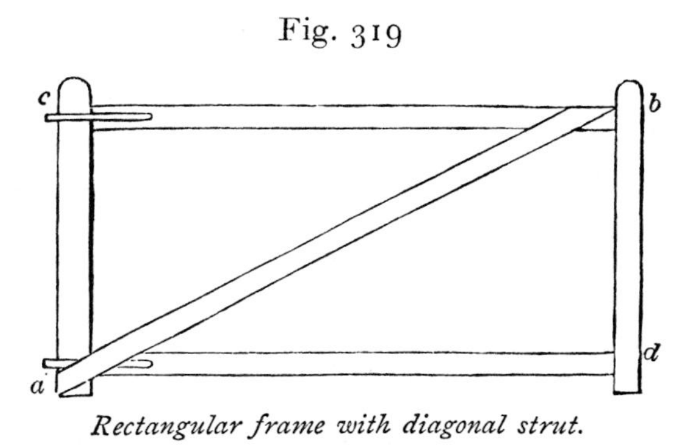

Rectangular frame with diagonal strut.

a c Heel-post.
b d Head-post.
c b Top rail.
a d Bottom rail.
a b Diagonal.
a c b 1 triangle.
a b d The other triangle.

field-gates constituted entirely of wood, the diagonal should invariably be applied as a strut, to rise from the foot of the heel and terminate at the top of the head-post. Placed in this position, the diagonal supports the swinging end of the gate by its resistance to compression, which it is well adapted to perform by the area of its cross-section being considerable, and hence capable of resisting lateral flexure. But a field-gate is liable, from various causes, to be forced up as the head-post, however well the diagonal is adapted to prevent the upper rail from being depressed, by any undue weight exerted upon its end. The advantages of a tie are the converse of a strut. If a tie is placed from the opposite angle to the strut crossing the strut in its centre — and an iron bar makes a perfect tie, the cohesion of which is such that a very small sectional area is sufficient for the purpose—the 2 antagonistic forces of the wooden strut and the iron tie, acting each in its own sphere, preserve within the whole structure the most perfect equilibrium. 3388.

A very common form of field-gate to be seen in this country is in fig. 320; and, applying the principles to it which we have been considering, we shall find it defective in several most essential particulars. It has a strut, but instead of extending across the entire diagonal, it stops short at the centre of the gate. The prolonged part of the top is liable to be broken off by any undue force being exerted upon its end, when it is converted into a lever whose fulcrum is supported at the end of the strut. It has also a tie, which is not only made of a wooden rail, but it stops short at the end of the strut, and in no part does it cross the strut so as to act with it in maintaining an equilibrium of forces. The consequence in practice is, that this form of gate is very frequently fractured at the head-post, and falls towards the ground. 3389.

Fig. 320

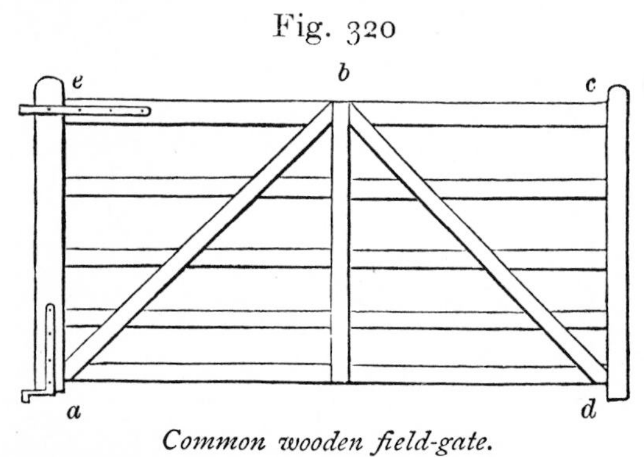

Common wooden field-gate.

a b Strut.
b End of strut.
c End of upper rail.
b d Tie.
c d Head-post.
a e Heel-post.
e Crook-and-band hinge.
a Heel crook.

Fig. 321

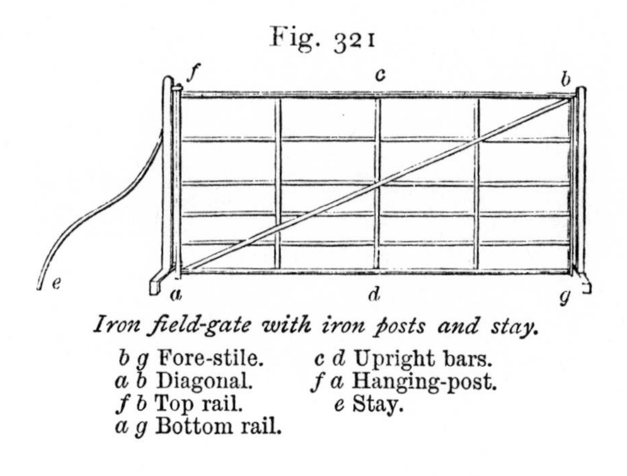

Iron field-gate with iron posts and stay.

b g Fore-stile.
a b Diagonal.
f b Top rail.
a g Bottom rail.
c d Upright bars.
f a Hanging-post.
e Stay.

Fig. 322

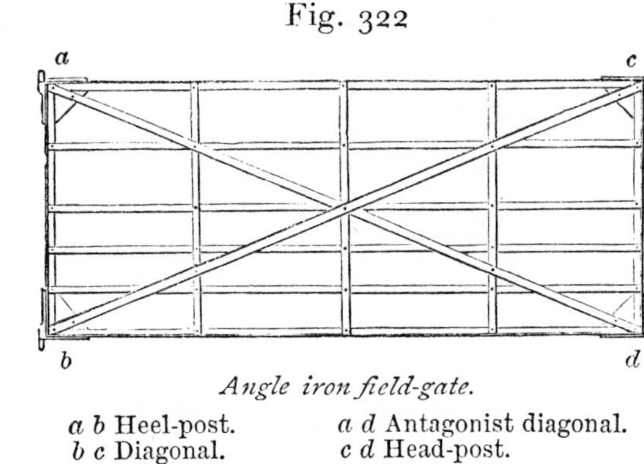

Angle iron field-gate.

a b Heel-post.
b c Diagonal.
a d Antagonist diagonal.
c d Head-post.

Fig. 323

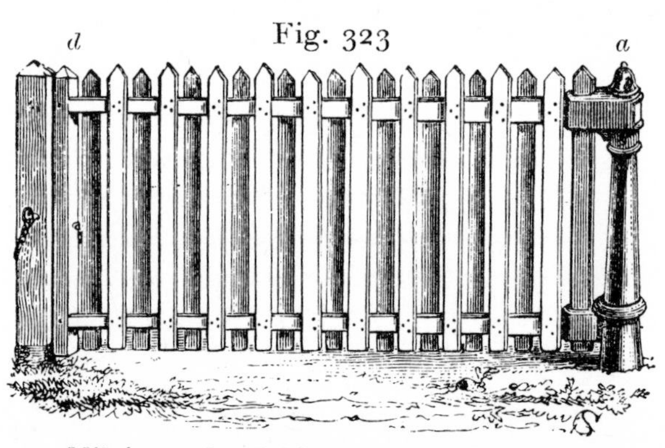

Miles's wooden field-gate with iron heel-post.

a Cast-iron heel-post. *d* Head stile.

DRAINING LAND.

Fig. 324

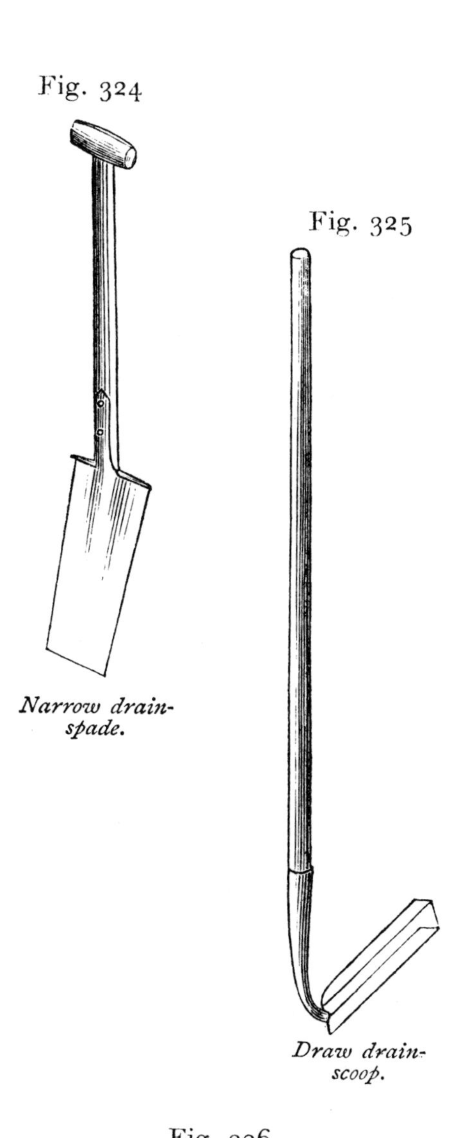

Narrow drain-spade.

Fig. 325

Draw drain-scoop.

Fig. 326

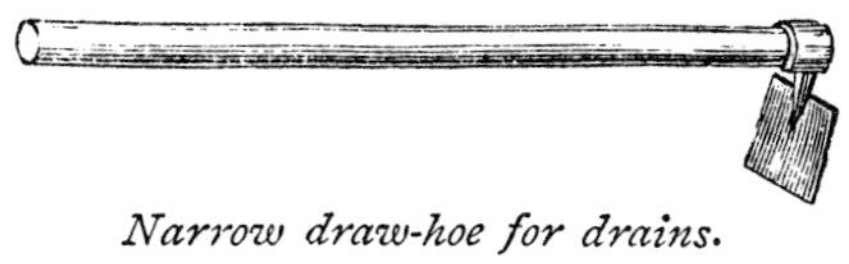

Narrow draw-hoe for drains.

Fig. 327

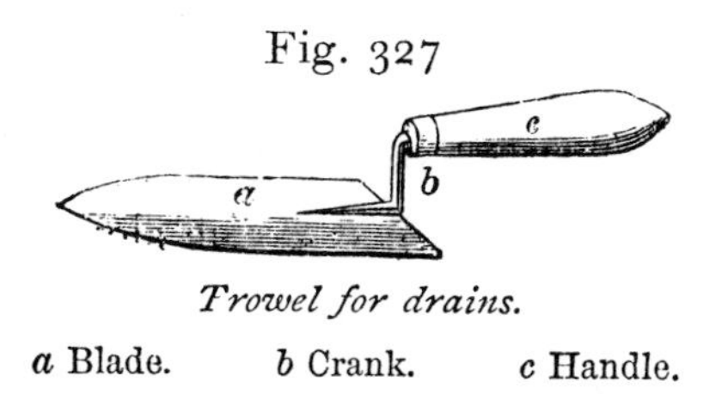

Trowel for drains.

a Blade. *b* Crank. *c* Handle.

Fig. 328

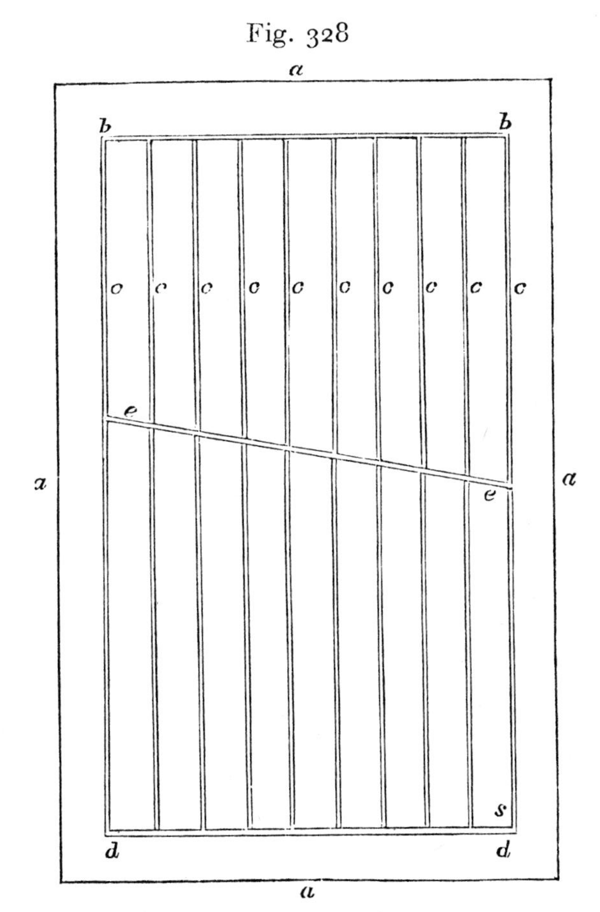

Parallel drains in the inclination of the ground.

Fig. 329

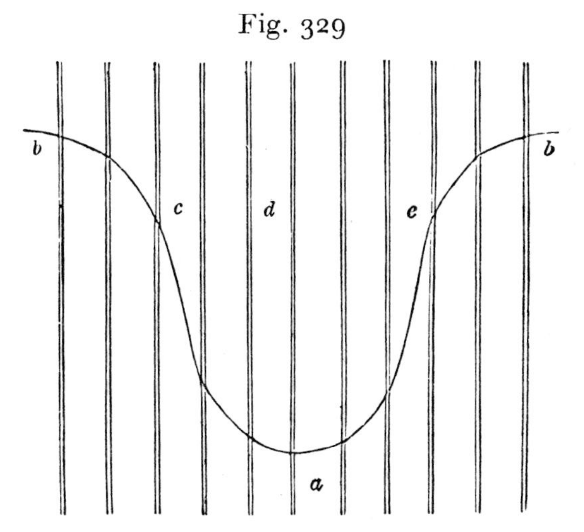

Drains improperly parallel against the inclination of the ground.

[*Digging and laying field drains by hand requires meticulous care. Stephens describes the operation at such length that it is not possible to reproduce his full text. The tools required for the job are designed to cut the narrowest trench possible so that the pipe tiles are held snugly.*]

Fig. 330

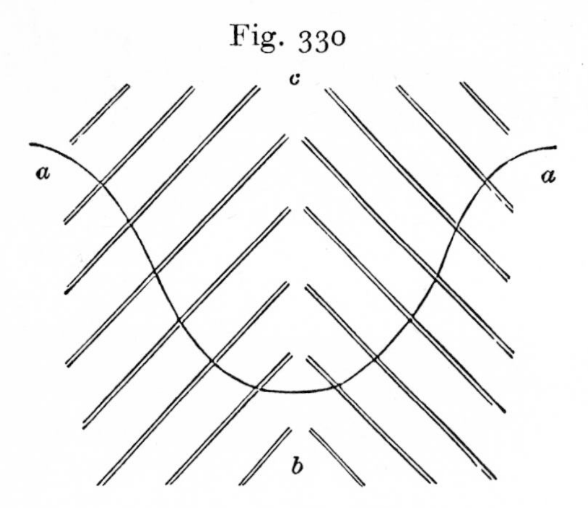

Drains in hollows parallel with the inclination of the ground.

Fig. 331

Fig. 332

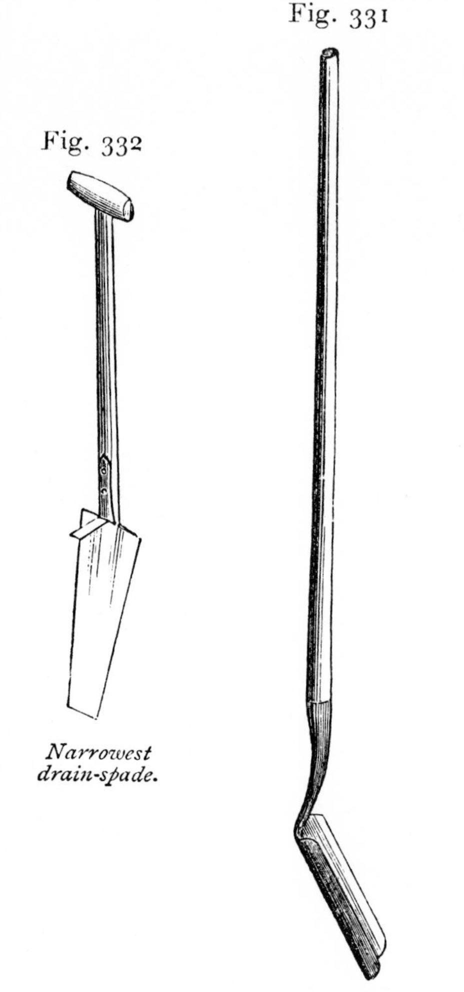

Narrowest drain-spade.

Pushing drain-scoop.

Of late years the *pipe-tile* has superseded the tile and sole, not only on account of its comparative cheapness, but of quick and easy handling in the manufacture and use. Its simplest form is the cylinder, fig. 333, 15 inches in length,

Fig. 333

Cylindrical pipe-tile.

2 inches diameter in the bore, and ¾ths inch thick. To reduce its cost to the lowest degree, it is made in many parts of England only 12 inches in length, 1 inch in the bore, and with a corresponding thickness. A good objection to this smallest size is the attempt of refinement in economy in diminishing the size, that they might be choked up with the smallest quantity of matter, when all the water they can convey must flow with but little force.

Fig. 334

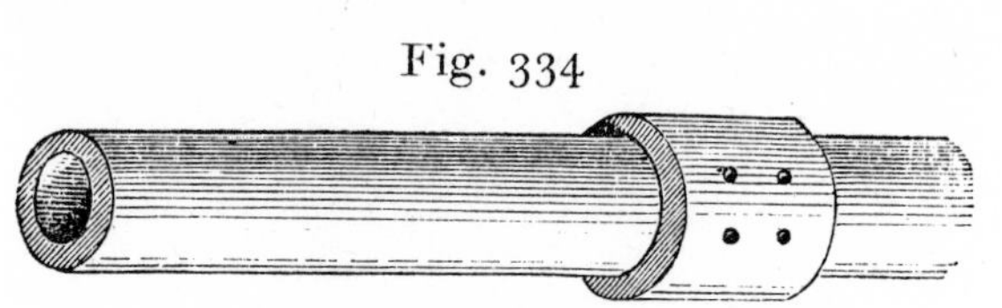

Cylindrical pipe-tiles with collar.

A very common form of pipe-tile is the horse-shoe, fig. 335, in which the

Fig. 335

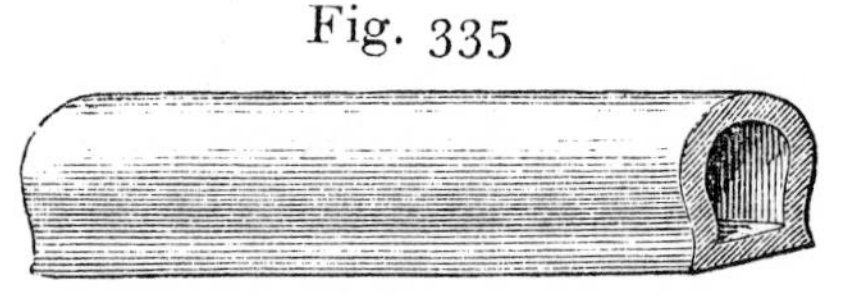

Horse-shoe pipe-tile.

sole occupies the space between the heels, which is the narrowest part of the shoe, and the upper part is rounded off capaciously in the form of the crust of the hoof. The sole is flat enough for the pipe to stand firmly upon the ground. There is no serious objection to this form. But the most perfect form of a pipe-tile is, in my opinion, the egg-shaped, the sharp end of the egg making a round and narrow channel for the water to run upon with force, and carry any sediment before it; while the rounded end provides a larger space for water should it rise to the top after heavy rains. Fig. 336 is an egg-shaped

Fig. 336

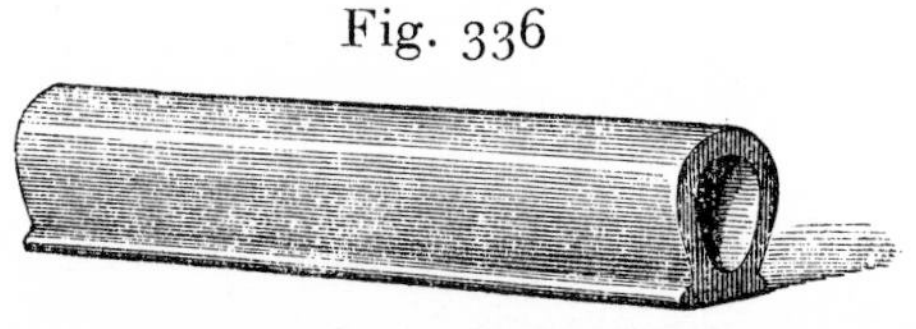

Egg-shaped pipe-tile.

pipe-tile, having a flat bottom to stand upon. Beyond this elegant form, I conceive little improvement can be effected in the pipe-tile. 3433.

Fig. 337

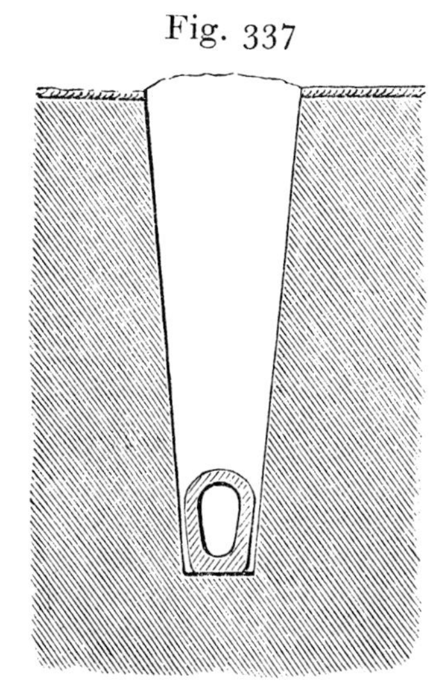

Section of egg-shaped pipe-tile drain.

Draining with *stones* is not now practised where pipe-tiles can be obtained, and railways at hand to carry them. Where suitable stones are plenty, they may be used in drains; so a few words may be said on that mode of draining. Main and small drains to be filled with *stones* are cut in the same manner as for tiles, only that they are the breadth of a common spade at the bottom. 3436.

Fig. 338

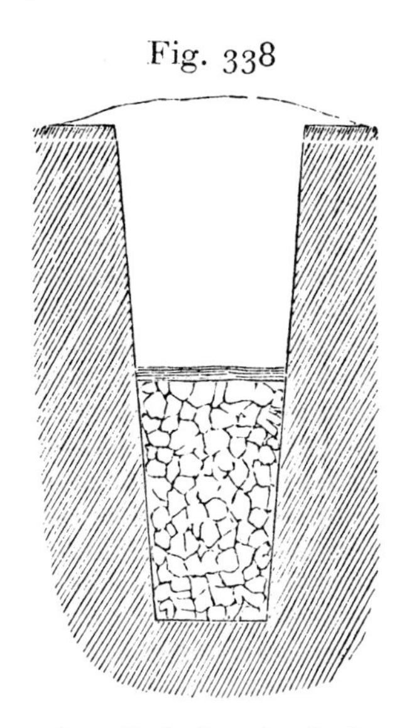

Section of small drain with broken stones.

Fig. 339

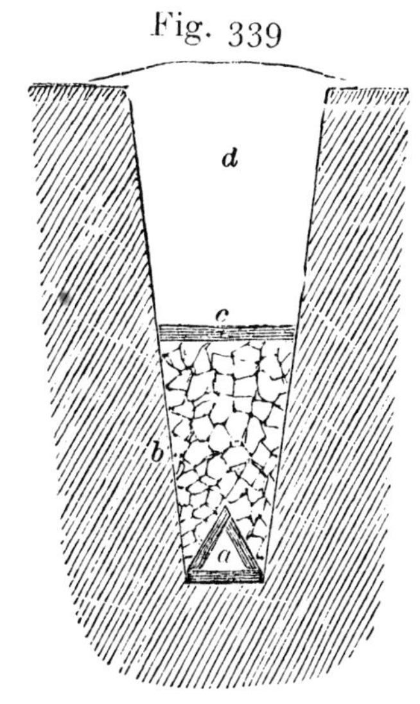

Section of triangular coupled stone duct drain.

a Triangular duct of 3 stones. *c* Turf-covering
b Broken stones. *d* Returned earth.

In comparison with the expense of execution, perhaps no draining has done so much good as *sheep-drains* on hill-pasture, which have dried its surface, and made it sound for stock, where formerly disease prevailed to an alarming extent. 3448.

Fig. 340

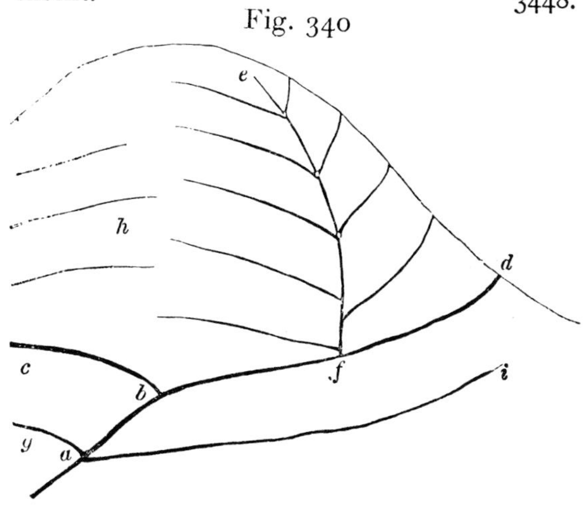

Plan of sheep-drains on a hill of impervious subsoil.

c f Leader of one set of main drains; its feeders meet on both its sides.
f Above this, 3 feeders enter the leader alternately.
e Below this, the opposite leaders should not enter the leader at the same point.
a b d Main drain.
a i Sub-main drain.
c b Main drain.
g a Sub-main drain.
h Ends of feeders placed alternately.

There are various ways of making drains in grass. One is to turn a furrow-slice down the hill with the plough, and trim the furrow afterwards with the spade. Where the grass is smooth and the soil deep, this is an economical mode of making an open sheep-drain. 3449.

Fig. 341

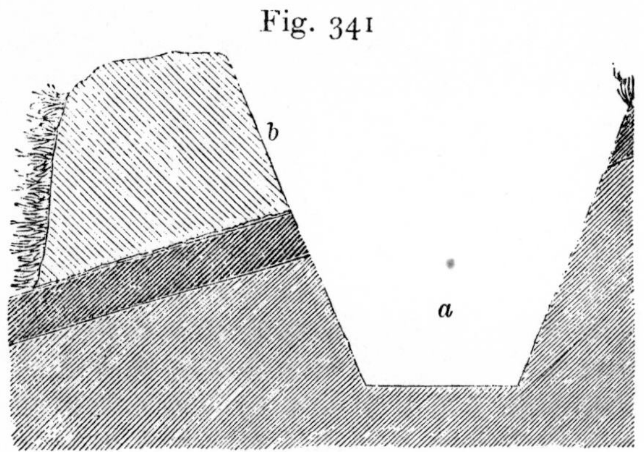

Open sheep-drain in grass.

Fig. 342 is a covered sheep-drain. A cut is first made 6 inches wide at bottom, 16 inches deep, and 18 inches wide at top. The upper turf *a* is taken out whole across the cut,

Fig. 342

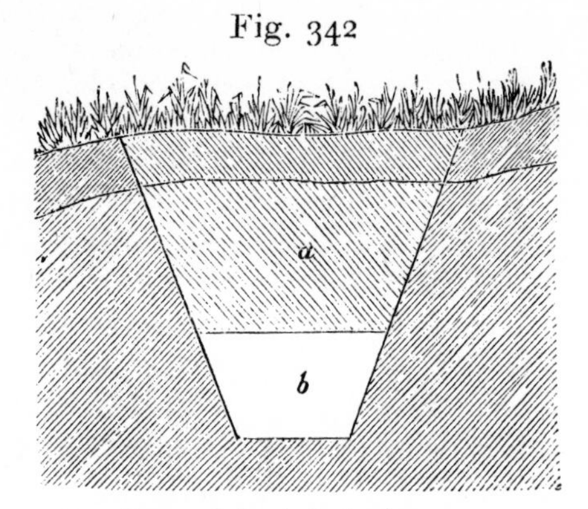

Covered sheep-drain in grass.

as deep and large as the spade can make it. 2 men will take out this turf better than 1. It is laid for a time on its grassy face upon the higher side of the drain, and the earth pared from the opposite face with the spade, giving the turf a trapezoidal shape. While 1 man is doing this, the other is casting out with a narrow spade the bottom *b* of the drain; and the earth and shovellings are spread over the ground. The large turf *a* is then replaced in its natural position, and tramped down, leaving the open space *b* below it for the water to pass along. 3450.

LEVELLING LAND.

Besides larger inequalities of surface, minor ones require emendation, the neglect of which renders the surface of improved arable land unpleasant to the sight. The inequalities I allude to are slight hollows, low heights running across several ridges, making 1 side or part of a ridge higher than the other, or part of the head-ridge higher than the ridges, and suchlike blemishes. The best and most economical method of getting quit of them is with the levelling-box, fig. 343, which, according to the nature of the soil to be removed and the distance to be carried, may be worked by 1 or 2 horses. 3468.

Fig. 343

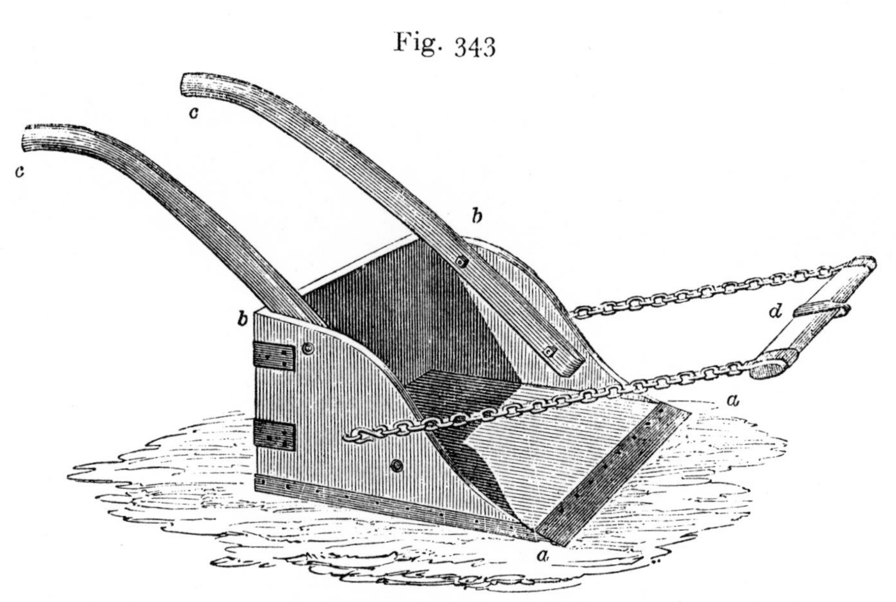

Levelling-box, or scoop.

b a, *b a* 2 Sides of box.
b b Back of box.
a a Sharp edge of iron sole.
c c Handles.
d Stretcher attached to the draught-chains.

SLAUGHTERING.

The Scotch and English modes of cutting up a carcass of beef are different. The Scotch mode is in fig. 344. 3533.

Fig. 344

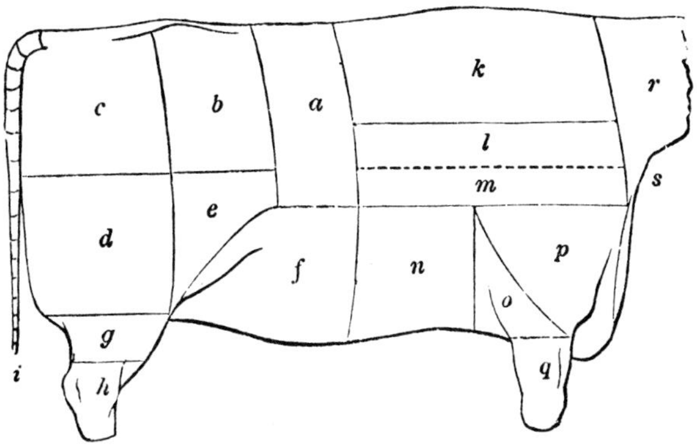

Scotch mode of cutting up a carcass of beef.

The different pieces of meat receive these names :—

In the hind-quarter.	In the fore-quarter.
a Sirloin, or back-sey.	*k* Spare-rib or fore-sey.
b Hook-bone.	*l* Runner, } large & small.
c Buttock, } the	*m* Runner, } large & small.
d Large round, } rump.	*n* Nineholes.
e Thick flank.	*o* Brisket.
f Thin flank.	*p* Shoulder-lyar.
g Small round.	*q* Nap or shin.
h Hough.	*r* Neck.
i Tail.	*s* Sticking-piece.

Fig. 345 is the English mode, which gives these names to the pieces :—

Fig. 345

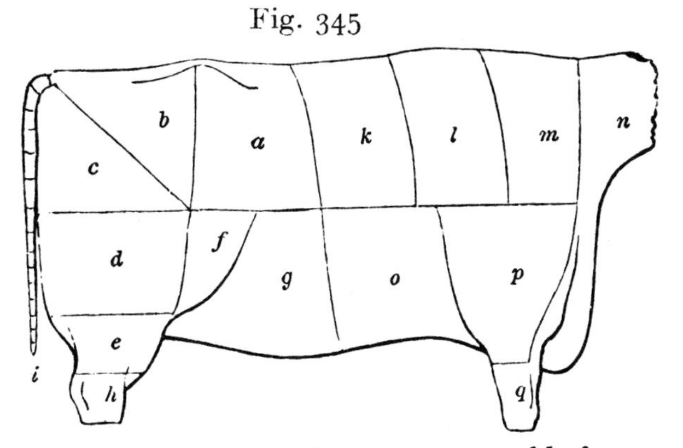

English mode of cutting up a carcass of beef.

In the hind-quarter.	In the fore-quarter.
a Loin.	*k* Fore-rib.
b Rump.	*l* Middle-rib.
c Aitch-bone.	*m* Chuck-rib.
d Buttock.	*n* Clod, and sticking, and neck.
e Hock.	*o* Brisket.
f Thick flank.	*p* Leg-of-mutton piece.
g Thin flank.	*q* Shin.
h Shin.	
i Tail.	

In almost every town is a different way of cutting up a carcass of mutton. I shall select Edinburgh and London, and distinguish them as the Scotch and English modes. 3538.

Fig. 346

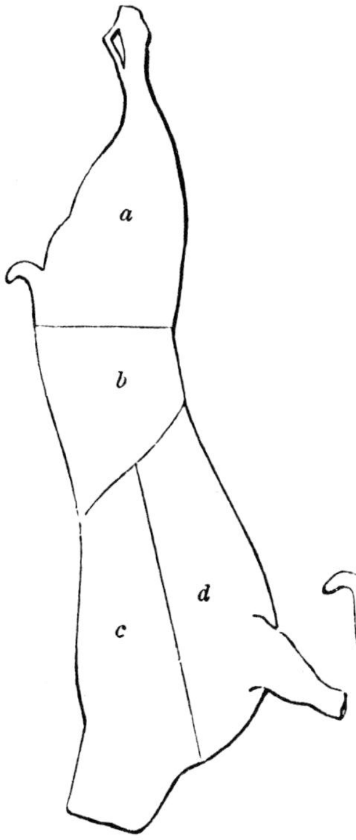

Scotch mode of cutting up a carcass of mutton.

In the hind-quarter.
a Jigot. *b* Loin.

In the fore-quarter.
c Back-ribs. *d* Breast.

Fig. 347

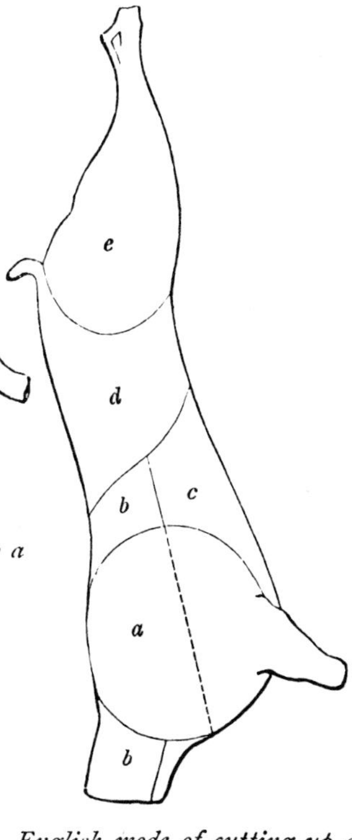

English mode of cutting up a carcass of mutton.

In the fore-quarter.
a Shoulder. *b b* Neck, and *c* Breast, both extending beneath the shoulder.

In the hind-quarter.
d Loin. *e* Leg.

The English mode of cutting up a carcass of mutton is in fig. 347. The English mode is preferable to the Scotch, being eminently adapted to the tastes of a people long acquainted with domestic economy; and the beauty and cleanliness of a butcher's stall in London call forth the admiration of every connoisseur. 3539.

Fig. 348 is the Scotch mode of cutting up a carcass of pig. The leg makes excellent pickled-pork, and the loin a juicy roast. The ribs make a roasting-piece, and pork-chops. The fore-end of the ribs and the whole of the breast are fit for pickling. The head, split in 2, is also pickled, and considered a delicacy, the fat upon the cheeks being gristly. 3542.

The English mode of cutting up pork is different. Fig. 349, where in the fore-quarter is the spare-rib, so called because the flesh and fat are taken off the ribs for salting; and the ribs are roasted; the hand or shoulder is for pickling; the belly or spring is also for pickling, or for rolling up, when well seasoned with stuffing, for brawn. In the hind-quarter are the fore and the hind loin, for roasts; the fore-loin also for making excellent chops; and the leg, which is cut short, is for pickling. The *neck* is called a *crop* of pork, and when divided into its vertebræ is cut for chops, and called *griskins*. The head, when divided in 2, is again divided at the jaw into an upper part, the *face* or *cheek*, and the lower the *chap*. Sometimes the 2 chaps are not separated. 3543.

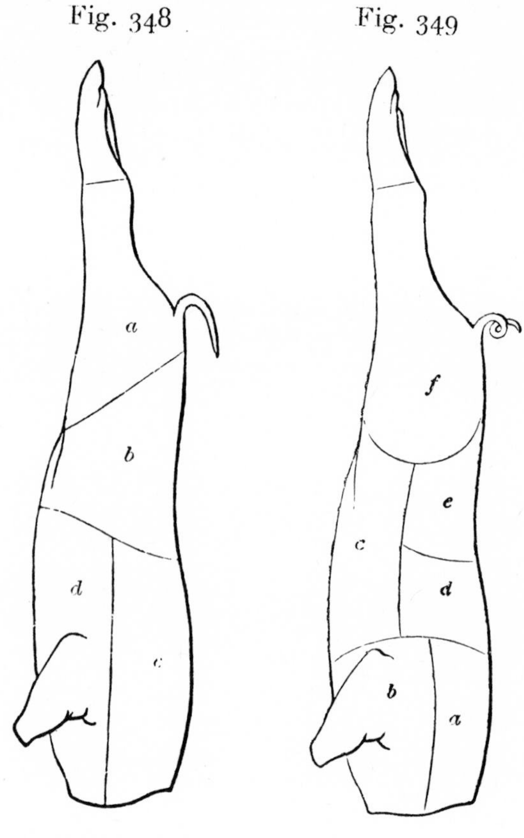

Scotch mode of cutting up a carcass of pork.

In the hind-quarter.
a Leg. *b* Loin.

In the fore-quarter.
c Ribs. *d* Breast.

English mode of cutting up a carcass of pork.

In the fore-quarter.
a Spare-rib.
b Hand or shoulder.
c Belly or spring.

In the hind-quarter.
d Fore-loin. *e* Hind-loin.
f Leg.

Bibliography

BOOKS BY HENRY STEPHENS

The book of the farm: detailing the labours of the farmer, farm-steward, ploughman, shepherd, hedger, cattleman, field worker and dairymaid. Edinburgh and London: Blackwood 1844. 2nd ed. 1851; 3rd ed. 1871; 4th ed. revised and in great part rewritten by James Macdonald 1891; 5th ed. revised and largely rewritten by James Macdonald 1908–9.

A manual of practical draining. Edinburgh and London: Blackwood, 1846. 2nd ed. 1847, 3rd ed. 1848.

The book of the farm: detailing the labours of the farmer, steward, plowman, hedger, cattleman, shepherd, field-worker, and dairymaid. To which are added explanatory notes, remarks, etc., by John S. Skinner. New York: Greeley and McElrath, 1847.

A catechism of practical agriculture. Edinburgh and London: Blackwood, 1855. New ed. revised and largely rewritten by James Macdonald, 1895.

The Yester deep land-culture: being a detailed account of the method of cultivation which has been successfully practised for several years by the Marquess of Tweedale at Yester. Edinburgh and London: Blackwood, 1855.

A practical system of farm book-keeping: being that recommended in The book of the farm. Edinburgh and London: Blackwood, 1856.

The book of farm implements and machines, by James Slight and Robert Scott Burn; edited by Henry Stephens. Edinburgh and London: Blackwood, 1858.

The book of farm buildings: their arrangement and construction, by Henry Stephens and Robert Scott Burn. Edinburgh and London: Blackwood, 1861.

The farmers' guide to scientific and practical agriculture: detailing the labors of the farmer, in all their variety, and adapting them to the seasons of the year as they successively occur, by Henry Stephens; assisted by John P. Norton. New York: L. Scott, 1862. "That portion of the Farmers' guide written by Mr. Stephens is a reprint of the second ed. of the Book of the farm".

On non-nitrogenised food: in a physiological point of view, by William Seller and Henry Stephens. Edinburgh and London: Blackwood, 1867.

Physiology at the farm in aid of rearing and feeding the livestock, by William Seller and Henry Stephens. Edinburgh and London: Blackwood, 1867.

CONTEMPORARY SOURCES ON VICTORIAN FARMING

CAIRD, James. *English agriculture in* 1850–51. London: Longman, Brown, Green & Longmans, 1852.

COPLAND, Samuel. *Agriculture, ancient and modern.* 2 vols. London: Virtue, 1866.

DONALDSON, John. *British agriculture.* London: Aitchley, 1860.

JEFFERIES, Richard. *Hodge and his masters.* 2 vols. London: Smith, Elder, 1880.

LOUDON, John Claudius. *An encyclopaedia of agriculture.* London: Longman, Hurst, Rees, Orme, Brown and Green, 1825.

MORTON, John Chalmers. *A cyclopedia of agriculture: practical and scientific*, edited by John C. Morton. 2 vols. Glasgow, Edinburgh and London: Blackie, 1855.

WILSON, John Marius, *The rural cyclopedia,* edited by John M. Wilson. 4 vols. Edinburgh: A. Fullarton, 1847–52.

MODERN WORKS

COLLINS, E. J. T. *From sickle to combine.* Reading: University of Reading, Museum of English Rural Life, 1970.

FUSSELL, G. E. *The farmer's tools*, 1500–1900. London: Andrew Melrose, 1952.

HASBACH, W. A. *A history of the English agricultural labourer.* London: Cass, 1966. (First published 1894.)

JONES, E. L. *The development of English agriculture*, 1815–1873. London: Macmillan, 1968. (Studies in economic history.)

ORWIN, Christabel S. & WHETHAM, Edith H. *History of English agriculture*, 1846–1914. 2nd ed. Newton Abbot: David & Charles, 1971.

THOMPSON, F. M. L. The second agricultural revolution, 1815–1880. *Economic history review*, 2nd ser., vol. 21, no. 1, April 1968, pp. 62–77.

THOMPSON, F. M. L. *English landed society in the nineteenth century.* London: Routledge & Kegan Paul, 1963.

TROW SMITH, Robert. *A history of British livestock husbandry to* 1700. London: Routledge & Kegan Paul, 1957.

TROW SMITH, Robert. *A history of British livestock husbandry*, 1700–1900. London: Routledge & Kegan Paul, 1959.

WATSON, James A. Scott & HOBBS, May Elliot. *Great farmers.* London: Faber, 1957.

Index